LAKELAND ROCKY RAMBLES:

Geology beneath your feet

Bryan Lynas

Published by Sigma Leisure – an imprint of
Sigma Press, 1 South Oak Lane, Wilmslow, Cheshire SK9 6AR, England.

First published 1994

Reprinted with minor corrections 1995

British Library Cataloguing in Publication Data
A CIP record for this book is available from the British Library.

ISBN: 1-85058-396-X

Cover picture: Part of the Langdale Horseshoe (Bill Stainton)

Illustrations by: Bryan Lynas

Typesetting and Design by: Sigma Press, Wilmslow, Cheshire.

Printed by: Manchester Free Press

FOREWORD

I have been fascinated by rock ever since I first discovered it when I started rock climbing at the age of 16. Of course my interest lay in its shape and form, whether the cracks, wrinkles or rugosities would make suitable hand or foot holds, or whether a flake or block would be a safe belay point, rather than in how it all came to be formed.

I have, however, always been aware of the different types of rock and the diversity of their properties, from the soft sandstone of Tunbridge Wells, through the grey pocketed limestone of Yorkshire to the hard pink granite of the Cairngorms and the rough gabbro of Skye, each of which requires a different climbing technique to tackle it.

In my early climbing days I didn't think further than this but gradually over the years my awareness and appreciation of the scenery has grown, especially for the incomparable beauty of the Lake District where I live, and I found that knowing a little more about the origins of the various rocks increased my appreciation.

Lakeland Rocky Rambles is an ideal companion for someone like me who has some knowledge but would like to know a little more. It adds a further dimension to some of my favourite walks and I shall look forward particularly to learning more about Blencathra and Buttermere, two of the areas I am especially fond of.

Since I came to live in the Lake District over twenty years ago there has been a huge increase in the numbers using the fells and crags and this is beginning to leave its mark, especially in the form of footpath erosion and traffic congestion. Even on a mid-week day in winter, Helvellyn top can be crowded and the car parks of Langdale busy. This must lead us all, as users of the crags and hills, to an awareness of how we can lessen our impact on the environment, pursuing our activities in a responsible way, so that we can pass on the landscape to future generations as we are privileged to enjoy it now.

CHRIS BONINGTON

PREFACE

Like many people, I fell in love early in my life . . . with the Lake District. I have vivid memories of school expeditions to Helvellyn and the Langdales where I began dimly to see that there was more, much more to these mountains and valleys than beauty. They were there, I realised, shaped as they are because of what lay underneath the thin mantle of grass, bracken and woodland; the old bones of the land, the rocks. Years later, as a fledgling geologist with a girlfriend who would become my wife, it occurred to me from something she said, that few people realised rocks could be not just interesting, but actually *exciting*. We were waiting at Fhionnphort, Isle of Mull (Scotland) for the little ferry to take us to Iona. The rocks in this part of Mull are a striking bright pink granite and here she noticed, seemingly for the first time, that rocks were not just 'grey all through'. For they are not necessarily grey and are certainly not boring if you understand what you are looking at. The Lake District 'old bones' are often spectacularly non-boring... but you have to notice them; to look at them more than fleetingly as you stride past so as to notch up yet another summit and get down in time for tea. Indeed you probably have noticed that rocks are not all grey and that some show strange markings which seemingly shout at you, but in a language you probably don't understand, like Chinese graffiti.

So what can the rocks tell us about Lakeland history millions of years ago? And what about the shapes of the mountains and valleys themselves? Why are mountains sometimes craggy and precipitous and yet in other places, rather flat and uninteresting? Why are valleys sometimes broad and 'U'-shaped? Why are they sometimes steeply incised? Why are the lakes there? The answer is always there in the rocks – geology – beneath your feet.

In writing this book, I hope to satisfy a need which many folk who walk the hills have told me about: people who have no formal training in geology but who really do want to know something about the rocks, scenery and nature around them. Knocking off summits is one thing; getting a feel, an understanding, for the country you're passing through is quite another. With this book to guide you – the first, I trust, of several which will include other parts of the country – I hope you too will be able to make some real sense of the rocks and scenery. My intention is not only to make each of the ten walks exciting by explaining what you see, but also to make inroads into some of the basic ideas in earth science. I deliberately avoid having separate 'lecturing' chapters on particular topics. I prefer to wait until you can see for yourself some exciting set of rocks which – because you can touch them and scramble over them (for geology is a 'hands on' subject) – will help you to understand not only why they exist and how they formed, but also some of the broader aspects of the endlessly fascinating subject of the science of our Earth. I want you to enjoy this process and, most importantly, I want to make the point that you can and should disagree – if you feel like it – with what I suggest for the origin of this rock or that scenery. In geology, we cannot see the actual processes which created rocks eons ago. All we can do is make comparisons with what we observe today: floods, active volcanoes, earthquakes and so on. So there may often be several possible explanations for what you see and uncertainties are normal. Don't worry about it! Enjoy the stimulation of dreaming up and discussing rival theories with your friends. Ask searching questions but don't mind if you can't get the whole answer. That comes increasingly with experience... and sometimes, not even then. 'The best geologist, other things being equal, is the one who has seen the most rocks.' That wise quote by H.H. Read (geology professor) many years ago is just as true today.

So please use this book in the way it was intended: as a guide offering explanations of what you see on certain well known walks. It is not exhaustive. It is not another 'geology of the Lake District', for these works already exist in several versions aimed at people who have some earth science training. If you have an enquiring mind and love the Lake District and want more out of walks than simply walking, then this book is for you. Enjoy it!

Bryan Lynas

NOTE!

In the short time since the first edition of this book, some details of the landscape have changed. These range from the minor reconstruction of a stile as a gate on the Loughrigg Fell ramble to the moving of a stile by a not-inconsiderable 1 kilometre where the path crosses a mountain wall on Lower Hartsop above How Ridge (Dovedale ramble). Such changes are rare, but unpredictable, so be sure to consult a current OS map before starting a walk and, if you find that there are changes, please write to me c/o Sigma Press.

CONTENTS

INTRODUCTION

Reading the Story in the Rocks

The aim of this book is to help you find out for yourself more about the *whys* and *wherefores* of the rocks, scenery and natural history of the Lake District. It is not just one more guidebook of walks you already know or can pick out for yourself from a good map.

Without the ancient and hard rocks and the forces of erosion which have been operating since the planet formed 4.6 billion years ago, there would not be a Lake District and you wouldn't be here, looking at this book whose subject is natural history with special emphasis on the old bones of the area – the rocks themselves.

The rocks here, as everywhere, have a story to tell; a story which can be read by anyone if they understand the language. You don't have to be a professional to make sense of what you see around you. All you need are a desire to walk, interest, sharp eyes and this book. Maybe you've always thought, as my wife used to, that all rocks are 'grey and boring'. This was because she'd never *looked* at them. Once you develop the habit of looking, not glancing, you begin to notice that rocks are not all grey – and are most certainly not boring. Many of the rocks – like those on Pavey Ark in the Langdales – are so obviously peculiar that they just cry out for your attention and curiosity. Others are more subtle, but just as interesting. With this book in hand – its descriptions, maps and many sketches – you also can begin to learn to read the story in the rocks. And an incredible story it is too, beginning around 500 million years ago.

A brief history

So far as the Lake District was concerned, it all started under the sea; a deep muddy sea. The mud, silt and sometimes sand from distant rivers, flowed into the deep water as bottom-hugging, turbulent, muddy currents before settling out onto the sea floor. Strange life forms, now long extinct, burrowed in the mud, swam or floated about. But the tranquillity of this setting was soon to be disturbed, first by strong earth movements which uplifted the old sea floor.

These movements heaved up the muddy sediments which had been laid down there, pushing them high above sealevel, where they were partially worn away by the same weathering and erosion processes which operate today.

Then the excitement really began: a paroxysm of volcanic eruptions. This volcano – or volcanoes, for nobody knows how many there were – spewed out lavas and other materials, often in an exceedingly violent and destructive fashion, giving rise to the immensely thick Borrowdale Volcanic Group (named from the famous dale in which the rocks outcrop everywhere). It is this group of volcanic rocks (conveniently shortened to BVG), which forms most of the high and rugged mountains of the area. It is also a most diverse group of rocks and you will, if you follow the walks in this book, get to know it quite well.

'Outcrop' is a word I use a lot. It simply means part of a rock formation which sticks up through the soil so that you can see it. (In most places, rock formations are buried under plants, soil, and loose debris.) So an outcrop (changed to its verb form) is said to 'crop out' (stick up) through the soil.

After the BVG eruptions and another period of erosion, the area subsided and was again invaded by the sea and there followed a long period in which sediments were quietly laid down on the seafloor. The sea was warm and often teeming with life, for at that time this part of Britain lay south of the equator within the tropics. Today, we can find the remains of this life as fossil shells and other small creatures which are very common in some rocks. You may be surprised to learn that Britain once lay south of the equator, but there is a wealth of evidence for this both from measurements of the ancient Earth's magnetic field (see Appendix) and from the fossils in the rocks themselves which are typical of tropical seas.

The long period of calm after the BVG didn't last. Around 400 million years ago, a mighty series of earth movements came to a peak, squeezing and crushing the rocks and uplifting the entire area as two of the huge plates which then, as today, formed the Earth's crust, slowly smashed into each other and jammed irrevocably together. This was the climax of the Caledonian mountain building episode which resulted in what is now Scotland (and eastern Canada) joining with England (and what later became the Appalachian mountains of the eastern USA) to form a Himalayan-scale mountain range and part of a new continent: Eur-Asia (p. 54). England, Wales and Scotland – for better or for worse – were never to be parted more.

After the Caledonian earth movements ended, the old and dead volcanoes of the Lake District lay buried for hundreds of millions of years beneath younger rocks. During this long period, a great rift began to develop about 200 million years ago in the old continent, a rift which was to become the Atlantic Ocean.

The continent slowly split apart, accompanied at times by great outpourings of lavas. The great conveyor belt of *plate tectonics* (I explain all italicised words in the Glossary) relentlessly drew apart what was to become the eastern seaboard of the USA and Canada, from the west of Britain, Ireland and Scandinavia. In Britain, you can still see the remains of this huge outburst of lavas: in Northern Ireland (the Giant's Causeway) and the Hebrides, in Scotland.

Meanwhile erosion (an example of 'Time wounding all heals' as Groucho Marx once said) continued its persistent destruction of the area which would become Lakeland. The great *Caledonian* mountain building had created the uplifted area but now erosion was beginning to fashion and carve the mountains we know so well today. But Time, the great leveller, and Erosion, its destructive consort, were to be assisted in a spectacular way when the Earth's climate cooled around 2 million years ago, triggering a major set of ice ages from which we have probably not yet emerged (though our inadvertent tampering with the climate may, by way of the greenhouse effect, change all this). During the cold periods which spanned many tens of thousands of years each, huge ice sheets covered all but the highest Lake District mountains, and moving rivers of ice gouged out the deep valleys and rock basins in which today's beautiful lakes collected after the ice melted. Windermere, Coniston, Buttermere, Stickle Tarn – all exist because of glaciers. And without the glaciation, the area would look very drab by comparison, with gently rounded mountains and shallow valleys – and certainly no lakes.

The last ice melted just 11,500 years ago – a mere blip in the immense period of time which had elapsed since the *BVG* volcanoes some 450 million years earlier (give or take a few million years). Trees colonised the barren landscape left by the ice, covering all but the highest mountains; animals, both hunters and hunted, roamed the forests – and then came Man.

At first, he contented himself with making tools out of some of the hard volcanic rocks, erecting stone circles, growing cereals and building simple settlements of huts. Then the Roman legions arrived, building roads and small fortresses. The Romans probably started some of the mines which generations of miners continued to work for the next two millennia. Later came makers of charcoal, cutting the oak woods to smelt iron ores and other base metals which the miners had dug out of the mountains. Quarrymen began to cut away certain bands of the volcanic rocks which split easily into attractively-patterned roofing slates and lintels for doors and windows. Then came the railways, bringing the first tourists. Now, with motorways and cars, tourists and walkers flood into the district in their hundreds of thousands to enjoy the landscape whose creation had taken so long.

So what you see today is not just the result of ancient geological events. The landscape has been fashioned by both ice and, more superficially, by Man. The vegetation we take to be natural is the result of thousands of years of tree-felling or planting, and grazing by domestic animals. If there were no people, the district — except for the higher mountains -would undoubtedly be heavily forested; and wolves, bears and eagles would hunt the otherwise destructive browsing herds of deer. There would be no mines, no quarries, no drystone walls, no sheep or cows, no towns, no roads or railways, no cars — and no you or me. It's a fascinating 'thought experiment' as you walk through this lovely country, to imagine just how it would have looked without Man.

In fact, I've modified this sort of 'thought experiment' on several of the rambles to help you visualise the way things once were. I hope you'll be able to join me in my 'mind time machine' as we zip back thousands or hundreds of millions of years. My aim is to get *you* to picture the goings-on I attempt to describe for you, whether it be volcanoes blasting out ash or glaciers grinding their way through the mountains to give the landscape we see today. For this time travel, I recommend a comfy spot out of the wind to sit and contemplate.

A simple philosophy

I have deliberately not attempted to explain any more details of the geology of Lakeland in this introduction than you have already read. The walks themselves will show you, little by little, how the rocks formed and were later moulded into the landscape of today. You don't have to know any geology at first, but as you both see and think for yourself — with a little guidance from me — the ideas involved should fall into place for you. If you find some parts heavy going (what I've written; not the walking), don't hesitate to skip bits. There's no exam at the end and I've tried to achieve an even balance between 'not enough' and 'too much.' At any rate, towards the end of the book, I hope you'll be 'reading the rocks' for yourself quite effectively.

I don't want to intimidate you with new words and concepts before you've even started so, unlike most books on geology, I've placed the geological map of the area, together with a timescale diagram which summarises the rock and glacial history, at the end of the book in the Appendix. Just refer to them, like the Glossary, whenever you need to.

Above all, I want this book to be fun. I want to help you feel the excitement which I always do when I start 'reading' the rocks beneath my feet in Nature's own classroom: the great outdoors.

A little common sense

You will have read time and again about following the Country Code, so you won't need reminding that it applies in this most beautiful of English National Parks as much as anywhere. It is equally important to remember that most of the rambles take you through quite high mountain country, so be aware of likely weather conditions – and be prepared for rain and cold winds. Indeed, I wouldn't recommend that you attempt any of the walks in poor weather. You wouldn't be able to – or want to – 'read the rocks' in rain and gale-force wind, let alone read the notes for each walk. And of course being on the fells in bad weather can be downright dangerous.

As you'll notice, erosion is not only a natural process. The constant pounding of fell paths by myriads of walkers' boots is a severe problem. The plants, which normally protect the underlying soils from erosion by rain, are destroyed. The National Park and National Trust have rebuilt many of the more popular paths by laboriously cobbling them, so please keep to these as much as possible – and don't take short cuts.

Some of the walks take you around old quarries and mines. Beware! Mines and quarries are by their very nature unstable. Rock falls do occur and entering mines is dangerous, even if you're experienced.

Do take with you the appropriate copy of the Ordnance Survey (OS) Outdoor Leisure maps (1:25,000 scale; $2^{1}/_{2}$ inches to one mile; 4 centimetres to 1 kilometre). Four sheets (4 – North Western Area, 5 – North East, 6 – South West and 7 – South East) cover the whole district and they are indispensable. You may find it helpful, before attempting a walk, to pencil onto your Outdoor Leisure map the route I show on my own maps of each ramble. Almost all are on well-defined footpaths clearly marked on the OS maps. My sketch maps cannot, without becoming hopelessly cluttered, give the route-finding detail you may need. So be sure to take both. The OS maps are also highly accurate representations of the mountains and have for years been 'metric' in that all heights (contours etc.) are given in metres above sealevel. So I too have followed the metric scheme.

It's a good idea to take a smaller-scale map with you too (e.g. OS 1:50,000 Landranger map, Sheets 89, 90 & 96) if you want to identify the more distant mountain summits.

Using this book

These are the ten rambles:

1. Buttermere and Haystacks: 7 kilometres (4 miles)
2. Dovedale and its mountains: 12 kilometres ($7^1/_2$ miles)
3. Coniston: 11 kilometres (under 7 miles)
4. The Langdale Pikes: 10 kilometres (under 6 miles)
5. Troutbeck and Wansfell: 10 kilometres (under 6 miles)
6. Loughrigg Fell: $9^1/_2$ kilometres (under 6 miles)
7. Bow Fell and Esk Pike: 18 kilometres (11 miles)
8. Catstye Cam and Helvellyn: 16 kilometres (under 10 miles)
9. Greenside Mine area: $11^1/_2$ kilometres (over 7 miles)
10. Blencathra: 11 kilometres (7 miles)

(For the approximate locations of these, see Appendix: geological map.)

As you'll see, I've selected rambles from different parts of the Lake District. My basis for the selection is that the rambles are well known or especially interesting. All the paths are public rights of way and each walk offers a variety of fascinating things to see, ending back at the starting point. You'll notice that though the rocks dominate the text, I touch on other matters such as the birds, plants or fungi you might see, together with industrial archaeology – pottering around abandoned quarries and mines.

I've arranged the text for the walks so that the **directions** are set in a different type style from the descriptions – in order that you can find out quickly which you are dealing with. Each ramble has its own map, each with a scale showing distances in both kilometres and miles. The rambles are based on a series of **localities** at which I hope you'll stop and take a little time to look around you and see what you make of what I've described. Some of the localities are optional extras: spurs off the main ramble. You can take them or leave them according to the weather and how you feel. For this reason, I've offered little idea of how long a ramble may take. In fact, most are almost certainly full day excursions if you are to have time to take stock of what you see – and enjoy yourself. Most of the routes stick to well defined paths.

I don't like 'jargon' and neither, I imagine, will you. But there are times when I have to introduce terms which simply have no equivalents in ordinary life. *Tuff* is a word you can apply to almost half of the volcanic rocks in the district. It means one thing only: volcanic ash which has become hardened into rock, but there's no use for this word in ordinary life. Yet I cannot keep on referring to 'ashes which have hardened into rock' again and again. So I use 'tuff'. Similar words pop up inevitably now and again. I place them all in *italics* which not only identifies them as words that you may not know, but tells you that they're fully defined in the Glossary at the end of the book.

The rambles are laid out in the order in which I suggest you do them. You don't have to, of course, but I've tried to introduce a few new ideas during each one, so you could find yourself a bit lost if you were to do the Catstye Cam and Helvellyn ramble first. By then, to avoid being boringly repetitive, I assume you will be familiar with some ideas and terminology. But remember, the Appendix and Glossary always back you up should you forget what *'Younger Dryas'* or *'hyaloclastite'* mean; or whether *'Coniston Limestone'* is *Silurian* or *Ordovician* in age.

I strongly recommend that you skim through the beginning parts of each ramble before actually doing it. I tend to load you with information of interest in the earlier part of a ramble whilst you're still fresh and enthusiastic. A quick pre-read will help you get moving over the first few localities. Forgive this uneven loading for, by the end of a long day out on the fells, only the most dedicated rambler remains gripped by the differences between *tuffs* and *turbidites*, *lapilli* and *limestone*. Probably you'll be more interested in the thought of draught cider at the Drunken Duck Inn (between Coniston and Ambleside). Anyway, when you've done your ten walks, you'll be able to amaze your friends when you let drop (over a pint) words like *'volcaniclastic sandstones'* and *'phreatomagmatic eruption.'*

Although you'll have no trouble finding most of the localities, some are less-easily described ('humpy rock 15 paces past the third rowan tree') and so I include full National Grid References for these: example [2723 9782]: the summit of the Old Man of Coniston. All the Ordnance Survey maps describe how to use grid references if you are not familiar with them. The 8-figure reference theoretically gives you the point to within 10 metres of its precise location, so a scaler helps. Most compasses include a perspex scale of some sort. 'Eyeballing' the location of the reference should be quite adequate in most cases.

When you set out on a walk, I'd recommend taking a compass for I often refer to directions. Your compass should preferably have a dip needle for measuring the inclination of strata. Also essential is a x10 magnifying hand lens for examining rocks and minerals – and small plants too. Hang it round your neck on a strong string. Binoculars are not only useful if you're keen on birds but also for examining inaccessible rocks. A camera is obviously worthwhile. Although geology is traditionally associated with hammers, such tools are frowned upon nowadays – banned in many places – and are almost always unnecessary for what you will be looking at. Because of the notorious weather, it's useful to have some means of protecting your map and this book. There are several different styles of map cases available with clear plastic windows so that you can look at your (dry) map or book in the worst weather.

Spelling of place names is always something of a nightmare as there are often many variations, both on the maps and in books. Since you'll be using an Ordnance Survey Outdoor Leisure map on the rambles, I've employed the spelling given on the latest (metric) editions of these maps. So "Bowfell" becomes "Bow Fell," "Hause" is sometimes "Hawse" and so on. Many of these do not accord with Wainwright's versions, if you are familiar with those.

The 'stuff' of science: facts and theories

The aim of the game here is to help you to 'read the rocks' and in so doing, to allow you to make up some of your own ideas about how a particular structure or formation came into being. It is a cornerstone of science that an idea or theory of something, or some event, should be testable. Let us take a simple example.

A gardener goes down to her vegetable patch and finds all her cabbages full of holes. She also notices small green caterpillars on the plants. So she quickly develops a theory for the origin of those holes because she knows that understanding the origin will be the basis for saving her cabbages. She can test her theory by observing the caterpillars. If she actually *sees* them eating holes, she knows her theory is correct and can either pick the caterpillars off or spray them with poison. If her theory was wrong (yes I know it's unlikely) and the caterpillars were just passing the time of day, the holes having been eaten by snails, then she'd be wasting her time killing the caterpillars.

Geology is a slightly odd science because many of its ideas are not directly testable. We cannot travel backwards in time to see what actually happened to create those oddball markings in this or that rock. Instead, geologists have to look for similar things forming now – and make an assumption that the same process operated way back in time. This gives rise to the rule that 'the Present is the key to the Past.' It works well for rocks like lavas where you can see features in 450-million-year-old rocks just like with those in lavas spewed out yesterday by Mount Etna (for example). It doesn't work when the process has never been seen operating in the present – or cannot be seen owing to its extreme violence. Such an example is the type of volcanic eruptions which created rocks called *ignimbrites,* now known to have been produced by colossal eruptions never witnessed by man.

In similar fashion, it has not been possible until very recently to see processes happening in the deep oceans. We can now 'see' either directly (via specially designed submarines) or indirectly (by means of sophisticated sonar and remote probes). As a result, we now know about huge seafloor slumps and slides and bottom-hugging turbid currents which can, over time, fill deep-sea basins with thousands of metres of sediments. It is our understanding of these processes that can help us to make sense of peculiar structures in ancient *sedimentary* rocks. Even deep-sea volcanoes have now been seen pouring out lavas onto the seabed.

But there's another problem to grapple with and that is 'secondary' alteration: changes in rocks which happen sometimes long after they have been formed. These ,changes can be small scale – for example when water gets squeezed out of sediment (*dewatering*) – or they can be very large scale indeed, such as those produced when crustal *plates* collide. Then, mountain ranges may be forced up. Many of these things no one could ever see, but it is possible to model the high temperature and high pressure processes on a tiny scale in modern laboratories, so that generally we can be pretty sure we are correct in our ideas about why, for example, *cleavage* forms in some rocks.

So you'll find time and again on the rambles that I offer more than one explanation for the curious rocks you see – and offer you the choice of how the rock actually formed. Interpretation of the meaning – 'reading the rocks' again – is fraught with difficulty, for in many cases the 'language' is ambiguous. You'll see the evidence, you'll maybe talk it over with your companions, and you'll come to some sort of conclusion. You may be right or you may be way off; you just cannot be sure in some cases.

Anyway, happy walking! And keep your eyes open.

I'd like to thank . . .

My friend and mentor, John Liverman, who lent me his cottage as a *pied a terre* whilst I carried out my researches and who has undertaken several rambles to check any errors I may have made. I'm also immensely grateful to fell-runner, orienteering expert and authoress Carol McNeill who slowed to a trot so as to check out some of the other rambles. Her comments and suggestions were first-rate. My wife, Val, and younger son, Richard, accompanied me on most of the walks, partly to act as scales in photographs and partly to ask questions from a layman's point of view and keep my flights of fancy in check. Finally, my mother copy-edited the manuscript so it's been a real family affair. Even so, any errors are my fault.

ROCKY RAMBLE 1:
BUTTERMERE AND HAYSTACKS

How to get to the start of the ramble

From Keswick, there is a choice of routes to Gatesgarth [194 150], the start of
the ramble. The quickest is over Newlands Pass down to Buttermere village and
then south alongside the beautiful lake to Gatesgarth. Alternatively, you might
like to go through Borrowdale (B5289) and over Honister Pass, going by the
famous slate quarries. You can park at Gatesgarth, though the farmer makes a
small charge.

The ramble: needs, distances and times

The ramble starts at Gatesgarth, immortalized in *The Tale of Mrs Tiggy-Winkle*
by Beatrix Potter. It follows Warnscale Beck to an old slate quarry before
conducting you along the ridge past Innominate Tarn -where A. Wainwright's
ashes are said to have been scattered – to Haystacks, the highest point on the
ramble. From there, you drop down to Scarth Gap Pass and so back to
Gatesgarth; a round trip of about 7 kilometres (4 miles). The amount of
climbing is about 580 metres (1900 feet), so reckon on most of a day for the
circuit. The route takes you through mountain country, so be prepared to cope
with bad weather, as *parts can be dangerous in mist or rain.*

You'll need the OS Outdoor Leisure map, Sheet 4: North Western area.

Introduction

On this ramble, you'll see rocks which formed, some under the sea, nearly half
a billion years ago. Many of them were blasted out of volcanoes, or welled out
as thick, treacly lava flows. You'll also see some of the effects of the great ice
sheets which did so much to influence the scenery of Lakeland.

First stage: Warnscale Bottom

**Walk up from the car park past the cottage on the right and then take a
right turn along a bridle track towards locality 1.** As you start along the
track, you'll see some of the landforms which have been fashioned by ice, the
most recent of the important geological events which have affected the area.

On your right side is the flat valley floor – Warnscale Bottom – once
occupied by the waters of a much larger Buttermere which, like all the lakes in

the district, is slowly being filled in by debris washed down in times of flood from the mountains. The flat area is now covered by sands and gravels brought down by Warnscale Beck but the valley was shaped by the action of glaciers during a series of very cold — glacial — periods which began in Britain about 2,000,000 years ago and finished only 11,500 years before the present (see Appendix: Timescale, Column D). Like all the other Lake District valleys, it was carved by great, slow-moving rivers of ice, flowing down towards the lowlands in just the same way as glaciers in the great mountain ranges of the modern world. The ice contained rock debris which had become frozen into it higher in the mountains and it was this debris, held like sand on sandpaper, that scratched and chiselled the bedrock below as the ice passed over it.

Looking carefully at the smooth bedrock surfaces near the bridle path, you'll find that they've been grooved and scratched by the stones held in the ice. The grooves and scratches are called *glacial striations* and tell us that the ice moved, as you'd expect, along the length of the valley. You can also see many bedrock outcrops which are moulded into smooth, rounded forms like sheeps' backs. These tell us of former ice action and you'll see a good example shortly.

The rock basins occupied by Buttermere and Crummock Water were gouged out by the former heavy and powerful glacier which over-deepened the valley.

Valley over-deepening is a sure sign of former glaciation. Unlike streams and rivers, glaciers can flow slightly uphill as well as down. A river can never carve out a rock basin and create a lake which is why glaciated areas abound in lakes and unglaciated areas don't.

When it melted, the glacier left a hollow which quickly filled with water. The deep, flat-floored, 'U'-shaped valleys tell us clearly that glacial processes took place here not so very long ago. Other indicators which you can see from the track are corries and 'hanging valleys'.

'Corrie' is an Anglicised version of the Gaelic 'coire' (which also means 'kettle' or 'cauldron'). This word has the same meaning as 'cirque' (French), 'cwm' (Welsh) and 'combe' or 'cove' (Lake District): all refer to the distinctive deep hollows, often containing a tarn, scooped out of mountainsides by glaciers.

'Hanging valleys' form because the powerful main valley glacier has so deepened its course that it leaves the side valleys with their puny glaciers 'up in the air'. Once the ice has gone, magnificent waterfalls may develop and away to the west, you can see Comb Beck plunging down from Burtness Combe to join Buttermere.

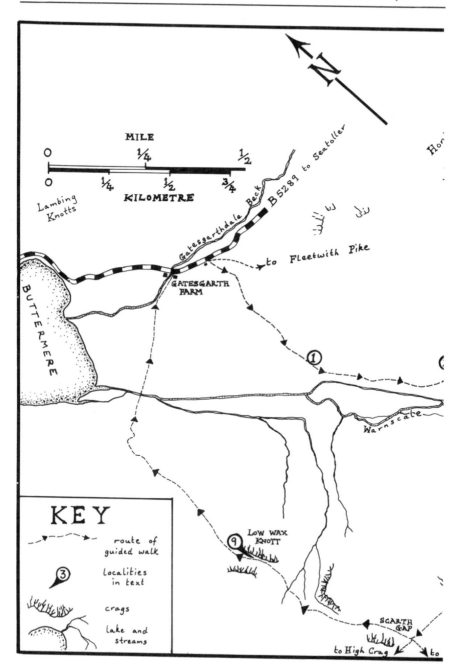

MILE

0   ¼   ½

0   ¼   ½   ¾

KILOMETRE

Lambing
Knotts

Gatesgarthdale Beck   B5289 to Seatoller

Hor

to Fleetwith Pike

GATESGARTH
FARM

BUTTERMERE

①

Warnscale

KEY

route of
guided walk

③ localities
in text

crags

lake and
streams

LOW WAX
KNOTT

⑨

SCARTH
GAP

to High Crag   to

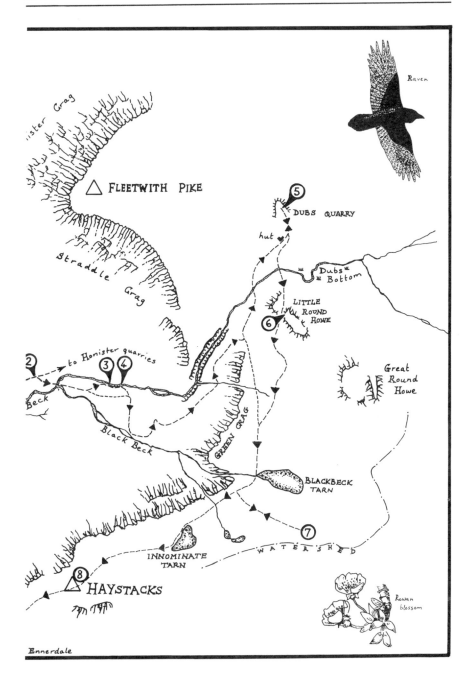

Towering above you to your left as you walk along this track is Fleetwith Pike.

The white cross at the base of the rocky buttress is a memorial to Fanny Mercer, killed in a fall nearby in 1887.

The crags above and the rocks beside the track are *slates* known collectively as the *Skiddaw Slates*. (Geologists call the rocks you see here the 'Kirkstile Slates', a subdivision of the *Skiddaw Slates;* see Appendix – Timescale). The *Skiddaw Slates* form all the mountains to the north, such as Robinson and Grasmoor and, of course, Skiddaw. These grey, monotonous rocks were laid down on the seafloor as mud and silt between about 500 and 470 million years ago (in the lower *Ordovician Period*). That ancient sea was inhabited by small animals called *trilobites* which scurried about on or above the seafloor, searching for food. Other creatures, called *grapto-lites* (Fig. 1.1), drifted with the ocean currents as colonies, each animal living in a tiny chamber attached to others above and below to form a long rod or stipe.

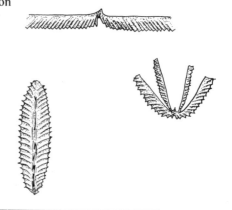

Figure 1.1: Graptolites: the outstretched arms of Didymograptus, the leaf-like Phyllograptus and the four-armed Tetragraptus. All of these have been found in the Skiddaw Slates but they are very uncommon.

Both these animal types are long extinct: *graptolites* died out about 330 million years ago, though *trilobites* hung on for about another 75 million years. Lucky fossil hunters can find their preserved remains in the *Skiddaw Slates* though finding them is difficult unless you are very determined and know what to look for. I did once find a perfect trilobite near the summit of Grisedale Pike. It was just lying on the path . . . so you never know.

The rocks have recorded for us not just thousands, but millions of years of deposition of sand, silt and clay particles, originally swept into the ancient sea by rivers. Currents flowing along the seabed carried the particles away from the shallows into deeper waters where they were laid down in thin layers or *laminae*, groups of which form *beds*.

Often the *laminae* are so regular that they are probably like tree rings, corresponding perhaps to yearly weather cycles or, more likely, larger storms happening every few years. So the *laminae* act as a crude clock and we can estimate how quickly the muds and silts were laid down. The rate in these rocks was perhaps a few tens of centimetres per thousand years, quite fast by comparison with some other types of sediment found in the deep ocean basins.

Sheep rock and cleavage: Locality 1

To the left of the track, just before it bends round to the left, is a large outcrop of slate. This is our first Locality. A dry stone wall which has been following below the track curves away here towards a circular copse of Scots pines near Warnscale Beck.

The outcrop has the typical ice-smoothed form which French geologists in the last century termed *roche moutonnée* or 'sheep rock'. If you look carefully, you should be able to make out crumpled layers – *laminae* – cut across by the *cleavage*.

Cleavage is what geologists and quarrymen refer to when a rock can be split into very thin parallel wafers. Not all rocks have *cleavage*, and how it formed is a complex story (p. 56). Generally, this sort of *cleavage* develops best in rocks made up of mud or silt particles. The rocks are heated and squeezed by the enormous stresses set up during mountain-building episodes. During these periods of stress, which probably lasted for millions of years, flaky minerals called *micas* began to grow forming myriads of parallel crystals at right angles to the main squeezing direction. Eventually, so many mica crystals formed that the rock could split more easily parallel to them than in any other direction. This is called slaty *cleavage*. The *micas* grew from clay minerals, normally the most important ingredient of mud rocks.

The seafloor upon which these sediments were laid down probably sloped gently so that from time to time, perhaps triggered by a severe storm or earthquake, the soft sludgy sediments would slide and slump down the slope into deeper waters. In doing so, the beds became contorted into chaotic *slump folds*: these are the strange crumpled layers you can see here. You may be able to make out much larger examples on the slopes of Robinson overlooking Gatesgarth, in crags called Lambing Knotts [194 155].

Twenty metres beyond Locality 1, a tiny stream crosses the path. In the damp grass by the streamlet, you may find some small yellow-red waxy-capped toadstools called *Hygrophorus* (Fig. 1.2). Growing with these are the common but attractive little yellow tormentils (Fig. 1.3). In the damper patches, you should find sundews (*Drosera*) with their tiny, club-shaped leaves covered in long hairs, each with a droplet of sticky liquid at the tip (Fig. 1.4). These are insect-eaters and often grow in these wet, acid soils along with butterworts, the only other insectivorous plants of the Lake District.

Figure 1.2: Hygrophorus. *The name means 'moisture bearing' reflecting this edible toadstool's preference for dampness.*

Figure 1.3: Tormentil, a four-leaved *Potentilla and member of the Rose Family. They are common almost everywhere in the Lakeland mountains.*

Figure 1.4: Common sundew (Drosera), a lover of acid, peaty bogs.

If you continue now along the track, you'll notice a neat, circular sheepfold on the opposite valley side which has been built upon the lower part of the rock *screes* from Haystacks far above. The upper limits of the *screes* more or less coincide with the upper limit of vegetation, because above this level, there is mostly bare rock and little or no soil. Most *screes* in the Lake District were formed during periods much colder than now – at the end of the last ice age. They form when water freezes in *joints* and fractures in rock crags, expanding and prising the cracks open until, when the ice melts, another piece of rock topples over and crashes down to the *screes* below. You can tell that most of the *screes* are not now forming because they are covered in grasses and bracken which would not be able to survive on active *scree* slopes. If you look up to your left, Fleetwith Pike is also draped with *screes*, again mostly stabilised and overgrown by bracken.

Bracken is somewhat toxic to both animals and humans and it's a serious menace in many upland areas of Britain for there is no easy way to control it. Well not quite no way . . . it appears that there are a couple of species of insect which munch away happily at bracken in South Africa. But is it safe to introduce them here as biological controls?

As you turn a corner along the track so that the Scots pines behind are only partly visible, look again at Fleetwith Pike up to your left. High above, you can see quite clearly the sudden change of rock type as the massive, craggy volcanic rocks of the *Borrowdale Volcanic Group* rest upon the *Skiddaw Slates* underneath. This junction between rock types, one of the most obvious in the whole Lake District, *dips* down towards the head of the valley and crosses Warnscale Beck. It *dips* in this way because the once flat-lying junction, or contact, between the two rock groups has been tilted to the southeast by earth movements. It is made very clear because the base of the volcanic formations is marked by the beginning of the *screes* and a different style of rock outcrop. The hard volcanic rocks tend to form great crags, whilst the underlying older and softer slates form small, rounded outcrops. The line of change follows the base of the crags and you'll note that the heather grows only on the slates.

This change between mud and silt rocks and what you'll shortly see to be thick *lava* flows from a nearby ancient volcano, is of great importance to geologists. It marked a dramatic change about 460 million years ago, from stable conditions to volcanic eruptions on a prodigious scale. Why this sudden change?

Not far to the northwest, a huge battle was being fought. Two of the great plates which formed the Earth's crust at that time, were relentlessly ploughing towards each other, so something had to give. It did, with the thinner, weaker crust of an ancient ocean (Iapetus Ocean, p. 55), which at this time separated the thicker continental plates, being forced down and consumed underneath the more buoyant, rigid continent plates: a process, part of *plate tectonics*, called *subduction*.

If you ever visit the Arctic or Antarctic oceans, you can see some of these processes in action – on a very small scale. When floating pack ice (= plates) is forced by winds and currents into collision with other ice, huge pressure ridges form (= 'mountain ranges'; a nightmare for explorers trying to cross them). In addition, the leading edge of one floe (= plate) may ramp up onto another, overriding it and forcing the other flow down underneath it (= *subduction*). If the currents change, the crumpled floes may break apart and start spreading away from each other, forming 'leads' in the pack ice. The same process occurs with crustal plates which can be torn apart, new ocean forming in between. This is how the Atlantic Ocean formed, though starting only 200 million years ago. The parallels between 'ice tectonics' and *plate tectonics* are remarkably instructive.

But the friction heat generated in this tussle between the plates became so great that some of the rocks along the downgoing ocean plate melted and then rose – by a combination of melting and extreme pressure -through the over-riding plate to form volcanoes. What we now know as the Lake District was on the leading edge of the over-riding plate, which is why volcanoes formed here.

Black Beck and waterfalls: Locality 2

Continue until you reach two large, waist-height stones on either side of the track which, though not erected by me, mark Locality 2. Before you is a fine scene (Fig. 1.5) of crags and waterfalls as Warnscale Beck plunges down from the valley head. It is joined not far in front of you by Black Beck, which has an even more spectacular descent through a great chasm high above on the right, the outlet of Black Beck Tarn. Because of its steep descent this stream is powerful in times of heavy rainfall and has brought down many large blocks and boulders to build up a cone or fan of debris where its descent becomes less steep and its energy is lost. You'll be crossing this *alluvial cone* shortly.

Figure 1.5: *Green Crag and Warnscale Beck waterfalls; the lowest rocks of the Borrowdale Volcanic Group. The old quarrymans' track runs up to the left. Your route is dead ahead.*

From Locality 2 the main track continues on the left side of the valley up to the old slate quarries, known as Dubs Quarry (Locality 5). But you take a different route and continue on slightly to the right, directly towards the waterfalls. Cross the beck on a small, wooden bridge and begin to climb along a gentle, grassy track.

As you walk, notice the scattered trees growing on the slopes: they are all birch, hawthorn and ancient yews. The large boulders you see around you were left when the glaciers melted. You'll see a particularly good example of such a boulder at Locality 7. As the path crosses a small offshoot of Black Beck, look at the water-polished boulders and cobbles which are all volcanic rocks brought down from the crags high above.

Wet, water-polished outcrops or boulders are the very best way of seeing the fresh detail inside a rock. Normally, outcrops are crusted with lichens and mosses, and the rock itself is weathered, causing many minerals to decay.

Figure 1.6: Club moss, a member of the Fern (Pteridophyte) Family, its creeping stems covered with tiny, overlapping leaves.

At the point where the grassy part of the track ends and it becomes steeper and stonier, bear off to the left to follow Warnscale Beck up through grass and bracken and a few rowan trees.

In the marshy patches, if you look carefully, you should see tiny insectivorous sundews. Also enjoying the wet patches are sphagnum moss and the branching clubmosses which look like green rats' tails (Fig. 1.6).

Passing small waterfalls and deep pools in the beck, some forty paces slightly uphill from the track you just left behind, you should find yourself above the first large waterfall.

Skiddaw Slates: Locality 3

Here you'll find outcrops in and beside the beck of the lead-grey *Skiddaw Slates*. Look closely at wet, water-polished surfaces and you'll see delicate pale and dark stripes or bands in the rocks depicting the *bedding*. These formed because of slightly different grain sizes and compositions of the original muds and silts as they were laid down on the ancient seafloor. The whole rock is affected by intense *cleavage*. The angle between *bedding* and *cleavage* is clear in many outcrops in the stream beyond the third living rowan tree above the base of the waterfalls.

When a powerful river discharges its load of mud, silt and sand into the sea, the different particle sizes of the sediment load mean that the deposits which 'fall out' onto the sea floor become sorted; as if passed through a series of sieves. The largest sand particles settle out first, followed by the finer silt and, much later, by the mud and clay. This is why *beds* or *laminae* form in rocks made up of sediments which have 'fallen out' from suspensions in water (or air). You can prove this to yourself by putting some soil, generally a good mix of different particle sizes, into a large water-filled glass jar. Shake your jar and watch what happens. You should actually get a graded bed.

Continue a short way up the stream to a waterfall about 3 metres high. Your next stop is where you see a medium-sized rowan tree and two small ones.

The mighty Borrowdale Volcanics begin: Locality 4

Here you can see the actual junction, the contact, between the *Borrowdale Volcanic Group (BVG)* and the *Skiddaw Slates*. This is the junction which I mentioned before Locality 2 and it's worth spending a few minutes here looking carefully at the rocks beside the stream. The slates are, as before, strongly *cleaved* and banded or *laminated.* The *plane* of the *cleavage dips* steeply (75°) towards the southeast. The *plane* of the contact *dips* less steeply (about 60°) which means that if you walk up the stream to the southeast, the rocks you cross are becoming younger, because older rocks almost always *underlie* younger ones.

You can best make out the actual change from slates to volcanic rocks on the left bank of the beck (on your left looking upstream), beneath the rowan trees. You'll find this lowest unit of the thick *BVG* to be a hard, grey-green, fine grained, vaguely banded rock. Unlike the underlying slates, it is tough and so does not have a *cleavage*. It is an *andesite lava,* and this rock type forms the base of the *BVG* everywhere in the Haystacks area. It is very thick, probably more than 100 metres, and in places became folded and contorted whilst it was still molten as you will see later. Above the waterfall here, the *lava* is cut by networks of white *quartz* veins. This mineral crystallised out from fluids which flowed through cracks in the rock that formed as the *lava* cooled.

Look out for the little sundews, mosses, ferns and liverworts (Fig. 1.7) which grow in the damp places by the stream.

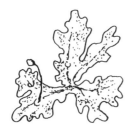

Figure 1.7: Liverwort, a primitive, seaweed-like Bryophyte with stems and leaves but no true roots. Another lover of damp places.

Mosses and liverworts are the most ancient of all land plants. Geologists have found traces of them in rocks older than the *BVG* (up to 470 million years old). Another 50 million years passed before the earliest vascular land plants definitely appeared. These were the forerunners of today's trees and flowers which all have a system of tubes – the vascular system – to carry water and nutrients between roots and leaves. Interestingly, the first land animal colonisers preceded the vascular plants by around 30 million years. These were arthropods, the land equivalent of the *trilobites* which were so successful in the world's seas at that time.

Now walk back up to rejoin the track you left earlier for the detour to Locality 3 and climb the steep incline which at first heads southwest.

Now you'll pass outcrops and huge boulders of brown-grey *BVG lavas,* many with colour bands and cavities. The banding was formed by the flowing movement which occurred when the *lava* was still hot but very thick and sticky.

In the summer months, wheatears (Fig. 1.8) nest in the *screes* near the track. You can easily recognise these attractive little summer migrants by their light grey breasts, white flashes in their tails and their loud 'weet, chack, chack' calls.

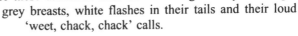

Continue up the track and cross a small stream. Some 70 metres further, wet outcrops of rock beside the track are covered with insect-eating butterworts (Fig. 1.9). In early summer, they bear delicate purple flowers. Also around the track, you should find harebells and club-mosses.

Cross a ruined wall. High above the track to the right, you'll notice a small stone building. This has been partially rebuilt with a window which, if you care to enter and look through it, frames a beautiful view down the Buttermere valley. Once a shepherd's or quarryman's shelter, the hut is now used as a mountain refuge. It has a fireplace and a bible, should you wish to read something other than this guide whilst waiting for bad weather to clear.

Figure 1.8: Wheatear

Continue along the lowest track with cairns (there are several possible ways here) and cross Warnscale Beck wherever you can. Then climb up the left bank to join the old miners' track (from Locality 2). Follow this for about 300 metres to Dubs Quarry, where you find another building, marked on the O.S. map as a 'climbing hut' (Fig. 1.10).

Figure 1.9: The insectivorous common butterwort (Pinguicula) with its rosette of sticky, inrolled leaves and gnome-hat, violet flower.

Dubs Quarry: Locality 5. Relic of former industry

Have a wander about here and examine the remains of the quarry operations: the rock faces, the tips, the old railway lines and the collapsed level (tunnel) lower down, through which the slate blocks were hauled from underground quarrying operations. To see the level, walk 40 paces past the climbing hut (which has a water supply running down an inverted rail) and follow an old incline on your right, down to the collapsed level and several ruined buildings. The slate blocks would have been dressed and split here by hand.

Dubs Quarry was but a small part of the great Honister Quarries, which have been worked continuously since 1643. Before about 1870, when tramways with iron rails began to be widely used for moving the slate blocks, the quarrymen used to drag the blocks on sledges specially made for this purpose. Each block weighed about a quarter of a ton and had to be dragged down screes and rock to the splitting sheds. Today, they are moved by lorry.

But what are the slates? In the top part of the main quarry, you can see the green-grey strongly *cleaved* rock, the source of the slates. You have to be careful to distinguish the *cleavage* from the *bedding*. Here, you may like a few definitions. *Bedding* is a general term given to individual layers or beds of sediment grouped together. The horizontal trend (the compass direction of a horizontal line drawn along the *bedding plane*) gives us the *strike* of the beds whilst their *dip* can be measured in degrees from 0° (flat-lying beds) to 90° (vertical beds). The *cleavage* which, of course, developed long afterwards rather overwhelms the *bedding* in the quarry, making the latter a little difficult to see.

But the *cleavage dips* at 75° to the southeast, whereas the *bedding,* when you can measure it, has a much gentler *dip* of about 30° to the south.

Figure 1.10: *Dubs Quarry with the climbers' hut on the left. You can see the steeply dipping (top left to bottom right), cleaved BVG in the centre of the picture, surrounded by slate tips. In the top part of this quarry, you should be able to make out the difference between cleavage and bedding and examine some of the fresh, green BVG rocks in detail.*

If you look carefully with a lens at the fresh rock in the quarry, you'll see that it's made up of particles, called *clasts*, about the size of fine grains of sand. These are eroded bits of volcanic rocks. They are unlike the mud and silt rocks of the *Skiddaw Slates* you saw earlier, and have the characteristic green colour of many of the volcanic rocks of the Lake District. You should also be able to make out beds of larger, pea-sized volcanic particles or *volcaniclasts*. As most of this rock is made up of sand-size volcanic particles, it's called a *volcaniclastic sandstone.*

    (Sorry about these last two paragraphs . . . a bit heavy going, aren't they!

Don't worry: you don't have to remember any of it because you can always look up the words in the Glossary and as you get more familiar with these names and ideas, you'll soon wonder what the problem was.)

Because you can see definite beds in this *sandstone,* you can be sure that it is a *sedimentary* rock. The grains, *clasts,* settled out from suspension in either air or water. In Dubs Quarry, the rocks were laid down in water. How do we know this? We can tell from various small structures they contain such as ripple marks. They may have fallen out directly from clouds of ash from nearby eruptions, probably into a shallow lake.

To continue the ramble, drop down towards the southwest, crossing the stream once again as it flows out of Dubs Bottom. This was once occupied by a small lake but has long since become filled by sediments and peat, and is now just a marshy area drained by the meandering stream. In the marsh grow sphagnum mosses, rushes and cotton grass, the raw materials of peat. **Follow the broad and clear track which makes its way up the slope towards Black Beck Tarn. Away to your left are Grey Knotts and Brandreth and ahead of you is a rounded crag on the left side of the track with a smaller companion on the right. This is Little Round Howe and is about 250 metres from the stream. The track passes through the opening between these two craggy outcrops which is where you stop.**

Chaos and confusion at Little Round Howe: Locality 6 [2076 1325]

The rocks here repay close examination for they are a veritable jumble. You'll notice first that the main mass to the left of the track is not uniform; it's a confused mix of variably sized and shaped fragments -*volcaniclasts* – some the size of a small dog (Fig. 1.11). This is a *volcaniclastic breccia,*which tells you what the rock is but not how it formed. Underneath the obvious *breccia,* most of the fragments are smaller (pea or grape size) and you can see pieces of broken-up *beds* 'floating' raft-like in the mixed fragmental material which encloses them. One such raft has been folded into a tight 'V' (about 1 metre long but lying on its side).

On the right side of the track, below the *breccia* outcrops, you can see *flow-foliated lavas* with white *feldspar* crystals. Some of these *lavas* show signs of having started to break up, in this instance because of a process known as *flow brecciation.* This occurs when a *lava* flow develops a solid crust, whilst the hotter inside part remains liquid and mobile. The pressure exerted by the flowing liquid breaks up the solid crust and drags the fragments produced into the continuing flow.

But *flow brecciation* cannot account for the jumble of material which overlies the *lava* to the left of the track, the main crag of Little Round Howe (Fig. 1.11). You might have noticed that all the *volcaniclasts* within this *breccia* are made of *lavas* -mostly without noticeable crystals – but the event which produced the *breccia* was almost certainly a gravity-driven *debris* or *mass flow*. An unstable slurry of water-saturated *lava* blocks (remember that many of these rocks were erupted or laid down under water) mixed up with muds and silts began to move, probably because of an earthquake shock, for earthquakes always occur in areas with active volcanoes. They then would have flowed and slumped down an underwater slope coming to rest where the slope flattened out, for the same reason that Black Beck has built up a fan of debris which you crossed earlier.

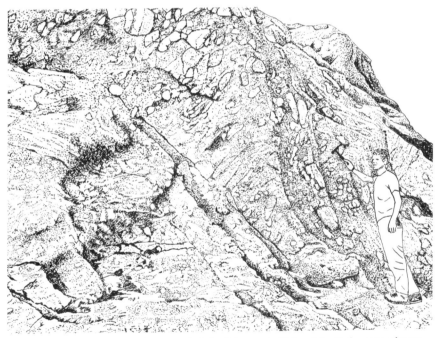

Figure 1.11: *Little Round Howe to the left of the track. Volcaniclastic breccia, slumps... The choice is yours. The 'floating rafts' are in the lower left of the sketch.*

Such *mass flows* are very common events indeed and can occur on land or in the sea. We cannot, of course, observe them directly when they occur below the sea but on land, their effects are sometimes disastrous for they may form certain types of landslips, mudflows or debris flows. The Aberfan disaster (p. 222) was a man-made example.

So we can explain the rafts of material 'floating' in muddy, sandy gravel by *mass flow* origin, in which beds are torn apart and mixed up with any other material which happened to be around. The very coarse *breccia* (Fig. 1.11) may have the same origin, though it could have formed in other ways, such as by avalanching from a nearby active volcano. It could even have been the material which blocked up the vent of one of the ancient volcanoes. You've now seen the evidence before you; these rocks are telling us a story, but there is more than one way to 'read' their obscure language. What do *you* make of them?

Leaving the spectacular outcrops of Little Round Howe, continue along the track towards Black Beck Tarn. As you do so, you'll have regular glimpses to the northwest, down over Buttermere and Crummock Water. Buttermere village is built on the higher part of a large *alluvial fan* of gravels and sands brought down by Mill Beck in times of flood. Buttermere and Crummock Water would once have been one continuous lake, but are now cut into two by this fan. The river connecting the two lakes has been forced right across to the base of the steep slopes of High Stile as the fan has built out towards the southwest.

As you approach the shallow rocky basin occupied by Black Beck Tarn, you'll see on the ridge above a large, isolated, triangular perched block which you will be visiting shortly. Behind are the great ridges of Kirk Fell and Pillar, on the other side of Ennerdale.

Crossing Black Beck, the track continues on in a rather dramatic way, with a steep drop off on your right back down to Warnscale Beck. Black Beck itself plunges down into a forbidding rocky chasm. On your left now are further crags which look as though they are *bedded*. Some of this 'bedding' is gently folded, though the folds are nothing to do with later earth movements; rather they are due to the process of flow in the once-hot and sticky *lava*. You'll later see perfect examples of such folding on the summit of Haystacks.

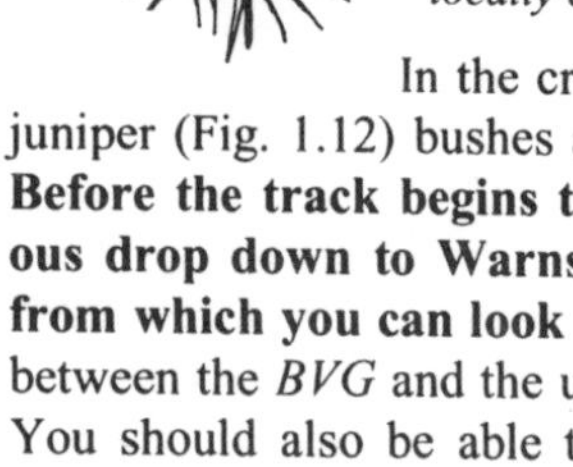

Figure 1.12: Dwarf juniper (Juniperus), member of the Cypress Family, with its bright red, berry-like fruits. This small tree is locally common in the Lake District.

In the crags and gullies hereabouts, you'll notice many dwarf juniper (Fig. 1.12) bushes and yellow bog asphodels growing in damper places. **Before the track begins to climb steeply upwards, away from the precipit-ous drop down to Warnscale Bottom, there is a fine viewpoint (Fig. 1.13) from which you can look across to Fleetwith Pike** and see clearly the junction between the *BVG* and the underlying *Skiddaw Slates* which we discussed earlier. You should also be able to see that the thick and uniform *lavas* of the main crags of Fleetwith Pike (and Haystacks) are overlain to the southeast (to the right) by a succession of thinner sheets of *lavas* and *tuffs*. These form a striking series of *beds* dipping gently to the southeast at about 30° (as you saw in Dubs Quarry, a part of this sequence).

Tuff and *volcaniclastic sandstone* can be the same thing, or they can be different. Strictly, a *tuff* is a hardened volcanic ash which has fallen out directly from an eruption cloud. A *volcaniclastic sandstone* is simply a sandstone made up of particles which had a volcanic origin. They may have been laid down as ash somewhere else on land first, to be then washed into a lake by heavy rains (which often accompany volcanic eruptions). These things are notoriously hard to tell apart and such minutiae of rock terms don't need to concern us at all. Just be aware that this is one reason for the Tower of Babel of complicated names. The aim is precision, but the result is often confusion for the amateur!

Figure 1.13: Fleetwith Pike with thick lavas forming the summit and crags, all dipping to the right. You can make out vague bedding features in the Skiddaw Slates (on the left) which also dip to the right of the picture.

Now head up the steep section of the track for some 30 metres, away from the chasms. The track flattens out as it makes its way towards Haystacks summit but don't continue along it just yet. Turn sharp left along a smaller path marked, once you have started along it, by stone cairns. This heads south-southeast, towards Great Gable, meandering over a rocky plateau with *flow banded lavas* cropping out almost everywhere. The landscape you are

looking at has been heavily scraped by ice sheets which rounded and smoothed
the rock outcrops, now separated by stagnant peaty pools or bogs.

Figure 1.14: *Perched block (looking closer than it really is in the left of the sketch) and
a complex contact between a lava flow (below the hammer shaft) and laminated
sediments.*

Lavas, drapes, slumps and a perched block:
Locality 7 [2010 1258]

**After a while, the path passes the perched block (about 25 paces to the left
at its closest) that you saw in the distance from Black Beck Tarn.** Here, you
are on the watershed between Buttermere and Ennerdale. Locality 7 includes
this block (looking much closer than it really is in Fig. 1.14, left), dragged here
by the ice sheet which covered the ridge. It was left in this 'perched' position
when the main ice sheets finally melted about 14,500 years ago.

There is much of interest at Locality 7, mostly close to the left (Black Beck
Tarn side) of the path. Here you'll notice a sudden change from the thick
flow-banded and folded *lavas* that you've been walking over since Black Beck

Tarn, to beautifully *bedded,* fine grained, *graded, volcaniclastic* sediments which overlie the *lavas.* A contact between the two is particularly clear right by the path (Fig. 1.14) and if you look carefully, you can make out beds slumped and draped over the very irregular, broken up top of the older *lava* flow beneath. As the *beds* settled and became squashed – loaded – by the weight of later sediments overlying them, they were disrupted by small *faults* with tiny movements of just a few millimetres. You can examine these little *faults* for yourself in an outcrop nearby (Fig. 1.15). When these delicate beds were laid down, volcanic activity had temporarily ceased giving way to tranquil conditions. From time to time, slight tilting must have occurred, probably due to local, larger scale *fault* movements. Some of the beds affected by this tilting would then have protruded a little from the lake floor or sea floor and so would

have been scoured and planed-off by water currents. Fresh layers of sediment would then have been laid down, but with a slight angle between the older tilted and planed-off sediments and the later ones. You can see this clearly at the top of the outcrop in Fig. 1.15. All the beds dip (note the pen for scale) gently to the right of the sketch, but the topmost beds cut out the ones beneath them, forming a small angle. They themselves would have been horizontal, but because of later tilting, now dip a few degrees more steeply to the right. This is a very small-scale *unconformity.*

Figure 1.15: *Delicately bedded muddy and sandy sediments cut by tiny faults. Note the small, angular unconformity at the top of the outcrop. The topmost beds dip more steeply to the right than those underneath, cutting out the underlying beds progressively towards the right.*

Unconformities are an important concept in geology for wherever you see such a relationship, you know that there has been a break in deposition. If the rocks, like tree rings, record the regular passing of time, alarm bells ring when you see an unconformity which tells you that some of the rock sequence is missing – like missing pages from a book – so the time record is not complete. Some well known *unconformities* can represent gaps in the record of millions of years. In fact, the contact you looked at at Locality 4 is probably unconformable. There may have been a prolonged period of erosion of the *Skiddaw Slates* before the *BVG* eruptions began. On the other hand, the breaks we see here (Fig. 1.15) may have been only months.

Once you have appreciated the meaning of this contact between the *lavas* and the overlying rocks, you might like to try and follow it northwards. With care, it is quite easy to do this for some tens of metres. It is complex because the top of this sort of *lava* flow is always a jumbled mass of rubbly blocks. The flow itself often contains blocks up to the size of a small dog. The nearby perched block rests upon this complex contact.

After a few minutes of studying the *lava* and overlying bedded sequence, you may find that as you 'get your eye in', you can indeed follow the junction between the different rock types. You will then have discovered one of the principles which geologists use for making a geological map. All the 'lines' on a geological map are boundaries such as this. Some are easy to trace; others more difficult.

Now retrace your steps to the main track to Haystacks from which you turned left to visit this locality. After you have rejoined the main track, you'll pass Innominate Tarn on your left (Fig. 1.16), beloved of A. Wainwright whose cremated remains are said to be scattered hereabouts and whose beautifully produced guides are admired and used by so many walkers in the Lake District.

At one end of the tarn, white-flowering bog beans grow in the shallow peaty water. These are closely related to the gentian family.

You now begin to ascend the track on the final part of the route to the summit of Haystacks. As you proceed, stop and admire the ridges of Pillar to the southwest and look down into the head of Ennerdale where you'll notice, apart from the stark and unattractive spruce forest plantations further down, that the bottom and lower slopes of the dale are covered by large grassy mounds. These, too, are relics of the latest glacial period and are called *moraines.* If you were to dig into a *moraine,* you would find that it is made up of sticky clay with angular stones and boulders. *Moraines* form when a dirty ice sheet decays, leaving behind all the loose material it had plucked or ground up when it was active.

Figure 1.16: *Innominate Tarn, Wainwright's resting place. The great bulk of Pillar rears behind with lonely Ennerdale between. This beautiful tarn would not exist if there had been no glaciation.*

Haystacks summit: Locality 8 [1934 1318]. Folds and a view.

When you reach Haystacks summit, you must obviously admire the view, for although this mountain is not high by Lake District standards, it is in a way the more impressive for that reason. For around you rear the crags and precipices of Steeple, Pillar, Kirk Fell, Fleetwith Pike and High Stile whilst further afield are Great Gable, Whiteless Pike, Robinson, Hindscarth and Dale Head. Most of these nearby peaks are higher but if you peep carefully over the edge of the precipices of Haystacks down towards Gatesgarth, you'll see that this mountain, too, is no dwarf.

As you look around the summit area, defined by rounded rocky outcrops with – a few paces before the summit – one particularly noticeable grassy trough running between them, you'll realise that the rocks are all *flow-folded lavas* (Fig. 1.17) like those you saw near Black Beck Tarn. In fact in this grassy trough, you'll see some of the best examples of *flow-folding* anywhere. These folds continue down towards **Scarth Gap, to which you should now begin to descend.** *Please note that this descent is steep and potentially dangerous if you are careless.* **You have to make your way down one of the cairned tracks through steep gullies and onto loose screes below. If you follow the regular track, you shouldn't have problems here, but do keep your eyes**

open for cairns. At Scarth Gap, you meet the track which joins Ennerdale and Buttermere. Descend towards Buttermere on a long, steady incline, passing more outcrops and boulders of *andesite lavas,* some with obvious crystals.

Figure 1.17: *Spectacular flow folding in the lavas just below Haystacks' summit. The hot lava must have had a treacle-like consistency to concertina in this way, but this is quite normal in lavas which contain an excess of silica.*

After a short while, you cross a wall and then a small stream. In the stream, you can see once again the *Skiddaw Slates* which you saw at Localities 1, 3 and 4. But just a moment; things are not so simple here for further down the track when you should be well down into the *Skiddaw Slates,* you find more outcrops of *BVG* rocks, some of which are full of *feldspar* crystals. This suggests at least two possibilities: The contact between the *Skiddaw Slates* and the *BVG* is very irregular, not flat or smooth. Indeed, the landscape before the *BVG* volcanoes may have been cut by erosion into a series of hills and valleys which were later 'drowned' by the *BVG* deposits. In other words, what we see here may be evidence for be an irregular *unconformable* contact (Locality 7). Alternatively, these outcrops of *BVG* may have been brought down into their present position by buckling of the rocks and *fault* movements. And I'm afraid that there's a third possibility: the volcanic rocks you see here aren't *BVG* at all. They may be older volcanic rocks. There are some within the *Skiddaw Slates,* known as the Eyecott Lavas (see Appendix: Timescale).

Hot bodies: granite at Locality 9 [1877 1400]

The final stop on this walk is between High and Low Wax Knotts at a point where the path kinks to the right. Here, you should see a few pale coloured outcrops beside the track. If you look closely at these, you'll see that they are unlike anything you've seen earlier. This is *granite,* and is composed of large crystals of pink and white *feldspars,* white *micas* and *quartz.* The *mica* is shiny and metallic-looking; the *quartz* colourless. This rock is an offshoot of larger *igneous intrusions* which lie to the west (Ennerdale) and northwest (see Appendix: Geology Map), where they form the north part of High Stile and Red Pike. The rock was forced into the surrounding older rocks as a hot, partially crystallised mush at, perhaps, 800°C. It was formed deep in the Earth's crust and squeezed into the host rocks – the slates and volcanics – by the tremendous forces which operated during the mountain building period about 400 million years ago.

When liquid rock, such as this once was, reaches the surface, a volcano forms – an *extrusion*. But at this locality, the molten rock did not reach the surface. This is why it contains such large crystals for crystals only become large if they have time to grow. Obviously, a molten rock which erupted rapidly and violently at the surface of the earth would cool and solidify almost immediately, so any crystals which do form are often too small to detect with the naked eye. By contrast, *intrusions* are well insulated by the rock into which they are forced and so cool very slowly, allowing the crystals time to grow. So the granite which you see here looks very different from the rocks of the *BVG* nearby, though chemically they may be very similar.

Finally, complete the descent along the track which has suffered greatly from erosion in recent years. Pass through the gate at the bottom, cross the bridge and walk back to Gatesgarth, noticing as you do that you are ascending very gently the whole time as you walk along the lane to the farm. This is because Gatesgarthdale Beck, which drains from Honister, has built out an *alluvial fan* like Mill Beck at Buttermere village. The fan has forced Warnscale Beck over to the foot of Haystacks, though the former beck now drains directly into Buttermere from Gatesgarth.

As you walk back to the farm with thoughts of your evening meal in mind, look back once more to that splendid sight of the great dale-head panorama formed by Fleetwith Pike, Warnscale and Haystacks and consider the ramble you have just completed. Before you started, these were just handsome mountains. Now you have seen for yourself a little of how these mountains came into existence and why they look as they do. You can trace the *unconformable* contact between the older *Skiddaw Slates* and the *BVG*. You know what rock forms most of the mountains above and from whence it came. Congratulations! You have begun to understand the rudiments of 'reading' the rocks.

ROCKY RAMBLE 2:
DOVEDALE AND ITS MOUNTAINS

How to get to the start of the ramble

If you are driving from Keswick or the north, you'll need to pick up the A592 south along Ullswater, passing through the villages of Glenridding and Patterdale. About one and a half miles south of Patterdale, the road crosses Goldrill Beck and bends to the left at Cow Bridge. Immediately to your right is a small carpark which is the start of the walk.

If you are coming from Ambleside or the south, take the A592 over Kirkstone Pass and so down the long gradient to Brothers Water. The road bends left just before the turn off right to Hartsop village and the carpark is then 300 metres ahead, bearing left off the main road.

The ramble: needs, distances and times

You'll need a full day for the complete ramble. It is about 12 kilometres ($7\frac{1}{2}$ miles), though because there are optional parts which you can miss out, it could be less – or more if you decide you want to forge on to Fairfield (873 metres). The amount of climbing involved – largely the ascent to Dove Crag – is around 700 metres (2,300 feet).

This is definitely a fine day ramble though even when the cloud is down the walk up Dovedale is easy and there's no danger of getting lost. But to continue up onto the fell tops is both pointless and dangerous if the weather is poor.

Priest's Hole makes an unusual and sheltered picnic lunch spot for those with a head for heights, though there is no shortage of pleasant lunch spots in any case.

The Outdoor Leisure map is Sheet 5, North East area.

Introduction

This ramble takes you through some of the most beautiful of all Lakeland scenery. In addition to the fascinating rocks, I've included some history and prehistory. There's even an old mine, and there are marvellous views in all directions from the higher parts of the walk.

The rocks you'll see are all part of the *Borrowdale Volcanic Group,* those hard rocks mostly thrown out of volcanoes about 450 million years ago which now form the rugged mountains of the central Lake District. They tell a fearful

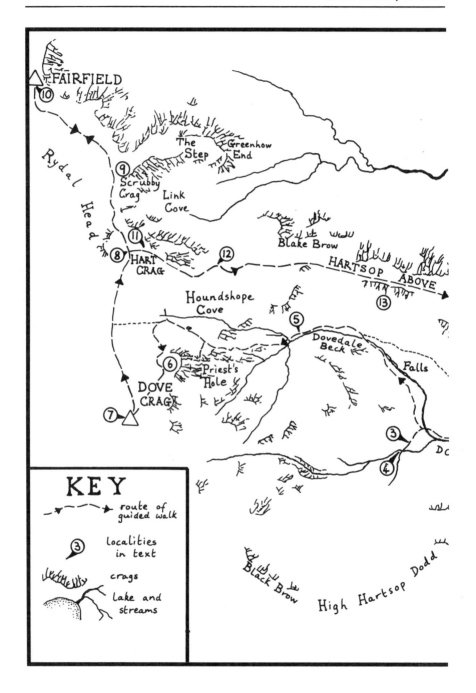

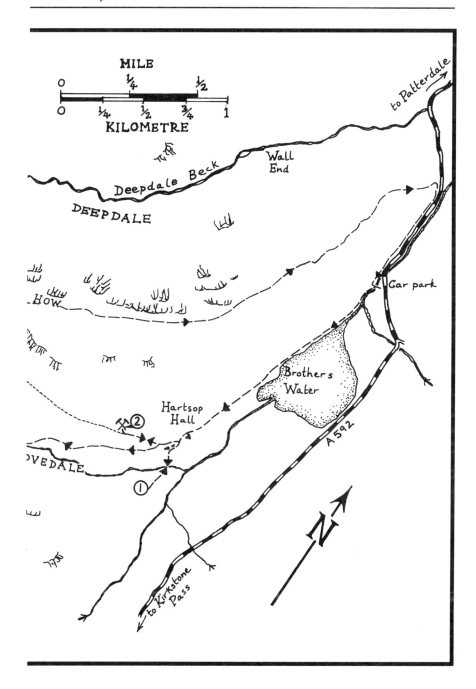

story of violent eruptions, *lava* flows, powerful mudflows and hot avalanches as well as quiet shallow lakes; a story which you can read for yourself in the rocks.

Brothers Water, Hartsop Hall and Dovedale

Cross the bridge and turn left onto the broad track running initially by Goldrill Beck which shortly opens out into Brothers Water. This lake, like all others in the Lake District that are not man-made, was gouged out by powerful glaciers during the ice ages which gripped most of Britain between about 2 million and 11,500 years ago. This valley was filled, probably at several different times, by a slow-moving river of ice which because of its weight and the rocks caught up in the moving base, ground and crunched its way down into the bedrock. The end result was a huge, 'U'-shaped valley with a flat floor, eminently suitable for a lake to form. Ullswater and Brothers Water are two examples of lakes which have formed in an valley overdeepened by such powerful glaciers (p. 11). But like all lakes, Brothers Water is ephemeral. It is slowly filling in with stones, silt and mud brought in by flooded becks every time there is prolonged rain. The reeds and rushes growing well out into the lake are a testament to this infilling, showing how shallow much of it now is and, luckily, providing shelter for various types of wild ducks and other waterfowl such as the shy coot.

The woodlands clothing the steep slope to the right of the track are dominated by oaks, with grass and bracken growing beneath. In the cooler, damp days of autumn, you can find various sorts of fungi here, most commonly the cep or penny bun (*Boletus*) (Fig. 2.1). This is different from what we normally regard as 'mushrooms' because instead of radial gills underneath its fleshy cap (e.g. field mushrooms), this one has spongy pores, usually bright yellow. Surprising to many is that some of these are edible but I don't think they're very good. Some are poisonous too, so avoid them unless you have a special knowledge of which to go for.

Figure 2.1: *Boletus, a mushroom with yellow spongy pores instead of gills.*

The woodland plants are growing in a mixture of stable *screes* and *solifluction* material, stony soils which have slowly slipped down the steep slope from higher up, mainly because of winter freezing and thawing continually heaving and melting the ground. The *screes* probably formed during the *Younger Dryas* period, the last gasp of the great ice ages which ended only 11,500 years ago. During this period which lasted for about 1,200 years, the cold became sufficiently intense for small glaciers to form once again in the high corries and valleys (p. 11 and 83). These glaciers left distinctive *terminal moraines* which you can often see forming natural dams across the valley floors. The *Younger Dryas* ice (see Appendix: Timescale) probably reached as far as Hartsop Hall, leaving characteristic *moraine* ridges on the valley sides, showing us where the glacier tongue once reached about 12,000 years ago.

As you continue along by the lake, you'll see that rocks crop out from time to time under the trees showing that the soils and screes are really quite a thin skin.

When you emerge from the wood at the southwest end of the lake, walk down to the left over the sheep-cropped grass of the lakeshore and look across to the northeast. On the skyline are the two 'cat's ears' of Angle Tarn Pikes. Below and to the right is the tiny hamlet of Hartsop which Wordsworth described in his *Guide to the Lakes* as 'a decaying hamlet . . . remarkable for its cottage architecture'. The hamlet now consists mostly of holiday homes. It is sited on the banks of Hayeswater Gill which, being quite large, has built out a substantial *alluvial fan*, most of this forming during the enormous flood of meltwaters released by the decaying glaciers at the end of the ice age. This is the reason that you now find Goldrill Beck forced right against the steep rocky slopes of the long ridge of Hartsop above How. The accumulating debris of the Hayeswater Gill *alluvial fan* has gradually built out westwards, filling in a formerly much larger Brothers Water as it did so.

Alluvial fans are common throughout Lakeland, mainly as a result of the enormous volume of debris-charged meltwaters released by the decaying glaciers. You see them wherever a powerful tributary stream emerges from a side valley. Often villages are built on them – Patterdale and Glenridding for example – because, being mostly sand and gravel, they are usually well drained.

And now for a little fluvial etymology. A 'gill' or, sometimes, 'ghyll' is a narrow stream, often in a wooded ravine. The word dates from the 11th century and is a British dialect adaptation of the Old Norse, 'gil' meaning a steep-sided valley. 'Beck' is a north English term for a swift-flowing stream. It comes from the Old English 'becc' and Old Norse 'bekkr.'

Now continue along the track to Hartsop Hall. Notice that the track runs along a distinct change of slope angle with steeper more hummocky ground on the right and smooth river *flood plain* on the left. The ground on the right is made up of masses of clay and stones which were dumped here by the *Younger Dryas* glaciers, for this was their maximum extent.

Approaching the lovely 400-year-old Hartsop Hall, now owned by the National Trust, you'll walk under some fine sycamore and ash trees. The hall itself is a classic of Lake District architecture with stone mullioned windows (Fig. 2.2) and barns built as part of the main, roughly 'T'-shaped house.

Figure 2.2: Hartsop Hall with Kirkstone Pass behind.

Go through the gate and across the yard and look for the public footpath guide post labelled 'Kirkstone Pass'. Walk through the gate and continue south along this path (this is an optional extra involving a short walk to a prehistoric settlement opposite Caudalebeck Farm). **After going through the gate, you pass some more barns to your right in which, at sheep shearing time, you'll see piles of rolled up fleeces ready for transport. Before the silage pit, bear left along a grassy track to cross the beck on a wooden bridge and continue through the lush pastures to Locality 1.** This diversion gives you a beautiful panorama of High Hartsop Dodd, Black Brow, Dove and Hart Crags (from left to right). The contrasts between the lush, sheep-cropped pastures of the flat valley floor, punctuated by fine trees, patches of woodland and neat drystone walls and the forbidding black crags and wild mountainside overshadowing make this one of the most beautiful of all Lake

District valleys – the more so because there is no road within it. Yet if you had been standing where you are now some 18,000 years ago, you would have been crushed under a huge river of ice probably hundreds of metres thick: the glacier which once flowed out from here to merge with that from Kirkstone Pass.

Old settlement and erratics: Locality 1 [398 117]

The settlement is no more than a few grassy hummocks on your right before you get to the barn and walls at the base of High Hartsop Dodd. But what a lovely spot; well drained and with clear views both up and down this great north-south valley and ancient line of communication. If you wander around the hummocks, you find that there is clear evidence of boundary walls to the north, east and especially west.

Figure 2.3: *Glacial 'erratic' boulders at the old settlement near Hartsop Hall. Behind and to the right are the dumps of Hartsop Mine.*

Some huge 'erratic' boulders, once held tightly in the ice, were dumped here when the glacier melted (Fig. 2.3) and some are incorporated into the settlement wall. In fact the settlement, in which you can see several indications of former huts or structures of some sort, was built on the *medial moraine* which formed where the two glaciers merged into one. Normally, glaciers carry a whole lot of broken rock debris which falls onto them from the exposed rock walls of the upper valley sides. From the air, this appears as a ribbon of black rubbish at each edge of the glacier so if two glaciers join (forming a Y shape), the two *lateral moraines* merge to form the stem of the Y, the *medial moraine* (p. 152). When the ice stagnates and melts because of warmer conditions, it dumps the *moraines* as prominent 'dykes' of material, very obvious in the Alps for example, where they are still being formed.

Have a quick look at the biggest boulders. You'll see that they are made up of angular rock fragments up to half a metre in size. These are *volcaniclasts* making this a very coarse *block tuff.* You'll see a good deal more of this later as you might expect because obviously the boulders have been brought down by the ice from somewhere higher up the valley.

Finally, take a look at the lower hillside to the northwest, to the left of Hartsop Hall. There are obvious whitish patches of rock fragments just to the right of a curving wall. These are dumps from Hartsop Mine, the next locality.

Return to the main track at Hartsop Hall and continue up it, branching right along the way marked 'Dovedale – permitted fell path' up to the mine dumps about 200 metres further on. This is also an option. If you aren't interested in old mines, keep on the lower track beside the wall which follows along the bottom of the valley.

Hartsop Mine: Locality 2 [395 119]

Old mines, so the saying goes, never die. Certainly Hartsop Mine had a long stop-start history, closing 'finally' in around 1860. But it reopened for exploration in 1931 and was again 'finally' closed in 1942.

This mine, though never large, once produced lead ore. The ore, *galena* (p. 227), also contained silver (80oz. per ton). The other minerals – for there are usually half a dozen or so in any mineral vein such as this – included minor copper ores such as *bornite.* Minerals such as *sphalerite, barite, pyrite,* and a little *fluorite* were also recorded and traces of gold showed up in assays. The vein was 3 feet thick, trending northeast at variable angles. The ores actually occur within other (valueless) materials such as *quartz* and *brecciated* volcanic rocks. You can usually find *quartz, galena* and pink *barite* (heavyspar) on the dumps. At the top of the dump, an entrance remains open, cut in solid rock with a stream flowing out of it. A small dam, now open, seems to have been made inside to control water levels.

Beside the dumps, you can see concrete machine beds which once supported small crushers and washers for ore processing. There's also a *leat* (marked on the O.S. map) which provided water for a water-wheel to power these machines.

Return to the main (lower) track and continue on up Dovedale. As you walk along, watch out for herons fishing in Dovedale Beck away to your left. **About 600 metres along the track from the permitted path branch, you'll spot a stone barn ahead,** and on your left is a striking grassy *moraine* mound, dotted with boulders like plums in plum pudding. Fresh *moraines* are exceedingly common in daleheads such as this and probably all date back to the *Younger Dryas* glaciers. Some of the best known are in Mickleden, Great Langdale (p. 105).

Pass the stone barn, a fine specimen of drystone construction, the thick walls being skilfully built of unshaped boulders and the roof made of heavy rough slates. From here on, glacial *moraines* form hummocky ground to the right of the track. These hummocks continue up as high as the upper intake wall (on the other side of which the permitted path runs). The wall follows the junction between *moraine* and later *screes.*

'Intakes' are walled fields penetrating up the valley sides, making maximum use of the land for improved pasture. Many of these are now abandoned to bracken and the rough grazing they once were.

The *flood plain* of the beck is now only 100 metres across and soon ceases altogether in a jumble of low outcrops and *moraines* which form the dale head. **As you approach the footbridge to cross the beck, look left and in the foreground you'll see ice-smoothed outcrops of rock, Locality 3.** If you then look up to the skyline – Black Brow – you can see a distinct bowl-shaped corrie which once held a small glacier. There is a clear lower 'lip' to this corrie, smooth, green and grassy compared to the crags behind. **Continue over the bridge to Locality 3, 100 metres further on.**

Roche moutonée and lavas: Locality 3: [3890 1131]

The first obvious feature of these outcrops, the middle one with three silver birch trees growing from cracks in it, is that they are rather smooth. This is simply because all the rough edges, so characteristic of the crags and outcrops higher up the fells, have been planed off by the glaciers which formed the smooth, sheep-back outcrops: *roches moutonées.* But there's far more to see in these exposures of the *Borrowdale Volcanic Group* rocks than you might expect. Take a look at the outcrops about 20 metres to the right (west) of the birch trees and you'll be able to make out a wavy-topped *lava* flow overlain by a jumbled mass of broken *lava* fragments (Fig. 2.4). This is an obvious junction, or contact, between two rather different rocks and, as usual, interpretation of what actually happened here is uncertain. If you scramble about on these outcrops, you should find that above this contact, there are many *blocks,* some the size of a small barrel, incorporated into this jumble and, if you look carefully, you'll find that some of the *blocks* are rather odd. One (Fig. 2.5) football-sized block is almost perfectly hexagonal. Another (Fig. 2.6) is full of parallel elongate cavities, and there are quite a few of these, some up to one metre in size. Furthermore, if you move up the outcrops towards the south, you'll easily notice another change: some of the southernmost rocks are distinctly *bedded* (Fig. 2.6). The *strike* of the beds is northeast-southwest and they *dip* at about 50° southeast. In fact in some places, the *bedded* rocks seem to be filling spaces between the *blocks* and boulders of the underlying jumble.

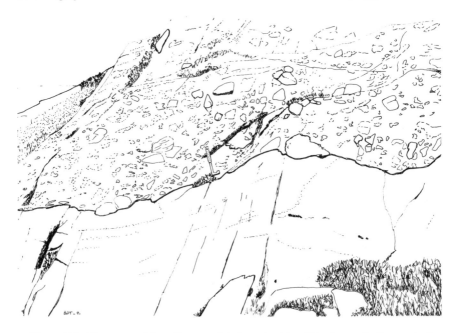

Figure 2.4: Wavy-topped lava flow overlain by a jumble of blocks; part of an ancient debris flow.

The outcrops cease before they reach the farm track on the south side. But what do they tell us? Let's start back at the bottom on the north side. The rock below the wavy-topped contact (Fig. 2.4) is an *andesite* which contains white crystals of *feldspar*. It shows evidence of having been liquid and has solidified in its present position. This means it was either a *lava* or a very shallow *intrusion* into the jumbled pile you can see above. Many of the *volcaniclasts* above the contact are made of the same *andesite* which suggests the broken-up top of a *lava* flow.

But you don't have to go many metres up from the contact to find yourself dealing with 'exotic' blocks which are much larger than those lower down. This coarsening-upwards of the jumble suggests some kind of avalanche deposit. It cannot be the direct result of eruption because of the mixture of rocks of different origins. We can guess that the avalanche, or *debris flow* ended up under water because of the water-lain *bedded* sediment infills and overlap to the south. It may have started on land, perhaps on the flank of a complex volcano, and the large angular *volcaniclasts* indicate that it cannot have moved far from its source.

Figure 2.5: *Hexagonal block, formerly part of a lava flow or shallow intrusion but swept away by the debris flow which produced the jumbled rock which now encloses it.*

So what are these *blocks?* The hexagonal one (Fig. 2.5) was part of a *lava* flow or *intrusion.*

It is quite common to find columns of this sort in what were the hottest parts of once-liquid rocks – *lavas* or *intrusions*. The slow and even cooling resulted in regular contraction and *joints* and can produce spectacular landforms (like the Giant's Causeway in Northern Ireland and Staffa island in the Hebrides) in some partially-eroded flows.

Figure 2.6: *Welded tuff blocks to the left and right of the hammer have been covered in finely layered sediments, dipping gently to the right. The infills of sediment show that the rock finally came to rest under water.*

The paler-coloured blocks with elongate cavities tell an exciting story. They were produced by an violent type of eruption – a giant *nuée ardente* or glowing cloud.

A number of small examples of *nuées ardentes* were first seen in Martinique in 1902, one of which destroyed the town of St Pierre and its 30,000 inhabitants (only two survived).

But *nuée ardente* eruptions are not large or hot enough to produce the rock type we have here. A much larger eruption which did produce such rocks occurred at Mt Katmai in Alaska in 1912.

The Katmai explosion was the greatest eruption of this century though it was not witnessed by anyone due to the remoteness of the location. Geologists have estimated that 500 million cubic metres of ash was erupted per hour for 24 hours! And yet this too was geologically speaking quite a small eruption. This stupendous eruption spewed out so much ash that 30 centimetres fell on Kodiak island, 170 kilometres distant – all within 2 days. For the terrified inhabitants, day turned to night, rent by continual explosions from the previously docile volcano. The eruption completely filled a former valley with about 10 cubic kilometres of hot ash some 200 metres thick. This became known as the Valley of Ten Thousand Smokes because of the numerous spouts of steam which rose from its surface for many years afterwards (and still do in some parts). Six years afterwards, a survey team measured temperatures up to 654°C in these steam 'fumaroles.' Geologists believe that some eruptions in the distant past may have been up to 100 times bigger than the Katmai explosion.

The Lake District volcanoes gave rise to many of these violent and devastating *ignimbrite* eruptions about 450 million years ago. The *blocks* you see here are examples of *welded tuffs* from such eruptions. The streaky *eutaxitic foliation* is highly characteristic of *welded tuff* (Fig. 2.7). The streaks were called *fiamme* by Italian geologists because they look like flames. They are, in fact, pieces of *pumice* which, because the flow was so hot after it came to rest, became soft enabling the weight of the overlying hot flow to flatten them from ball-shapes to disc-shapes, rather like rolling out a lump of pastry to make a pie crust. It is these discs which in cross sections look like flames and give *welded tuff* its unmistakable appearance. Fortunately for the human race, *ignimbrite* eruptions are rather unusual.

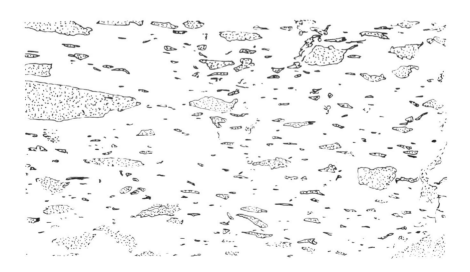

Figure 2.7: *Typical eutaxitic welded tuff in which the largest flattened pumice fiamme are about the size of a sandwich.*

So you see that these superficially dull grey rocks, surrounded by grass and covered in mosses and lichens, can tell a spectacular story of ancient violence, a far cry from the gentle serenity of this peaceful spot today.

A rather different story unfolds about 100 metres south of Locality 3, in the form of some curious remains between the two streams visible from the top of the Locality 3 outcrops.

Remains of ancient industry: Locality 4: [3888 1122]

What you see here is at first rather puzzling. There's a small ruined building and a pile of black glass. What do you make of this?

These are the remains of an ancient smelter . . . 'hearth and chimney being in the centre. Water from Hogget Gill was led into a small dam from which a launder carried it to the waterwheel propelling the bellows. Nearby are the ruins of a beehive-shaped charcoal house, and there is a pile of slag, both glassy and metallic, in which a careful search will reveal small pieces of metallic lead. This . . . dates from the late 16th or early 17th Century' (extracted from W.T.Shaw, *Mining in the Lake Counties*, Dalesman Press, 1972).

The question remains though: why drag the lead ore up here to smelt and then carry the metal back?

Now start the ascent to Dove Crag. Return over the rocks of Locality 3 to join an indistinct footpath through the oak, alder, hawthorn, birch trees and bracken on the south side of Dovedale Beck. It quickly starts to climb and though not much used, is never far from the stream bank. There are some fine waterfalls, more easy to hear than see amongst the dense vegetation. After about half a kilometre, cross a wall by a stile and continue up across ice-smoothed outcrops just like those you saw at Locality 3. You'll now be able to pick out the *welded tuff* blocks and the well bedded parts. There are some rather boggy peaty bits here too.

When the slope eases off as you enter the different world of the upper Dovedale valley, you'll immediately spot the *morainic* mounds like those you saw lower down. You'll now see the much more used 'permitted path' on the other side of the beck. Cross the beck to join it. From now on, rock outcrops begin to dominate the scene. Continue on until just at the start of a group of small rowan trees (Fig. 2.8), you'll see outcrops in and beside the track.

Figure 2.8: Rowan leaf, flowers and berries (which are bright red).

Lavas and a fallen block: Locality 5 [3800 1144]

Parts of this rock are fresh enough for you to be able to make out the green-grey *andesite lava* with white blobs which are decayed *feldspar* crystals. **Just as the path outcrops cease, you should find a striking fallen boulder on the left side of the track above the second rowan tree.** It is the size of a large sack made up of delicately interbedded whitish and reddish-grey *laminated tuffs* (Fig. 2.9), but the beds are repeatedly interrupted (at postage stamp scale only) by numerous tiny *faults*.

Figure 2.9: *Fallen block by the path at Locality 5: a wonderful example of soft sediment structures due to water saturation.*

Some of the beds are distinctly wavy – rippled due to current action on the sea floor (or lake floor; we can't tell which but we do know that the *tuffs* were laid down in water). Some beds pinch and swell; others are disrupted into strange curls, wisps and flame-like structures (though *not* like the *fiamme* you saw earlier). These features are all typical of what invariably happens to wet sediments due to later loading and probably earthquake shocks. Some of the beds temporarily liquify – like jelly paints if you pound them about. Because of the weight of overlying beds, the liquified layers get squeezed and squirt sideways, upwards or downwards to form small 'injections'. The tiny disrupting *faults* occur because of the loading from above and often act as channels for the liquefied, or *fluidised*, material to squirt along. The upward squirts are called *flame structures* and the downward ones *load casts* and they can produce some very strange-looking bed forms indeed. Some of these load structures probably occur simply because the overlying bed is denser than the underlying; the denser sediment then sinks haphazardly into the sloppy stuff underneath. There's a good example of these loading and *fluidisation* structures in the middle of this block, right under my pen (Fig. 2.9). These structures give geologists *way-up criteria*: we can tell which way up the rock was when it was laid down. In this block, the tiny curled flames point upwards, so the 'way-up' of the block is with the youngest (top) beds being to the top right of the figure – facing the beck.

About 100 metres further on, three streams join including the one from Houndshope Cove which crosses the track. The rocks are still green *andesite*. An ash tree struggles to survive here and you can see many lady's mantle plants (Fig. 2.10) hereabouts.

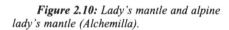

Figure 2.10: Lady's mantle and alpine lady's mantle (Alchemilla).

There's a short steep ascent from the stream and when the path levels off, you'll see numerous blocks of the same *welded tuff* as at Locality 3, **followed 10-15 paces further on** by green bedded *tuffs* and then *vesicular lavas*. So the rock sequence here is quite complex and you begin to realise that the grey crags all around which all look the same, are nothing of the sort.

Now you start the steepest part of the climb to Houndshope Cove, not yet visible over the craggy shoulder above. The path is well worn and the ascent is easy enough. Just past a ruined building on the right is a recent rock fall, also to the right a few metres from the track. If you look up above, you can see the scar in the crags on the skyline from which the boulders fell a few years back. They show up because they are green well *bedded tuffs* instead of the usual weathered grey. But in the topmost and biggest of these, the beds, regular elsewhere, are completely screwed up into a convoluted jumble. This is another example of wet sediment deformation where beds have *slumped*, rolling together and breaking up before the material became hardened into rock (see the superb examples on p. 172).

Something else we can learn from this rock fall is that the processes of erosion continue in the present day. We tend to think of this sort of landscape as permanent and unchanging and in terms of our trivial life spans, it almost is. Yet here we see how water, freezing in cracks and levering out blocks of rock, still plays its less obvious role in these mountains. Of course during the glaciations, erosion was orders of magnitude more rapid, but even now the landscape is a dynamic and changing thing.

Not far round Dove Crag near 'Easy Gully' (see Wainwright guide), there are several older but much larger falls of rock which have created a rather fearsome landscape below and to your left. This presumably caused Wainwright to refer to this boulder-strewn valley as 'the crater of a volcano'. The scene he rather fancifully described formed almost 450 million years after the volcanoes and is almost entirely due to ice action. Yet the rocks themselves are directly or indirectly the products of volcanoes as you've seen.

Continue on up the steep track and, if you don't suffer from vertigo, up to Priest's Hole. The indistinct path to this branches to the left as soon as the main track levels out over the lip of Houndshope Cove. You'll have to use your hands in some of the short climb to the hole but there's nothing very difficult. I took my 10-year-old with me and he didn't bat an eyelid (but then neither did he on Sharp Edge, p. 246).

The cave itself offers shelter in bad weather and a rather unusual 'framed' view. There is a visitor's book for you to sign and a few other odds and ends for emergency bivouacs. I'd say there was room for a dozen people inside and it's quite dry with a low wall at the front. It's a good place for contemplation and speculation: who were the first humans to shelter here? I'd be surprised if this cave hasn't been used on and off for thousands of years. It is even defendable from attackers.

But why is the cave here at all? It is probably entirely natural, excavated by weathering processes in much weaker rock. The rock is partially flat-lying, fine grained sediment and partially a grey probably *intrusive andesite* with swirls and bands of *vesicles*. The cave seems to be excavated along the contact between the two rock types, though there may have been some slight *fault* movement along this too. *Faulting* would help to explain the weakness since in these brittle but hard rocks, the rock next to the *plane* of movement tends to become rather smashed up.

Descending back to the track in Houndshope Cove, you cross well *bedded tuffs* which you may not have noticed on the way up to Priest's Hole. There's a boulder of this rock, which also forms this face of Dove Crag, **just to the right**

of the main track where it flattens off, some 50 metres before a tiny peaty tarn. This boulder (Fig. 2.11) allows you to examine the typical *bedded tuffs* without having to hang on in some precipitous perch. It is a beautiful specimen, worthy of inclusion in a museum — but who would carry it?

From here you have another option which would cut short your walk. You can turn right off the track which now heads southwest up the short climb to the col between Dove and Hart crags, and make for Hartsop above How ridge, due north across the cove (also filled by hummocky glacial mounds). On the crest of the ridge, you'll strike the well worn path (Blake Brow, between localities 12 and

Figure 2.11: *Boulder near Priest's Hole showing superb miniature faulting of well bedded sediments. My son's hand, enclosed in anorak, gives the scale.*

13) which returns, ultimately, to Brothers Water and the car park. This short cut means that you miss out Fairfield, Dove and Hart crags and a bit of a scramble down from the latter.

The main route continues southwest towards the col, meandering between *moraine* hummocks and peaty pools and bogs. Above on the left is the northwest face of Dove Crag. If you look at the base of the crag, you'll see that the rocks are rather *massive volcaniclastic* beds full of fragments up to football size. These rocks pass up into the well *bedded tuffs* you saw around Priest's Hole. **About 50 metres to the right of the track, just as it starts to**

**ascend again, is a small beck which comes down from the col. Turn right
off the track and cross the beck to examine the isolated rugged outcrop
which looks like a confused tangle of boulders and blocks.** Looks don't
deceive: it is a very coarse *breccia* which contains *lava blocks* the size of a
large rucksack (Fig. 2.12).

Figure 2.12: *Block and boulder rock near Dove Crag, probably the result of an
avalanche down the flank of a volcano.*

As usual, there are several possibilities for its origin. It is most likely some sort of rock slide or avalanche deposit, sloughing off the side of a volcano. It could even be part of the neck or vent of a volcano itself -such vents are typically found full of blocks like this – but there is no other strong evidence for this from the surrounding geology. **Return to the path and plod on up to the col. If the weather is fair, you can make a short cut off to the left of the path, heading for the north end of Dove Crag ridge and Locality 6.**

Dove Crag north, a view and some thoughts: Locality 6 [3742 1086]

At the north end of the summit ridge, nearly 400 metres north of the cairn which marks the highest point of Dove Crag, you can find light grey-weathering outcrops of coarse *tuffs* full of *lapilli*, volcanic fragments ejected directly from a vent. The *tuffs* overlie those we saw near Priest's Hole and, like them dip gently to the east. So what is this vertical slabby appearance so prominent here, you wonder? This series of close-spaced vertical '*joints*' has nothing to do with the original *bedding* and is a structure, *cleavage*, which was imposed long after the eruptions had ceased and these rocks had been deeply buried beneath thousands of metres of later and younger rocks, now long since eroded away.

Now there's quite a bit to say about *cleavage* (see also p. 15) and volcanoes, so find a comfortable spot with a good view and imagine you've travelled backwards in time some 450 million years.

Take a look at Fig. 2.13, left side. This is a reconstruction of the way 'our' part of the planet looked all those years ago. You'll see that there's an ocean called Iapetus where the modern Atlantic should be and a sea called Tornquist where you'd expect the North Sea. But that's misleading because no landmasses or seas would be recognisable to you or me then. To start with, the central part of this region was about 25 degrees south of the equator. You can see the landmasses such as Greenland and Labrador (America), Canada and Scandinavia (Baltica) which give you a guide as to where things were, though the familiar coastlines of today didn't exist. Britain, shaded black, is still in two separate pieces. North Britain (Scotland and the northern counties of Ireland) are part of the American plate. The rest of Britain, including the Lakes area, is about a thousand miles away to the southeast. The Canadian island of Newfoundland was similarly split.

Figure 2.13: *Two reconstructions of the geography of this part of the planet's surface about 450,000,000 years ago (left) and 370,000,000 years ago (right). See text for details. NN — north Newfoundland, SN — south Newfoundland, NB — north Britain, SB — south Britain, N — Newfoundland, B — Britain. The thick black arrows on the left-hand drawing show which way the plates were moving at that time. The barbed lines show plate boundaries, in this case subduction zones. The Iapetus Suture formed when the old seafloor finally disappeared beneath the overriding plates and Laurentia, Avalonia and Baltica fused together in a complex fashion and a cataclysm of mountain-building, known as the Caledonian.*

But because of the relentless movement of these rigid plates of the Earth's crust (which continues today), the plate containing South Britain (called the Avalonian plate) moving towards the north, the other (Laurentia) containing North Britain moving towards the southeast, something had to give. It did. The intervening Iapetus Ocean floor, always thinner and weaker than continental landmass crust, was forced *underneath* the leading edge of the Avalonian plate creating a *subduction zone*. This process typically results in frictional melting of the downgoing plate as it rasps against the overthrusting one.

You can demonstrate this for yourself by placing the outstretched fingers of your right hand over those of your left. Push both hands together *hard* so forcing your left fingers and knuckles down under the overriding (Avalonian) right hand. If you do this several times, the knuckles of your left hand will heat up because of friction. And if you kept up the movement, your left hand (ocean floor) would be subducted, then your wrist, then your forearm and so on until all the left arm had 'disappeared'. The Lake District would be a tiny mole on the first joint of the Avalonian middle finger.

This analogy mimics quite well the actual process which went on for tens of millions of years all those eons ago. The frictional heating melted great pods of liquid rocks which then migrated upwards, melting their way up through the crust like huge hot maggots, and erupting at the surface to form volcanoes. Some 'maggots' didn't reach the surface and formed *intrusions* such as the *granitic* rocks of Ennerdale and the Skiddaw area (pp. 34 and 248), now exposed by erosion.

The Lake District and parts of north Wales, also largely volcanic in origin, are remnants of these outbursts of *subduction*-related volcanicity. Many of the volcanoes which rim the Pacific Ocean today are *subduction*-related for *subduction* zones exist below Japan and South America's west coast and the movement of the downthrust plate under the leading edge of the landmasses is the direct cause of the frequent and serious earthquakes in that region. The Andes contain dozens of active volcanoes which produce – as you might guess – *andesite lavas*. In fact the analogy between the Lake District volcanoes and present day Andes is fairly close.

Cleavage, the platy structure in the rocks around you here, develops because of intense pressure and heat due to deep seated earth movements such as those which occurred here during the mountain building episode (about 60 million years *after* these rocks were formed).

This was the climax of the *Caledonian* mountain-building and occurred when all the ocean floor had been consumed by *subduction* and the two great continental masses crashed into each other not very far north of here (roughly the Scottish border), suturing together tightly and permanently so that no nationalist sentiment will ever sunder them. So Avalonia (South Britain, the Appalachian mountains of the eastern USA and Newfoundland south) and the Laurentian plate (North Britain, Labrador, Greenland and north Newfoundland) became united for the first time (Fig. 2.13, right) though millions of years later, this super-plate broke apart again to create the modern Atlantic Ocean.

Earth scientists first began to develop the theory of global *plate tectonics* in the 1960s (though the idea of continental drift had been around a lot longer). For the first time, the scientists found mechanisms for this apparent drift of the Earth's crustal plates and instruments became sufficiently accurate to actually measure the rate of movement. For the plates continue to move around and bump into each other to this day. The actual velocity of the movement is something like the speed of growth of a child's fingernail. Where plates collide, they may create huge mountain ranges like the Himalaya, *subduction* zones as off the west coast of South America, or complex *fault systems* such as the infamous San Andreas Fault in California (indirect cause of the 1994 Los Angeles earthquakes).

Now back to the present and our walk. The views from this locality and from here on are splendid. But now walk south across the *cleaved tuffs* towards the boundary wall and the broad track which forms part of the

famous **Fairfield Horseshoe walk from Ambleside.** The *tuffs* form a quite prominent flat ridge trending just west of south crowned by a cairn at its highest point.

Dove Crag summit: Locality 7 [3745 1048]

The actual top of Dove Crag, 792 metres high, is marked by a stone cairn but is otherwise nondescript. The rocks below the cairn are worth looking at, though. You'll see that they are rather dark grey *porphyritic lavas,* but here they were *foliated* by flow when they were hot. In fact, the *foliation* has been distorted into small folds as cooler 'plastic' *lava* was pushed by the hotter material behind it. The rock is dark enough to suggest another rock type which contains less *silica* than *andesite: basalt* or *basaltic andesite.* The actual distinction between the latter two is unimportant and quite difficult to make in these old altered rocks. If you have a hand lens, you should be able to spot clumps of *feldspar* crystals and other black crystals which are *pyroxenes.* Both these minerals are dominant in *basalt* lavas.

Basalts are rather different from *andesites* in that they are hotter when extruded and flow much more readily. *Basaltic* volcanic eruptions (such as those on Hawaii) are rarely explosive whereas *andesitic* volcanoes can be quite violent. The general rule is the more *silica* a lava contains, the more viscous it will be and the more violent the eruptions.

The walk now continues by joining the Fairfield horseshoe track, at first retracing your steps and then continuing on beside the wall down the col between Hart and Dove crags. The views are magnificent for you can see Windermere and Coniston lakes, the sea at Morecambe Bay in the far distance, the Coniston fells, Scafell, Bow Fell, Great Gable, Pillar and, nearby, Fairfield. To the north is St Sunday Crag. As you walk, remember that you are now crossing back down over all the rocks you've seen earlier; in effect going backwards in time for the further north you go, the older the rocks are because they underlie those behind you. Remember that the entire sequence of rocks hereabouts (starting right back at locality 3) dips to the southeast at 20-40°, like a giant tilted layer cake.

The wall stops at the col, but the track continues, clear and cairned, up to Hart Crag summit. Where the wall stops, as you start to ascend, the rock is shattered into *screes* by frost action and you'll see it is often stained a red-purple colour. Have a look at some pieces. The colouring, under a hand lens, turns out to be an unusual lichen. There must be some mineral in these rocks which encourages this red-purple lichen to grow rather than the commoner green and grey types. The rock itself is hard, dark grey and contains black iron-rich minerals and a good deal of *pyrite*. The local abundance of iron may explain the vivid lichen. But what is the rock? From its colour and minerals, it is probably a sort of *basalt*. But it contains small cavities and fragments up to marble size. This indicates that it is a fragmental rock – a *basaltic tuff* – and not a *lava* (or *intrusion*).

Hart Crag summit: Locality 8 [3682 1126]

Being higher than Dove Crag (822 metres), this viewpoint is slightly better because now you can also see Helvellyn and Catstye Cam plus all the lesser eastern fells. The rocks here have again been affected by *cleavage*, so that they stand up as vertical plates looking like beds. The *bedding* continues to dip moderately to the southeast, showing how confusing *cleavage* can sometimes be. The rocks are *tuffs*, full of angular lumps of *andesite* and more *silica*-rich material such as *rhyolite* or *dacite*. If you look around, some of the fragments are rounded as well as angular. Rounding usually indicates some sort of erosion by running water which in turn suggests that this rock is a *debris flow*, incorporating a mix of rock fragments.

Debris flows are easy to imagine. When volcanoes erupt, the eruptions often involve enormous quantities of water, either from condensed steam and rain or from crater lakes. Imagine all the loose rubbish in the steep gullies of a volcano, and then think what would happen if heavy rains and eruptions came at the same time. Water-saturated slurries would quickly gather in the gullies and coalesce to form fast-moving flows of liquified mud and boulders. Because these mudflows are naturally confined to stream valleys, they pick up anything loose in the stream – cobbles, pebbles, the water (and in the example of Mt St Helens in 1980, trees, houses, people and bridges). Such mud or debris flows were and are extremely common processes associated with volcanoes. Some in Indonesia (where they are called 'lahars') have killed thousands of people.

Back to Hart Crag and its mixed *volcaniclastic* rocks. If the weather is good and you feel like an extra bit of walking before the long trudge back (almost all downhill from here), it's only just over 1 kilometres, via Link Hause, to Fairfield. Otherwise, skip localities 9 and 10 and walk a little over 100 metres northeast to locality 11.

Scrubby Crag: Locality 9 [3663 1159]

Drop down to Link Hause and then scramble up the massive *volcaniclastic* rocks which form the lower slopes. The higher you climb, the lower in the sequence you are going (they are still dipping southeast and you're going northwest) and you'll find that the rocks become coarser and coarser until on the summit, you find *blocks* of a rock type you saw much earlier in the day – at Locality 3. These are *eutaxitic welded tuff* and are larger than footballs. It is quite possible that the deposit you see here was formed at the same time as that at Locality 3 though only careful geological mapping of the different rock units would confirm this.

Now continue west along the gentle grassy broad ascent to Fairfield. If you look south down into Rydal Head, you'll see once again the familiar signs of glaciation: the broad 'U'-shaped valley and the hummocky forms of the *moraines* on the valley floor.

Fairfield summit: Locality 10 [3595 1169]

The summit is a flat plateau with a magnificent view in all directions, especially of Helvellyn. The rather bleak flatness is relieved here and there by small outcrops of *tuffs* with *rhyolitic lapilli*. The *bedding* is quite flat-lying. The outcrops are much broken up by the bitter cold weather received by this and other high Lakeland summits. This frost-shattering can create large areas of broken rock known as *blockfields* (p. 179), characteristic of the mountains of high latitudes. Sometimes, the frost heaving and shattering can produce vague polygonal shapes and if there is a slope, downslope movement may occur giving the appearance of stone stripes. These *periglacial* features are common in the present day Arctic, and are present on most of the high British mountains including this one. You can see how easy the shattering process can be because the *cleavage* and *joint planes,* being vertical, readily soak up moisture. The freezing of the water is accompanied by an increase in volume as water turns to ice (which is why ice floats). This prises open any weakness in the rock and the process continues, slowly but inexorably, towards its total disintegration.

Retrace your steps to Hart Crag – up sequence – to the summit cairn. Then make your way for about 100 metres across rough *blockfield,* first towards St Sunday Crag and then towards Hartsop above How ridge, visible to the northeast. You will then intercept the rather rough track which drops steeply down the northeast side of Hart Crag and which is the return route. This path is not easy to follow in the mist, so beware.

Strange structures: Locality 11 [369 114]

About 10 paces to the left of the track, where you should have intercepted it – before the steep descent – there are some white-coloured *tuff* outcrops with fine examples of *flame structures* and *load casts*. You can also see that

the rock contains pea-sized pellets which may have been pieces of *pumice* or blobs of ash which coalesced during an eruption (*accretionary lapilli*). These outcrops are in place (not loose blocks): the 'flames' point upwards and the *load casts* bulge downwards. So the rock is, as you'd expect, right-way-up (Fig. 2.14).

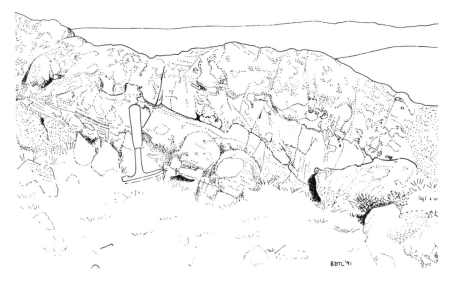

Figure 2.14: Sedimentary structures at Locality 11, Hart Crag.

If the *flames* and *load casts* had been the 'pointing' the other way, we'd be seriously worried for the entire rock sequence you've seen today would be upside down! Impossible, you might think. Certainly that's true here, but there are many mountain areas of the world which do show large areas of rock which are upside down. There are examples quite near at hand in Scotland and Wales, and many more in the Alps.

Our route continues down towards the peaty ridge of Hartsop above How with Houndshope Cove on your right and the great precipices of Scrubby Crag on your left. You'll notice as you scramble that you're following more or less the same beds as you've just seen, some showing *slumping*. Especially interesting are the 'puddingstone' bands which are interbedded with the finer *tuffs*. These have a range of ingredients from angular *tuff* fragments to pale *rhyolitic* pebbles and cobbles. All these features are unmistakeable evidence for the existence of water around these volcanoes.

As you approach the steepest part of the descent, roughly level with the north end of Dove Crag, note that the dip of the beds has steepened up to about 40° though the *strike* remains to the northeast as you've seen many times. The beds are quite similar to those at the other side of Houndshope Cove forming Dove Crag, but they are older as you can now see because, as you drop down, they are overlain by the *basaltic tuff* which forms the south flank of Hart Crag. And that, we have already seen, lies beneath the Dove Crag *tuffs*. I'll review all this from a good vantage point a little further on.

The descent, you'll now have noticed, is steep but it is not dangerous given due care and attention to balance. When you emerge onto the flatter peaty ridge at the bottom, head off a little to the left of the track (which goes through several very boggy patches) aiming for the clear track further ahead and a large craggy outcrop on the edge of the ridge overlooking Link Cove, and of especial interest.

Figure 2.15: Volcanic breccia at Locality 12, Hart Crag.

Volcanic breccia: Locality 12 [3738 1150]

By now, you'll see quite clearly what this rock is without me telling you. First, you'll have noticed the huge *blocks* and boulders (Fig. 2.15) varying from the size of an orange to almost that of a dustbin. They are all angular (and so have not been rolled about in rivers or the sea) and consist of two rocks we've seen several times already. One is a *vesicular lava* and the other, our old friend the *welded tuff*. So we're looking at a deposit very like that at Scrubby Crag (Locality 9) and way back in Dovedale (Locality 3). If you walk to the east end of the outcrops, you'll find that the fragment size drops right down and the deposit becomes bedded and so passes up into the rocks we saw higher up Hart Crag (Locality 12). So everything fits together – correlates – well.

Continue on along the ridge rejoining the track. After half a kilometre you are at Blake Brow which is a good place to stop and look back at the sequence. You can see very clearly how the rocks are all part of a *bedded* continuity, almost all dipping to the southeast at around 30⁰.

The track is now often very boggy. The peat in the hollows is quite thick and walkers' boots have really churned it up. You can usually avoid the worst by creeping round the edge of each bad patch.

But why is the peat here? How old is it? Obviously it post-dates the glaciers and so is younger than 11,500 years. But it seems not to be forming now and, indeed, is eroding fast in places – because of walkers and sheep . . . and rain. It is probably the sheep that prevent it from forming since they nibble the rough sedges and grasses which once provided much of the material for the peat. The entire upland plant population has changed and, with the exception of dwarf juniper, a few (poisonous to sheep and people) yews and rowans, there are no longer any naturally occurring trees (see p. 122) on the higher Lake District mountains. So we can hazard a guess that the peat probably goes back several thousand years, though its accumulation here must always have been slow.

Peat forms simply because the water is so acid that none of the fungi and bacteria which normally break down dead plant material can function effectively. Rainfall is naturally slightly acid (more so now thanks to cars and power stations) and acidity increases as initial decay makes 'humic' acids. This bumps up the acidity to such a degree that further decay stops. So the dead plant matter remains and those few plants which are acid-tolerant can grow upon their mummified predecessors. Peat can be dated by techniques such as pollen analysis and *radiocarbon dating* and has itself something of a rather specialised story to tell.

Hartsop above How summit: Locality 13 [3828 1200]

After the gentle ascent to the summit, rest awhile and take stock of what you've seen on this rather intense day out. From this vantage point, the final locality (whew! you say), you have a panorama of almost the whole day's walk laid out before you. I've summarized this in Figure 2.16 in which I've shown the outlines of the fells from Dove Crag (left) to Dolywaggon Pike (right, in the distance). I've outlined the *bedding* where you can see it and continued the imaginary traces of this into the sky so as to summarize the complete sequence. Dotted lines are simply projections of the visible beds. The dashed lines are approximate junctions between the different rocks you've examined.

Once again, the rocks underfoot are the same as those at Localities 3, 9 and 12, the *volcaniclastic breccia* ('V'). You can see the familiar *welded tuff* blocks here, though the beds dip much more steeply to the southeast. With this inclination, you can perhaps visualise in your mind's eye this 'sheet' of distinctive rock dipping down to Dovedale Beck, the dip shallowing out a little to the southeast and Locality 3. In the other direction, we know that it forms the backbone of the Hartsop ridge, the main part of Hart Crag and the upper part of Scrubby Crag. So we have traced this distinctive rock unit for 2.5 kilometres, not bad in one day.

Also from here you can see the entire sequence (Fig. 2.16) overlying the *breccia* starting with the *bedded tuffs* of Hart Crag (Locality 11) through which you descended a few minutes ago as you made your way down the steep track to Locality 12. Overlying these striking *tuffs* is the dark *basaltic tuff* ('BT') of the south flank of Hart Crag. Well to the left, you can make out the black mouth of Priest's Hole (labelled 'PH') and see the gently dipping sediments we know to form Dove Crag ('V') which start with the coarse *volcaniclastic* rocks of the small outcrop near the track in Houndshope Cove. These quickly become finer grained higher up the sequence. The great gash of Easy Gully is probably a *fault,* creating a line of weakness in the rock. The *cleaved tuffs* ('T') of Dove Crag north summit overlie the *volcaniclastic* beds below and are themselves overlain by the *basaltic lavas* ('B') of Locality 7, Dove Crag summit.

Naturally this broad picture is not wholly correct. We can refine it by geological map making, but it is the beginning of the process of understanding . . . *your* understanding. The general picture is fairly clear and certainly good enough for anyone to see − now − that these variable rocks do form a regular and understandable sequence. You have a fine view of the wild upper Dovedale Beck valley through which our path of the morning snakes upwards. You can also make out a few of the *moraines* near where the valley turns to the east.

Looking to the right, past the bedded rocks of Hart Crag, are Scrubby Crag, the Step and Greenhow End. You've not seen these rocks close to, except for the very top, but you can still get an idea of their form and structure. They are formed by *massive* volcanic units which also appear to be *bedded* and dipping in the same direction as those you have walked over. The rather forbidding austerity of Link Cove sets the scene for Deepdale which separates Hartsop above How from St Sunday Crag to the north. This dale contrasts vividly with the gentle beauty of Dovedale. Link Cove is a good example of a glacial corrie, complete with a steep lip and waterfalls. Characteristically, it faces northeast – the direction which receives the least sunshine and so stays coldest – and would have been occupied by a small glacier during the *Younger Dryas* period. The other branch of Deepdale runs up to the col of Deepdale Hause which from here frames the rounded bulk of Dolywaggon Pike, the south end of the Helvellyn range.

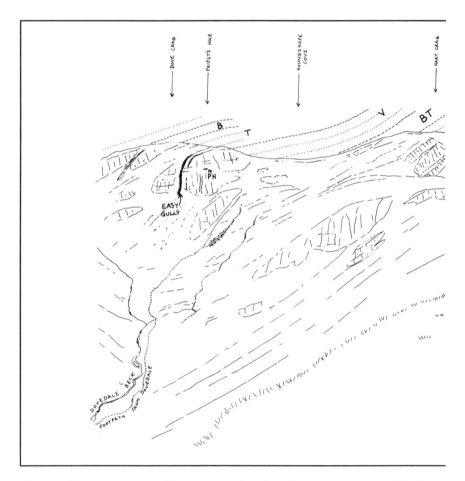

Figure 2.16: *Synoptic view of the mountains from Dove Crag to Dolywaggon Pike from the highest part of Hartsop above How. See text for details.*

Now all that remains is to make the long gentle descent of Hartsop above How ridge spine, always accompanied by lovely views on both sides. The 'cat's ears' of Angle Tarn Pikes become conspicuous as you get lower. After a while, a fine drystone wall joins the track from your right. About 2 kilometres after Locality 13, another wall comes up from Wall End in Deepdale (from your left) to meet the one on your right. There are two stiles and you take the righthand one. From here, you can see clearly both Brothers Water and the *alluvial fan* at Hartsop which has impounded the lake.

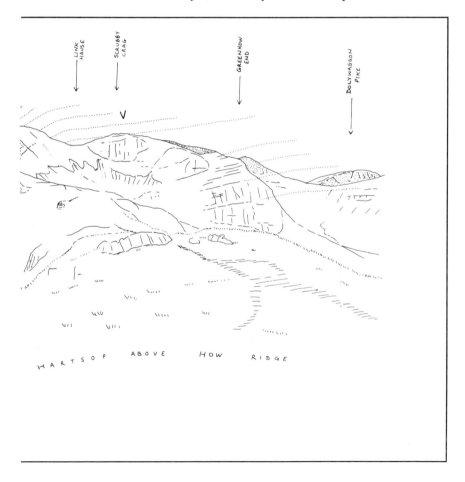

The path continues down along the ridge crest though now the wall is to your left. Keep the wall (which when you enter the woodland lower down becomes a fence) in sight right down to the main road. From here, turn right onto the 'permitted footpath' which takes you back through pleasant woodland to the car park and the end of the walk.

Summing up

The walk you've completed has taken you through a wonderful sequence of scenery and rocks. And now you have some insight into how the rocks, shaped and moulded by powerful forces of erosion, have given rise to the beauty you have seen. You also have seen for yourself that the rocks here are *not* monotonous grey nonentities: they have a story to tell if only you know how to read it. I hope this ramble has helped you to begin to do this for yourself.

ROCKY RAMBLE 3: THE OLD MAN OF CONISTON REVEALED

How to get to the start of the ramble

Make your way to Coniston village and turn up the road just to the south of the garage towards Dixon Ground (this road junction is at [3015 9750]). After 200 metres, the road swings sharp left, past the old railway station and starts to climb very steeply. This is the start of the old Walna Scar Road which crosses the south end of the Coniston range to drop down to Hollin House in Dunnerdale. Only the first part of the road is driveable. The narrow tarmac road does a couple of bends after the steep ascent, a sign says 'Coniston Old Man and Walna Scar' and after about 1,500 metres (1 mile) in total, you reach the fell gate which opens onto the rough pastures of the mountains. There is ample parking space on the other side of the gate, including in a small disused quarry on the left. This is the starting point for the ramble [2888 9702].

The ramble: needs, distances and times

Although there are optional parts (including the summit of the Old Man, 803 metres high), to be able to enjoy it to the full, you can reckon on the best part of a day to complete it. The total distance is around 11 kilometres (just less than 7 miles), involving some 600 metres (almost 2,000 feet) of climbing. The rocks around Goat's Water are a good place to picnic, and from here you can watch the coloured dots of climbers scaling the huge buttresses of Dow Crag opposite. If the weather is settled, you might prefer a picnic site with a more distant view, in which case you'll have to contain hunger pangs until at least Goat's Hawse, though remember there is no shelter on the ridges on a windy day.

Be sure to have a x10 lens with you to help you look at the fossils you should find. The OS Outdoor Leisure map you'll need is Sheet 6, South Western area.

Introduction

There's a little bit of everything to be found on this ramble around, up and over the famed Old Man. The rocks and scenery are themselves fascinating but there are old quarries and part of a once-huge copper mine to see as well as a return past some of the largest boulders in the Lake District. The rocks include both volcanic and sedimentary types, and there are fossil shells for you to find.

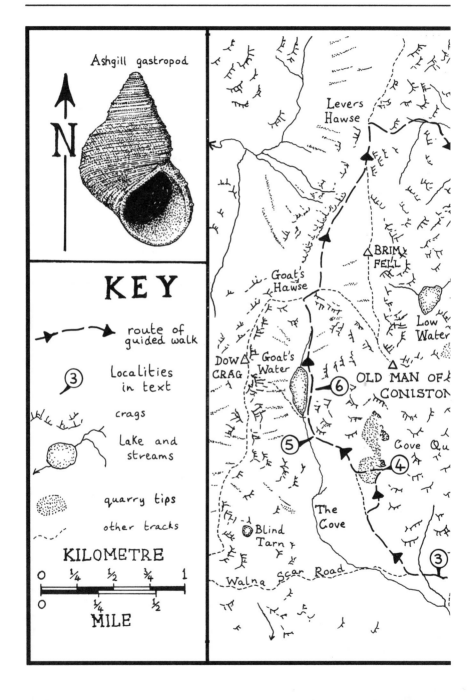

Ashgill gastropod

N

KEY

route of guided walk

③   Localities in text

crags

Lake and streams

quarry tips

other tracks

KILOMETRE

0   ¼   ½   ¾   1

0   ¼   ½

MILE

Levers Hawse

Goat's Hawse

BRIM FELL

Low Water

Dow CRAG

Goat's Water

OLD MAN OF CONISTON

⑥

⑤

Cove Qu

④

The Cove

Blind Tarn

Walna Scar Road

③

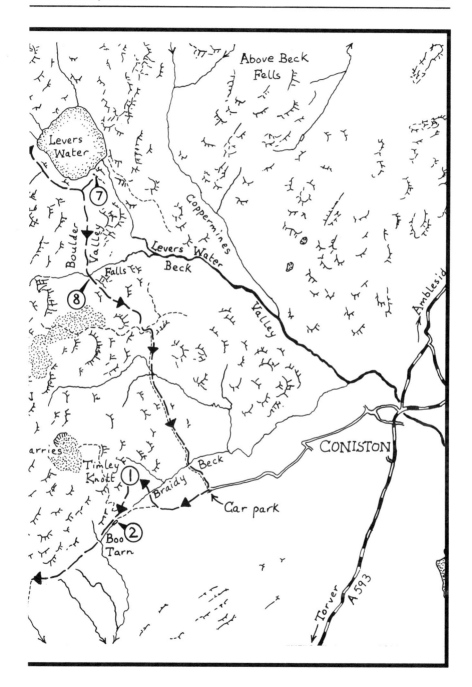

First stage: to Timley Knott and Boo Tarn

Set off on foot along the track with the quarries high up on the Old Man to your right. You can hardly fail to notice the dramatic difference between the rather dreary rolling moorland with its humps and hollows that you are walking through, and the steep craggy face of the Old Man of Coniston ahead. This, as you'd expect, is simply due to gross differences in the hardness of the underlying rocks. Those underfoot as you walk are relatively soft mud and silt rocks of *Silurian* age: the *Brathay Flags* and *Stockdale Shales*. Underlying these are rather unusual and interesting sedimentary beds collectively known as the *Coniston Limestone*, though much of the formation is not *limestone* at all. You can see these beds clearly at Timley Knott, the first locality of this ramble. They are the youngest representatives of the *Ordovician Period* in the district, and formed during the *Ashgillian Epoch* (about 440 million years old).

The original 'Ash Gill' from which this time epoch (see Appendix: Timescale) was named is Ash Gill Beck, just 2 kilometres southwest of here. Rocks of the chunk of time we call the *Ashgillian* are now recognised – by their distinctive fossils – throughout the world. So this otherwise insignificant little brook is immortalised in worldwide geological literature. In fact, this entire area of Coniston and Torver Common is a mecca for British geology, and the old quarries and rock outcrops around Ash Gill and Low and High Pike Haws are regularly visited by groups of geologists to this day.

Strangely, this boggy and rather drab moorland area was apparently favoured by the earliest of Lake District settlers, for there are a number of prehistoric remains, indicated on the OS map in Gothic writing as 'homestead,' 'enclosure' or 'cairn'.

The track along which you are walking ascends gently, bending first to the right, then to the left. On your right you'll notice a distinct marshy hollow, obviously once a small lake. Leave the road here and cut off to the right between the bracken-covered humps, heading straight for Timley Knott, about 200 metres away to the northwest. Shortly, you'll come to Braidy Beck. Cross the beck and scramble up the steep slope towards the large rowan tree which marks the right hand (northeast) end of Timley Knott.

Timley Knott; Coniston Limestone and fossils: Locality 1 [284 971]

As you puff your way up the rather steep slope to the top of the Knott, look out for fallen blocks of the *limestone,* many of which are full of small fossil remains. They usually appear as casts or moulds, the original shell having been leached out by acid groundwaters and rain. You should be able to find both *brachiopod* shells and *bryozoans*, but if you can't, don't worry. You'll see plenty more shortly. Notice too that many of the larger blocks that have rolled down this grassed-over *scree* slope show curious lines of parallel and often elliptical hollows (Figs 3.1 and 3.2). This is very characteristic of parts of the *Coniston Limestone*. The hollows have formed for the same reason that the fossils tend to occur as casts. The rock is not pure *limestone* (calcium carbonate, which usually occurs in nature as the mineral *calcite*), but parts are purer than others. It is these *calcite*-rich bands which are so readily dissolved away, leaving the less-soluble parts forming the ribs which separate the cavities. The cavities tend to occur in parallel rows because the rock was laid down as beds on the ancient seafloor. Where did all the lime for the calcite come from? Exclusively from the remains of living things, both plant and animal, which 'fixed' the lime as *calcite* to form their skeletons. The most obvious of these were the fossil shells.

Figure 3.1: *Block of Coniston Limestone showing the typical nature, the calcite-rich parts being dissolved out to leave cavities.*

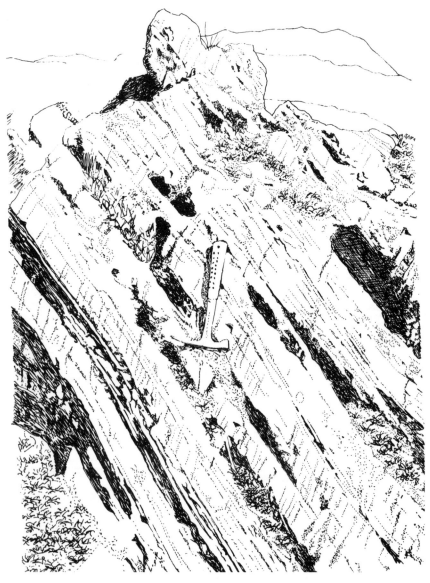

Figure 3.2: *Coniston Limestone at the summit of Timley Knott showing both bedding (dipping down to the right) and cleavage (which dips even more steeply, 70°) to the left. The shaft of my hammer bisects the acute angle between these two planar features or 'fabrics.'*

It is this same slow process, governed initially by the amount of carbon dioxide available in the atmosphere, which has produced the enormously thick *limestone* formations which you can see all over the world. Two examples with which you are probably familiar are the Chalk of south and east England and the Carboniferous Limestone of the Pennines.

You can see a fine example of the typical *limestone* 10 metres below the rowan tree (Fig. 3.1). The alternations (between rib and hollow) are almost certainly due to seafloor currents which sorted the coarser shell-fragment *limestone* into beds, winnowing the muddier sediment out. A calmer period would then have followed allowing the muddy sediment to fall out of suspension. The presence or absence of currents may have depended upon occasional tropical storms.

On the top of Timley Knott are many fine outcrops of these striking beds. You'll notice that there are two sets of *planar* features affecting most of these outcrops. I've already described how the alternating beds were formed, and you can see that these dip steeply (about 65° to the southeast). But there is a second planar fabric that cuts through the rock (Fig. 3.2) which is *cleavage* (pp. 15 and 56). Here, the *cleavage* is strong and penetrates the whole rock. It also shows refraction (Fig. 3.3) between beds of differing hardness, just as rays of light are bent because their velocity changes when they pass through transparent materials of different density such as air and water.

Here, you should see plenty of fossil shells. They are mostly *brachiopods* (of two important families called orthids and strophomenids) (Fig. 3.4) though you may be fortunate enough to spot a *trilobite* (Fig. 3.5). You may also see corals and bryozoa, both of which are tiny animals which formed colonies, using *calcite* to build the frameworks in which they lived. The fossils are not collectable here since they are part of the rock outcrop, but you can find plenty in the fallen blocks at the next locality.

Figure 3.3: *Cleavage refraction.*

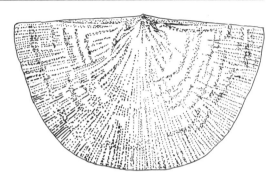

*Figure 3.4: Orthid and
strophomenid brachiopods.*

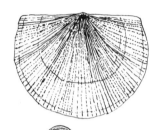

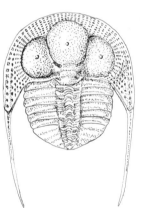

*Figure 3.5: Calymenid (Phillipsinella) and trinucleid
(Tretaspis) trilobites.*

It is these fossils which allow specialists (*palaeontologists*) to make time correlations with other rocks of the *Ashgillian* Epoch (see Appendix: 3. 'How old is a rock?') from around the world. Many life forms evolved quite 'rapidly' (in geological terms where a million years is not much more than a blip in time), whilst earlier forms equally rapidly became extinct. This means that the fossil remains of 'fast stream' animals – ones which quickly adapted to new conditions – can be used to correlate rocks from different places. If a new species came into being, became highly successful for a short while and then became extinct, its fossil remains in a rock tell us that that rock was laid down at about the same time as any other rock which also contains it, anywhere. That, at least, is the theory. In practice, it is more complicated because not many species are truly cosmopolitan: they didn't have the time or ability to spread all around the globe. Fortunately, many creatures had free-floating planktonic larval stages, just as they do today, and these could and did spread very widely and relatively fast – and these are the ones (in their hard-shelled adult forms) that are of vital importance in time correlation of rocks.

The flat top of Timley Knott is an ideal spot for contemplation about time and evolution – away from the huddled masses on the Walna Scar road. The *limestone* makes a special habitat for a number of lime-loving plants. If you look about, you'll be sure to see the delightful little natural 'rock gardens' in hollows which contain tastefully arranged clumps of moss and clusters of stonecrop.

From here, you have fine views to three points of the compass, the fourth being blocked by the craggy bulk of the Old Man. Look southwest, along the outcrop of the *Coniston Limestone*, followed by the Walna Scar road for several hundred metres (Fig. 3.6). The further to the left you look, the younger the rocks become as they pass higher up the *Silurian* sequence: first the *Stockdale Shales*, then the *Brathay Flags* occupying the fairly extensive and flat marshy area on the left. Further away are low ridges formed by the *Coniston Grits*, the youngest beds you can easily see from here.

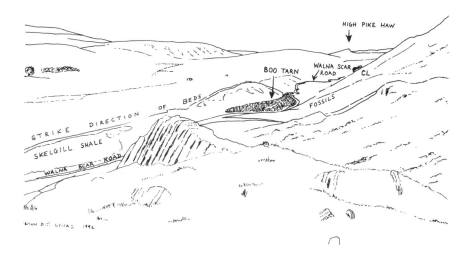

Figure 3.6: Looking southwest from Timley Knott. The Walna Scar road runs below with the insignificant Boo Tarn to its left. The abrupt change in slope from the marshy moorlands on the left to the steep slopes on the right define neatly the junction between the soft and hard beds. The Coniston Limestone is fairly hard, so the actual slope change is at its top, where it passes up into the Silurian Stockdale Shales. In the far distance, the little pike on the skyline (right of centre) is High Pike Haw, precisely the same rock formation as the one you are now standing on.

In their attempts to improve and refine the names which they give rock formations, geologists may end up creating confusion! A case in point is the *Coniston Limestone* – a useful term for a very distinctive rock which you can follow for many miles. This name had been in use for well over a century when it became more precisely defined as the 'Coniston Limestone Group'. Then it became the 'Coniston Limestone Formation'. Finally, it's been kicked out altogether and renamed the 'Dent Subgroup'. So officially, the Coniston Limestone doesn't exist! But because you and I don't have to bother our heads with the intricacies of rock naming, I decided to stay with the well-loved 'Coniston Limestone'. Now I'll be accused of creating mayhem. Sigh!

To the northeast, the picture is less easy to interpret because of *faulting*. The line of *Coniston Limestone* outcrop, the *strike*, is no longer simple because it has been chopped up and offset by *fault* movements. For example, the gully below the rowan tree which defines the northeast end of Timley Knott has been picked out by erosion along the line of weakness inevitably caused when a *fault* moves.

When this happens, the rocks close to the fault are broken up – *brecciated*. This is why faults can frequently be spotted from afar (from the air, for example) because they are often followed by streams.

This is the case here where a small tributary to Braidy Beck runs down the gully. If you try to visualise the projection of the beds from under your feet to the northeast, where *should* they be on the other side of the gully? They *should* be where you can see clear outcrops of the underlying *Borrowdale Volcanic Group*. So you can see that the *fault* has moved the Timley Knott side *downwards* (i.e. towards the northwest) for several metres. The *Coniston Limestone* on the other side of the gully has moved towards the southeast from where you'd expect it to be (Fig. 3.7).

This *fault* is very small but you can see how to spot them. If you were to try to follow the *Coniston Limestone* outcrop to the northeast, you'd find that it jumps from place to place because of similar *faulting*. In fact, you can follow it all the way to Ambleside and beyond where you see it again on Ramble 5.

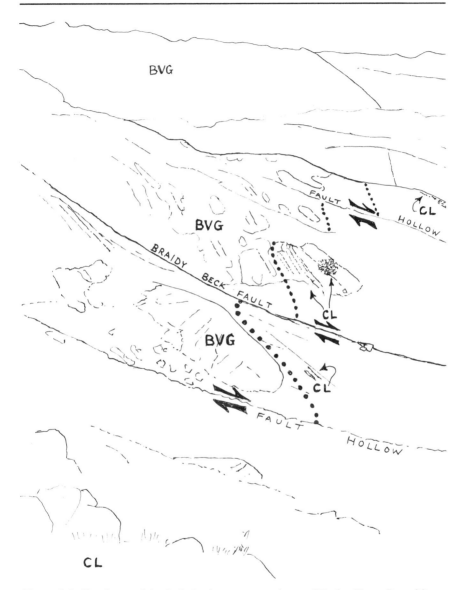

Figure 3.7: *Sketchmap of the fault displacements northeast of Timley Knott. Dotted lines show the projection of the strike: that is, where you should be able to see the Coniston Limestone had it not been moved by the fault. Key: 'BVG' – Borrowdale Volcanic Group, 'CL' – Coniston Limestone; large dots show the contact between the two. Double arrows show how the side of each fault has moved relative to the other.*

Musings on Time . . .

Now to examine the last feature of interest at Timley Knott. This is the relationship between the fossil-bearing rocks of the *Coniston Limestone* and the huge crags of older *BVG* rocks which underlie them. Because the *BVG* is hard and dips steeply southeast, it rears up behind the knott to form the Old Man. The relationship is important because it tells us the minimum age for the highest *BVG* beds: older than the start of the *Ashgillian Epoch* (around 443 million years or so). But how much older? Unfortunately there is little to go on. The rocks which underlie the thick (possibly up to 5,000 metres) *BVG*, and so are older, are the *Skiddaw Slates*. You've seen these on the Haystacks ramble and in a sense they are beneath your feet here too – but to reach them you'd have to drill down right through the entire thickness of the *BVG*! We know from *Skiddaw Slate* fossils that they are a minimum of about 468 million years old (upper *Llanvirnian Epoch*). So between them and the *Ashgillian Coniston Limestone*, a respectable chunk of time remains: around 25 million years.

It seems very unlikely that the *BVG* rocks were continuously laid down over such a lengthy period. That works out at about 2 millimetres every ten years (5,000 metres divided by 25,000,000 years); a ludicrously small figure when you look at the type of rocks which form this huge group. Much of the *BVG* is made up of coarse *breccias*, *welded tuffs* and *lavas* as you will have seen on the first two rambles. The type of eruptions which form these can spew out great thicknesses in a few hours or days! There's a time problem here so we're forced to suspect a long period when no rocks were laid down. This probably included the uplift and erosion of the older *Skiddaw Slates* creating an *unconformity* before the *BVG* eruptions even started (p. 30). The *BVG* rests upon *Skiddaw Slates* which had been previously squeezed by mid-*Ordovician* mountain building forces, and parts had been removed by erosion. Further evidence that the *BVG* is closer in age to the *Ashgillian* rocks which overlie it comes from the recent discovery of tiny fossils called *acritarchs* within the *BVG*. These are only visible under a powerful microscope after special extraction techniques, but are of *Caradocian* age. So the whole mighty group may be close to 450 million years old with most of the huge time gap having occurred before any of it was laid down.

The rocks of North Wales, visible from the Old Man on a very clear day, are also volcanic and are very similar to the *BVG*, though they are better known. They too are mostly of *Caradocian* age.

Why have I said all this now? Because you are almost at the junction between the *Coniston Limestone*, whose age we know, and the *BVG* underneath, whose age *must* (because it underlies) be older. But probably not much older. If we examine this junction and find that there is no evidence of any time break – no cutting out of the older beds or any other hint of *unconformity* – then this suggests the *BVG* was laid down just before the *Ashgillian*: i.e. *Caradocian*. I say 'suggests' because an absence of evidence is not a proof of anything. But what may be lacking here at Timley Knott may become strong evidence further along the *strike* of the junction between the two rock formations.

So now you can look at the evidence for yourself. If you walk a few metres to the northeast, towards the Old Man, you cross more outcrops of the *limestone* beds and pass down (in time) but actually up as you begin to climb the steep slope where, after only a few paces, you find that the rock has become entirely made up of bits of volcanic debris. Parts are rich in *pyrite* (fool's gold) which causes orange, brown and purple-black stains over the rock surface as the mineral oxidises. After a mere 3-4 metres thickness, this *volcaniclastic sandstone* passes abruptly into coarsely bedded *breccias*, composed wholly of angular pieces of volcanic rock up to golfball size. Being harder than the surrounding medium, the pieces stick out giving a knobbly appearance to the rock; the reverse of the *limestone* beds. If you continue on up the hill (not recommended), you find more and more knobbly beds of this sort, obviously part of the *BVG*. But what about the junction between the *BVG* and the *Coniston Limestone*? You've crossed it, but which is it? Are the 3-4 metres of *sandstone* between the definite *BVG* and the true *Coniston Limestone* part of the *BVG*? The answer seems to be that they are not, for a few *Ashgillian* shells have been found in it not far from here. So the actual contact – which may or may not represent a time break – is at the top of the *breccia* beds. As you see, this locality offers you no clue about time breaks. There is certainly no obvious *unconformity*. Figure 3.8 shows you what you've been walking across, seen from the southwest.

In fact, there *is* an *unconformity*, a time break, at precisely this point. High Pike Haw, just 3 kilometres southwest along the *strike* has beautiful outcrops of the *Coniston Limestone*. But there, the angular nature of the contact with the *BVG* is immediately obvious. The *bedding* in the *BVG* is not parallel to that in the *Coniston Limestone*. In fact, the beds trend not northeast-southwest as at Timley Knott, but somewhat west of north, which places them on a 'collision course' with the northeast-southwest *strike* of the *Coniston Limestone*. From this angular relationship, we know that probably hundreds of metres of *BVG* beds were eroded before the area subsided below the waves to allow the *Coniston Limestone* to form. How much time is represented by this break we can only guess – maybe a million years at most. From this you can see that it is only by careful note of the attitudes and trends of beds – *dips* and *strikes* – in such formations, often for long distances, that geologists can figure out what sort of contact they have. As for the *BVG*, it's 'suspended' in time, with a long time gap at the base and another moderate gap at the top.

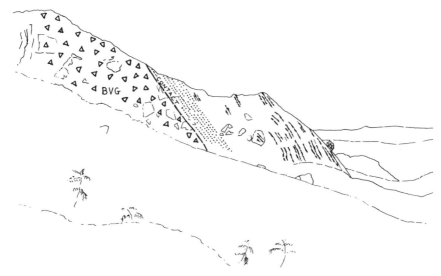

Figure 3.8: *Timley Knott from the southwest. The Coniston Limestone stands out with its rows of weathered-out cavities, but now you also know where the BVG (open triangle ornament) contact is. I've emphasised it for clarity. The sandstones I've also emphasised with rows of dots, although outcrops of these are scarce.*

Drop down towards Boo Tarn, looking back once or twice to 'review' what you've just seen (Fig. 3.8). Note another large *Coniston Limestone* bed surface just before you cross the road from the working quarry high above to the right, and rejoin the Walna Scar road.

Boo Tarn and fossils: Locality 2 [2824 9681]

Lakes, like people, have a limited life expectancy. They are all filling in. Boo Tarn is an example of a tiny lake which is gradually becoming little more than a marshy hollow. This little tarn supports its own distinctive sets of life, including those remarkable carnivorous insects, dragonflies, perhaps the most primitive (meaning in this sense, a long-surviving family) of all living insects. They first rose to prominence, often very large with wingspans as wide as your outstretched arms, back in the Carboniferous (see Appendix: Timescale) swamps, 300 million years ago. And here (on warm summer days at any rate) are their modern diminutive relatives, flitting back and forth over this even more diminutive tarn. You should also see pond skaters (Fig. 3.9) which use surface tension to walk on water. They, too, are carnivorous, catching insects which have fallen into the water. Amongst the plants are rushes and bogbeans (Fig. 3.10), lesser spearworts (a buttercup species) and sphagnum moss.

Figure 3.9: *Pond skater*

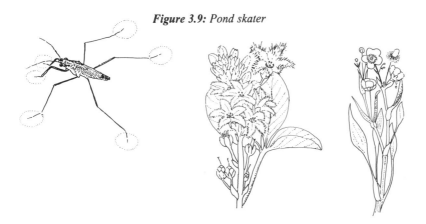

Figure 3.10: *Bog bean (left) and lesser spearwort (right)*

The tarn has formed in a hollow, excavated by erosion between the harder *Coniston Limestone* beds and the overlying *Silurian Stockdale Shales*. The ridge overlooking the southeast side of the tarn is covered in boulders of these softer rocks, all with a strong *cleavage*.

Along the right side of the road, there are many small patches of *scree* amongst the grass and bracken. Most of this has come from *Coniston Limestone* beds, identical to those at Timley Knott, which crop out higher up the slope. It's in these little *scree* patches just above the road that you should find a few fossils.

You may also find the bright orange, waxy toadstool, *Hygrophorus*, in the damp grassy places as you walk along looking for fossils. All species of this type are edible, though being tiny, are not much valued. Several small streams cross the track and upon their damp banks, you should find butterworts and sundews.

Continue along the Walna Scar road to the southwest, noting that each little beck that crosses the road has built its own small *alluvial fan* of debris which extends out into the hollow to the left of the track. A series of 'Boo Tarns' must have occupied this hollow a few hundred or thousand years ago, all now filled.

As the track bends to the right, a tiny spring emerges from fossil-bearing *Coniston Limestone* **to your right. This is marked on the OS map as 'Well in Crag.'** From this point on, you begin to cut obliquely down across the *strike* of the strata, getting closer to the *BVG*. The *Coniston Limestone* continues on, in sporadic outcrops, to the southwest, **but you are now walking west on what has become a rough track.**

Ancient glowing clouds: Locality 3 [2756 9643]

About 250 metres from Well in Crag, the Walna Scar track, now impass-
able to vehicles, cuts through an outcrop of the *BVG.* From here you can
see Brown Pike to the west, the first part of the Dow Crag ridge.
  You have now crossed the contact that you saw earlier at Timley Knott,
though there were no outcrops to show it. The rock at this locality, because it
was relatively recently broken when the track was enlarged for a now-defunct
quarry (Locality 4), is quite fresh and clean. You'll have noticed that most of
the natural outcrops are covered in a blanket of mosses and lichens which
makes every rock look the same as its neighbour, even though they may be
radically different. The rock you see here is an *ignimbrite* (p. 47). The violent
eruption which produced it was sufficiently large and hot for the bits of *pumice*
which it contained to be partially flattened by the weight of the overlying parts
of the flow to give the streaky *fiamme* structures. You can make these out here
if you look carefully at some of the fresh surfaces on the right side of the track.
It helps if the surfaces you examine are wet (and given the usual weather,
there's a good chance they will be). Then it's much easier to see other details
such as the pink and white pieces of unflattened volcanic material about the size
of a large coin. Some of the textures have a distinctly swirly appearance. This
outcrop may represent the top of the *ignimbrite* flow, where the heat was not
sufficient to cause actual full welding and flattening of the component fragments
as normally happens.

This is why early geologists didn't recognise *welded tuffs* as the products of
eruptions different from both those which produced *lava* and ordinary *tuffs*. They
thought *welded tuffs* were *flow-foliated lavas* and it is true that in their extreme
form – when they may actually start to flow as a liquid rock after initially coming
to rest from the ignimbrite eruption – they do effectively become *lavas* (though
geologists call them 'rheoignimbrites'). You can see examples of these extreme
ignimbrites on Crinkle Crags (p. 170).

Continue on along the track which passes through another smaller cut in
dark volcanic rocks. From here, you can see where the Goat's Water track
branches off to the right. Take this right turn, leaving the Walna Scar
Road winding upwards towards the col between Walna Scar and Brown
Pike. You'll notice that a second rather incised track is intertwined with the
walking track as you climb up through grassy or bracken-covered moorland. The meandering incised track reveals its purpose after about half a
kilometre, for it branches off finally to the right, up towards Cove Quarries
to which it leads. It has a fairly constant gradient so that laden carts could be
hauled down to Coniston. There may even have been a rail track though I've

seen no evidence of this. **The old quarry track, leading off to the right, takes you to Locality 4, an option since you must rejoin the Goat's Water track afterwards. But before continuing either way, look back between 20 and 50 metres before the quarry track splits off.** Here you can see fine examples of ice-polished rock surfaces for, as in all other Lake District valleys, this was at one time filled by a glacier. The ice contained blocks of rock – and sometimes huge boulders as you'll see later on this walk – which acted as powerful chisels, held fast into the base of the ice – gouging their way into the solid rock beneath. And here you see the result: parallel grooves in the polished rock surface, *glacial striations*. These grooves show that ice travelled downslope, as you'd expect.

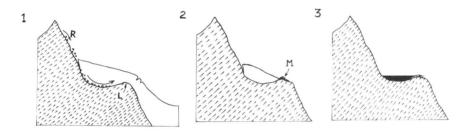

Figure 3.11: *Sketch section of corrie glacier. 'M' – terminal moraine dam at the lip of the corrie. 'L' – rock 'lip' which impounds the ice.*

Let's continue with glacial thoughts by looking over to the west where Brown Pike overshadows the appropriately named, invisible Blind Tarn [262 967]. The almost perfectly circular tarn is retained by a barrier of *moraine*, left by its small glacier before it finally succumbed to the sudden climate warming at the end of the *Younger Dryas* cold period. This is a classic example of a corrie formed by a glacier (Fig. 3.11) which grew during the 1,200-year 'cold snap' after all the older (*Devensian*) glaciers, which created the grooved rock beneath your feet, had melted around 2,500 years before (see Appendix, Timescale Column D). The reason for this brief plummet of temperatures – and also for the end of the *Devensian* glaciation 14,450 years ago – is now thought to be due to the restarting of an immense, deep, salty, 'conveyor belt' transoceanic current whose total flow is twenty times greater than all the world's rivers combined. It begins with north-moving surface currents in the North Atlantic which dive down to the abyssal depths of the ocean, liberating vast amounts of heat (so it is these currents and not just the Gulf Stream which keep northern Europe habitable) before setting off on their world tour as the 'deep salty current' via the ocean bottoms to end up surfacing again in the far eastern Pacific. For some reason, this current started again around 14,500 years ago but then shut down 1,800 years later, but not before temperatures had risen sufficiently to melt almost all the former ice sheets. After the shutdown 12,700 years ago, the start of the *Younger Dryas* cold period, temperatures fell by 6°C in 100 years, quite sufficient to bring back small glaciers in the Lake District. But when the ocean current restarted just over 1,000 years later, temperatures shot up to temperate levels within as little as 20 years. The small glaciers quickly melted leaving the beautiful, fresh *moraine* features you see today in many parts of the Lake District (e.g. p. 186).

Dryas octopetala (=8 petals) or mountain avens is a small member of the rose family typically found in the Arctic and mountainous regions of northern Europe. Pollen from this little plant suddenly becomes much more abundant in lake sediments 12,700 years old (see Appendix: 'Radiocarbon and the end of the last ice ages'), telling us that the climate had cooled again giving favourable conditions for *Dryas* to grow. One thousand years later, the pollen from this plant declined rapidly, marking the end of what is now know as the *Younger Dryas* cold period (also known as the Loch Lomond Readvance or Interstadial -confusing!).

The *Younger Dryas moraines* and corries remind you, poignantly, that climate is a dynamic system, constantly changing fast as well as slowly. A climatic 'flick of the fingers' can cause temperatures to both plummet and soar – and in as little as 3 years! You look up towards Blind Tarn and think, 'That's always been there'. But it hasn't. Such apparently slow and ageless, but actually near-instantaneous creations of the planet's capricious climate serve to remind us that we mess about with our atmosphere and oceans at our peril.

Blind Tarn is not only one of the smallest Lakeland *corrie* tarns, it is also the shallowest at only 7 metres (23 feet) depth. The deepest is Blea Water, below High Street. It is 63 metres (207 feet) deep.

Cove Quarries and their underground cathedral: Locality 4

With such a title, you just have to head up that track, don't you? If you don't, skip this locality and carry on up to Goat's Water. As you make your way up to the quarries, note how they form a series, inclining up the Old Man's Breast to exploit a distinct band (often called 'vein' by quarrymen) of strata dipping to the southeast, within the *BVG*. **Head for the right hand end of the quarries, the lowest part, scrambling up the waste tips as necessary.**

Standing on the floor of the quarry, you'll see that the overwhelming 'fabric' possessed by these rocks is *cleavage*. The rocks represent a period of tranquillity within the normally violent events of the *BVG*. During this quiet period, fine grained *tuffs* were laid down in water. Much of the resultant rock shows almost no sign of bedding, though parts show clear *graded beds* and small structures typical of sediments deposited in water. It is because these beds were fine grained and uniform that the *cleavage*, imposed later by earth movements (p. 54), was so strong, forming these slates which the quarrymen of the last century exploited for roofing slate. The beds are known as the *Tilberthwaite Tuffs* and have been worked for ornamental slate for centuries throughout the length of their outcrop: from Broughton Moor Quarry west of Torver, to Tilberthwaite, Little Langdale and Loughrigg (p. 163) and beyond.

At the back of the quarry, remains of rail tracks lead into a large open chamber, useful for sheltering from the rain (Fig. 3.12).

Figure 3.12: Entrance to the underground chamber at Cove quarries.

At this point, I have to give the usual warning about entering old workings. Yes, it can be dangerous (like driving up the M6 motorway to get here) and I'm not going to say it's perfectly safe to walk in here. Blocks do fall from the roofs of such chambers from time to time so, if in doubt, stay out.

But why did the quarrymen make these large chambers? The technique they used here was similar to that used in certain types of mining, and was common in the much larger underground quarries of Blaenau Ffestiniog in North Wales. The idea was to exploit the 'vein' of slate using gravity to do as much of the work as possible. Also, underground working was more efficient in that you only had to dig out what you wanted. If the 'vein' was thin, you could leave pillars of it to support the roof and just take the best. This would be impossible in the open air. Blocks were then prised and blasted away from above so as to slide down to where they could be collected onto railcars and pushed out into the open. There, the good quality pieces (without *quartz* veins or faults of any kind) were separated from the rest which was simply pushed over the edge of the waste tip. The larger quarries often had splitting and shaping sheds on site so that only finished slates had to be carried down to the nearest railhead but there's no evidence that this was done here.

If you decide to go in – safer with a torch – follow the rail tracks through the entrance chamber into a short tunnel and so out into 'the cathedral', a very much larger chamber which is totally dark so that you feel and hear its presence rather than see it. The tunnel continues further into the mountainside from the inside of 'the cathedral' though I have never been any further. If you stand in 'the cathedral' by the entrance tunnel, you'll be surprised how much you can begin to make out as your eyes accustom themselves to the small amount of light which passes down the tunnel. It's all very eerie: total silence except for the drip of water and . . . who knows? I've never seen a troll (Fig. 3.13), but surely here he should be, don't you think?

Figure 3.13: Troll. Note slavering jaws etc. Food preferences definitely not vegetarian. Particularly noted for preying on unsuspecting walkers following guided geology rambles.

Just outside the entrance is a gnarled mass of white *quartz* veins cutting the slate. *Pyrite* also occurs within the *quartz,* decomposing now that it is exposed to the atmosphere to brown-purple iron oxides and yellow sulphurous deposits which stain the rock surface.

Whilst it is perfectly possible to work your way up to the higher quarries from this bottom one using the cobbled zigzag quarry road, there's no advantage in doing so as there is little more to see and you have to rejoin the Goat's Water track, thereby losing height.

After rejoining the path to Goat's Water, continue along it and begin the ascent through boulders and outcrops of *BVG*. If you look at these rocks briefly as you pass, you'll see that they contain bands of pea-sized *lapilli* and parts are full of flattened *pumice* lumps, so this rock is a partially *welded tuff*.

Some of the *pumice* and *fiamme* are the length of an outstretched hand and are softer than the denser, *silica*-rich rock matrix enclosing them.

The rock changes abruptly at the point where the path stops ascending and bends a little to the right. Here you can just begin to see Goat's Water.

Volcanic violence and icy effects: Locality 5

You are now standing on the rock lip of the former Goat's Water corrie glacier and you can see clearly the *roches moutonées* shapes of the ice-smoothed rocks near the path. Looking more carefully, there are several examples of *glacial striations* right by the track. And if you're still doubtful, look at the train of huge boulders dumped by the decaying glacier all over the valley bottom. How else could they have got there? Giants playing volleyball perhaps?

Figure 3.14: *Sketch of block tuff at the rock lip, to the left of the track just before it starts to descend slightly.*

The rock which has been ground and polished by the passage of ice over it is quite different from the dark *welded tuff* you've just walked through, for it is a complete jumble of *blocks,* cobbles and boulders (Fig. 3.14). You could describe this as a *block tuff,* and it was probably the result of an avalanche of debris from high up on the slopes of a nearby volcano. The avalanche could have occurred either 'cold' – sloughing off of unstable material due to earth tremors – or 'hot.'

A 'hot' avalanche or *pyroclastic flow* can be due to a *nuée ardente* eruption or
what is termed 'column collapse.'

Column collapse: When a volcano is blasting thousands of tons of hot ash and
rock vertically upwards, it has to come back down again. If the eruption stops,
then the huge and heavy column of debris, often many kilometres high, loses its
upwards momentum and so falls back, flowing outwards off the volcano's flank
and forming *pyroclastic flows.*

In 1980, Mount St. Helen's (USA) exploded. This happened when the rising
magma body, already dangerously close to the surface, caused so much
bulging of the mountain's flank that it collapsed catastrophically, suddenly
uncapping and depressurising the hot, gassy *magma* which immediately blasted
out in a fearful eruption so powerful that it knocked down huge areas of mature
trees like matchsticks and picked up any loose material – mostly rocks but
including the odd car – and dumped them many kilometres away. Such
eruptions, a type of *pyroclastic flow*, depend for their extreme mobility on a
process called *fluidisation.*

Fluidisation: This property causes solids to behave as liquids and is now much
used in industry. You can see *fluidisation* for yourself when you drop a shovelful
of cement powder. It 'flumps' down and parts of it spurt out and flow just like
tiny rivulets. And this happens on a grand scale during very gassy eruptions
involving not cement powder, but a mass of boulders and rubble. They can
behave as a liquid and flow downhill very fast, and even up over low ridges too.
Fluidisation occurs largely because of the violent and continuous de-gassing of
the *magma* as the confining pressure is released, like foam from a bottle of
champagne after the cork pops. But since these eruptions are 'heavy' and
surface-hugging, they flow downhill – they do not project upwards like 'light' ash
clouds which form a huge column thousands of metres high above the erupting
vent (e.g. Mount Pinatubo, Philippines, 1991). As the ground-hugging flows
move, they rip up and incorporate boulders from earlier eruptions but because
they are moving fast (probably at least 100 kilometres per hour), they entrap air
which, since the inside of the gassy flow may be as hot as 800°C, adds to the
expansion and fluidity. Finally, as the expanding flow loses energy and the
slope slackens, the fluidisation ceases to be effective and the larger solid
materials fall out to form the sort of rock you see here.

This rock underlies (is older than) the rock you've just walked through and may
even be the basal part of one of these huge eruptions, for it passes up into
pumice-laden tuff which shows all the signs of having been partially welded.

    As usual, there are several possible explanations for what you see. Interpre-
tation of the *origin* of these ancient rocks is not always easy or certain. The best

we can do is to look carefully at all the evidence. And if you think that reading *this* rock is difficult, wait till you get to Locality 6!

Continue on towards the tarn. On your right and in the track, you pass by outcrops of whitish-weathering rock, parts of which are stained pink by iron oxides: *porphyritic andesites*. The white crystals – the porphyry component – are *feldspar* and are cemented in a dark, almost glassy groundmass of other minerals. This glassy appearance tells you that the *lava,* once erupted as a flow, cooled rapidly. Slow cooling *igneous* rocks like *granite* are always coarsely crystalline but glassy *lava* rock may be produced by rapid cooling giving no time for crystals to form.

By the time you reach Goat's Water, the *lava* outcrops have been replaced by another rock type – this time familiar: the rock has a strong rather delicate texture with *feldspar* crystals, flattened *pumice* and bits of broken glassy bubble walls, shattered by quenching (due to rapid cooling) and gas expansion. These broken bubbles are called *shards* and you need a lens to see them (Fig. 3.15). The rock is another *ignimbrite*: a *eutaxitic welded tuff.* Some of the *fiamme* are thirty times longer (up to a palm width) than they are thick – an indication of the intense degree of flattening of originally roughly ball-like *pumice* due to their total collapse. Blocks of this *tuff* litter the track and you can best see the delicate fabric on the flat *joint* faces.

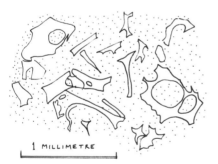

1 MILLIMETRE

Figure 3.15: Forms of glass shard. Some are complete bubbles whilst others are merely fragments of burst bubble walls. These are set in a fine ash matrix. Whilst with practice, you can see these with a x10 lens, they are best seen with a proper microscope. They are exceedingly characteristic of rocks of ignimbrite origin.

By the time you're half way along the length of Goat's Water, there is another sudden change . . .

Blobby, lumpy and swirly rocks – geological custard? Locality 6 [2670 9766]

Suddenly the rocks have become slabby and well bedded, with vertical dips and bed surfaces *striking* northeast-southwest. The best exposures are 20-30 metres up the *scree* slope to the right of the track. The beds are mostly water-lain (hence the good bedding) *feldspar* crystals and other minerals and show the usual tiny *faults,* small *slumps* and *fluidisation* features which occur in similar rocks (p. 50). But if you look around this locality, you'll find numerous examples of a bizarre form of this well bedded *volcaniclastic sandstone.* Certain layers of the strata seem to have been disrupted to make, in its extreme form, a weird honeycomb rock (Figs 3.16 and 3.17). This blobby, swirly and lumpy

'honeycomb' seems totally unlike the slabby *sandstones* within which it occurs. It seems (from the two sketches which are views of both the side and base of these curious beds) that the structure is the same whichever way you view it, all through the rock. Weathering has picked it out for you to see because of differing hardnesses: the hollows are made up of soft, reddish-weathering, fine grained sediment whereas the projecting lumps are harder and coarser grained.

Figure 3.16: Honeycomb rock at Goat's Water. This is a section across the bedding, but you can see no sign of it any more.

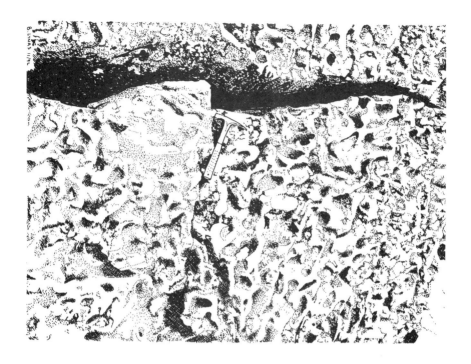

Figure 3.17: *Honeycomb rock again, this time the base or top of a bed.*

But why should they have developed in this way, you quite reasonably ask? Before we all throw up our hands in despair as to what it all means, there are clues here to be seen:

If you poke around the outcrops and fallen blocks, you'll find that there are places where you can see well *bedded sandstone* and honeycomb rock in the same section (Fig. 3.18). What you see here seems to be a transition between the normal beds and the weird honeycomb rock. It doesn't happen everywhere for here and there are remnants of bedding within the disordered honeycomb. Also only certain beds seem to have been susceptible. In fact, you can in Figure 3.18 actually see the various stages of development, frozen in time, which makes it very clear that this structure formed *after* these beds were laid down. Figure 3.18 (and other sections you can find) show various features which we already know to be associated with *fluidisation* and *dewatering* of shallow water sediments. There are water expulsion structures which seem to have blasted through rather sticky beds from below, owing to the increasing weight of overlying strata. *Load casts* may be an important part of the process too. Since we know that the overlying strata are *ignimbrites* and *lavas,* typically erupted rapidly, the loading (extra weight on top) of these odd-looking sediments could

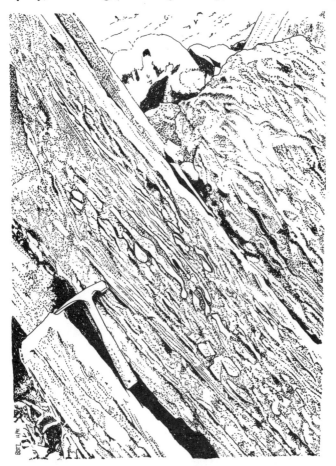

have happened quite suddenly whilst they were still very wet. Maybe the honeycomb beds developed as a response to this sudden loading. Earthquake shocks associated with eruptions would also trigger rapid *dewatering* by causing temporary but total *fluidisation* of the more favourable beds, which separated into the curious blobs, lumps and swirls before compacting – our geological custard. I may not be right but it makes a good story. What do you make of it?

Figure 3.18: *Transition between bedded sandstone and 'honeycomb'. The development for some reason stopped incomplete.*

Our problem rocks aren't quite over yet, for you may have noticed one or two large bed surfaces within the well bedded *sandstones* which show odd circular structures at their bases (Fig. 3.19). I'm not even going to try to explain these here, for you can see similar – and much better ones – on the Langdale Ramble (p. 121) where I have attempted an explanation.

Figure 3.19: This large bed surface (hammer for scale) shows odd circular moulds. Are they jellyfish? Or the work of prehistoric man? Your guess is as good as mine.

If you've heard a sharp 'tic, tic' sound as you've been puzzling over these rocks, it will almost certainly be a wren. Craggy places and *screes* seem to be favourites of this hardy, slightly nosey bird – the smallest of our native birds.

Goat's Water seems a dark and gloomy tarn, captured below the massive buttresses of Dow Crag, so popular with climbers whose paths cross the still-forming *screes* below the crag. If you look over the tarn to its northeast shore, you'll notice a low grassy ridge which runs due north for 250 metres, marking the junction between the *scree* and the boggy valley head below Goat's Hawse. It looks like a glacial *moraine* but is more likely to be a ramp of debris which formed after the *Younger Dryas* ice had melted away leaving only a persistent snowpatch on the steep northeast-facing slope below Dow Crag. As pieces of rock broke off the vertical faces high above, they would crash down onto the snow, bouncing and slithering to form this ramp at the bottom. Further warming caused the melting of the snowpatch, leaving a slight hollow now gradually being filled up by modern *scree* which has encroached upon the older debris ramp or *protalus rampart*.

If you turn left off the main path at the north end of the lake, you can cross to the rampart and walk along its crest. All about are huge fallen boulders from Dow Crag which show us, without need to climb and see, that the crag consists of a thick sequence of both *lavas* and coarse fragmental rocks, probably from one continuous series of huge eruptions. But at the north extremity of the crag, the rock becomes pale-coloured well bedded *tuff* so that both the *screes* and *protalus ramp* are made up entirely of this.

Climb now to Goat's Hawse, rejoining the track (if you have left it) wherever seems most convenient. From the hawse, you begin to have fine views of the Scafell range away to the northwest, then Harter Fell and Grey Friar. All these mountains are part of the same great *BVG* suite of rocks. **From this point, you can if you wish, make your way up to the summit of the Old Man (another 150 metres of ascent) by following the broad track to the southeast. Or you can climb a short way up the main track and contour round the grassy west flank of Brim Fell to Levers Hawse, so avoiding further climbing. There is a small track which you should be able to locate. Levers Hawse is at almost the same height as Goat's Hawse, a little over one kilometre to the northeast.**

If you do ascend to the flat and denuded summit of the Old Man, you should have fine views in all directions – if you can see over the heads of the other people there! Most important from our point-of-view is the contrast between the 'soft' *Silurian* country to the southeast and the resistant craggy *BVG* mountains all around and to the north. **Continuing along the fine ridge of which the Old Man forms the south end, you can look down into the perfect corrie of Low Water as you head towards Brim Fell.** It is not too difficult to visualise a small glacier occupying this great amphitheatre of nearly bare rock. Later on the ramble, you'll pass well below this lake and witness other dramatic effects of glaciation.

Continue on over Brim Fell and so down to Levers Hawse. From here you have a good view of Levers Water and the Coppermines Valley. You can also see clearly the highest workings of the Paddy End Mine, open vertical gashes in the rock (called *stopes*) above the southeast lakeshore. These *stopes* form Locality 7.

Descend the rather steep and slippery track into Gill Cove, towards the lake. Thick white *quartz* veins cut the rock hereabouts, and to the left, the crags are all formed of bedded *tuffs,* the *bedding* showing up as rows of hollows or disinct bands. **About half way down, look across eastwards to the ridges of High Fell (from Black Sails) and Above Beck Fell (from Wetherlam).** In both ridges, you can clearly make out a number of quite regular volcanic rock units forming a distinct 'grain', dipping from the upper left to lower right. In this way, we can begin to make order out of apparent chaos.

As you approach Levers Water, another glacial corrie lake, the track turns to the right, crossing a stream and continuing around the south of the lake towards Brim Fell End and Boulder Valley. Just before the low col

which passes over to Boulder Valley, you can turn left to visit the open *stopes* and dumps of Paddy End Mine.

The boulders which have fallen from Brim Fell End high above and which litter the path and slopes, are almost all pale grey-white, *porphyritic ignimbrite* just like those you saw at Goat's Water

Paddy End Mine: Locality 7 [281 991]

The open and distinctly unstable mine workings, fenced off to prevent sheep and people from entering, show you fairly clearly just how the minerals were found in the rock by the miners – as thick veins, now removed, which dipped at around 80° southwest. The miners were after the copper ores but a host of other minerals occurred with the copper. You should be able to find several by picking about on the old dumps just above the lake. The commonest minerals are *quartz,* a little *calcite, pyrite* (fool's gold), various iron hydroxide minerals (brown, purple and black staining indicating secondary minerals produced by weathering of primary minerals like *pyrite*). The copper occurred mostly as *chalcopyrite*, a bright yellow brassy mineral looking quite like gold. In some weathered lumps, you'll notice a green copper mineral: *malachite*. Minor amounts of bismuth, nickel and cobalt minerals were also found in this mine, so you can see that the suite of minerals is quite considerable and identification is not always easy.

The miners removed the veins containing the valuable minerals by *stoping*. This was usually done from underneath (overhand stoping) by boring a tunnel along the vein. The vein was then drilled and blasted so that it dropped down into the tunnel, to be removed by tubs on rails. A dangerous business indeed. The main entrance (and dumps) of this mine are about 300 metres to the southwest, south of the waterfalls of Levers Beck. Paddy End Mine had its heyday in the 1850s, producing up to 4,000 tons of 'dressed' copper ore each year. After this, output declined and it was abandoned in 1908 having produced overall some 52,000 tons of copper ore (averaging around 5-13 percent copper). The vein was the richest in the Coniston area and probably continues underneath Levers Water and well to the west.

Most of the original minerals (called 'primary' minerals – those first precipitated from the ore-bearing fluids, deep underground and in the absence of oxygen) were sulphides. It is only when these minerals become exposed to the atmosphere and circulating groundwater that the array of hydroxides and carbonates (called 'secondary' minerals) develop. How and why do veins of minerals form? The question is not easy to answer but in general, veins need some sort of pre-existing weakness in the rock along which they can penetrate. Almost invariably this weakness is provided by a *fault* which will, by its movement, have broken up the rock, creating connected cavities along which the vein fluids can flow. In this case – Paddy End Mine veins – the *faults* cut and broke up parts of the thick *ignimbrite* which you've already seen. The fluids were probably superheated brines which can carry many sulphides in solution. When the right physical and chemical conditions were satisfied, minerals precipitated out onto the walls of the cavities forming, eventually, the veins which have been so carefully removed by the miners. (This is akin to the precipitation, or 'furring up', of water pipes in hard water areas). It is common in such veins to find that first only one mineral crystallises, followed by a second and a third, giving a distinct banding to the veinstuff. The hot fluids probably came from deep seated bodies of magma (p. 180).

Levers Water has been slightly increased in size by a low dam. Water from this lake was once much used as a source of power for waterwheel-driven machinery in Coppermines Valley. The stones used for the dam spillway are a beautiful, *granite* with large crystals of pink *feldspar*. They almost certainly were brought here from Shap Fell, some 20 miles northeast where there is a famous quarry in the Shap *granite intrusion*. At the southwest end of the spillway are several examples of glacial 'perched blocks', dumped here on the corrie lip by decaying ice.

Return now to the track towards the appropriately named Boulder Valley and as you walk down, you'll see in front the hanging waterfalls which plunge down from the hidden Low Water, nestling high above under the brooding jowls of the Old Man.

It seems likely that the boulders you are passing have not moved far. The shape of this valley suggests that a powerful tongue of ice once emerged from Levers Water corrie over the low col by Paddy End Mine to carve this valley, gouging the crags below Low Water and so creating the hanging waterfall of today. Certainly, you can find *striations* – a sure sign of passage of ice – on the polished *ignimbrite* surfaces which form the rock lip of Grey Crag to the left of the track. Because the ice tongue steepened the precipices on its western side, huge boulders would have fallen from high above and bounded across the ice to form a crude *protalus rampart* like that you saw at Goat's Water.

Continue to the bottom of Boulder Valley where the largest boulder (Fig. 3.20) of all stands like a sentinel right by the track where it crosses the beck.

The great Puddingstone Boulder: Locality 8 [2805 9842]

This boulder is a *lapilli-block tuff,* and its very size tells us that it cannot have moved far. What probably happened in this hollow is that ice from the corrie now occupied by Low Water broke up as it was forced inexorably over the corrie lip, smashing itself to pieces as it avalanched down to where you are now standing. It would have formed a cone of shattered ice in the lower corrie. But this was not the end of the story. I have seen just this sort of thing in the high Andes so I know it really happens: the ice reforms a glacier as the broken pieces meld together under pressure from later avalanches. Thus a lower ice tongue, less powerful than that above, formed and merged with the tongue from Levers Water in Boulder Valley, gouging out a lesser corrie – the hollow where you are now. Like all corries, this too has a rock lip at its outlet over which Low Water Beck plunges for the second time to join Levers Water Beck in Coppermines Valley. The great puddingstone boulder must have fallen down from above as the ice was in a state of terminal decay – or it wouldn't be here now.

Figure 3.20: *'Puddingstone' boulder the size of a house.*

Beside the boulder is an old iron pipe which would once have carried water from Low Water at high pressure to power a turbine below in the old mines or quarries.

Continue on now along the footpath to join a vehicle track at the top of old slate tips below Crowberry Haws. The slates are the same *Tilberthwaite*

Tuffs you saw on the other side of the mountain at Cove Quarry. And like those, they have been worked underground and brought out of a tunnel which you'll see to the right of the track. The slaty *tuffs* show clear bedding with small structures in the coarser beds which developed due to loading and water escape (p. 49). The slates are still being worked in quarries both above and below this locality.

The level track continues southeast from here with *screes* **alongside**, which support low-growing dwarf junipers and a holly tree to the right of the track. You can hardly fail to notice the scene of ecological devastation revealed below in Coppermines Valley. Attempts have been made to redeem this somewhat, but imagine what it looked like a century ago when the mines were still in their heyday.

You come to a junction shortly. Turn left (downhill) for a short distance and then follow the main track which curves round to the right to continue its southwesterly course with The Bell on your left. Do not take the path which heads down towards Levers Water Beck and Coniston. Now you just have a gentle, downhill trudge for nearly 1 kilometre until you reach a bend in the track just before Braidy Beck. You saw this beck at Timley Knott, less than half a kilometre away to the southwest. And here again, as you'd expect, is the *Coniston Limestone.* There are few actual outcrops here, but the characteristic boulders such as you saw at Timley Knott are scattered about to the left of the track. Half a kilometre to the northeast, the little crags of Willy Scrow are again *Coniston Limestone* with trees on the *dipslope.* And you will certainly have noticed the sudden change from the rugged, rocky *BVG* landscape you've left behind you to the gentle, rolling *Silurian* moorland ahead.

The Walna Scar Road and parking place are now only a quarter kilometre ahead, after crossing Braidy Beck. Before leaving, look back to the mountain you've just walked over – The Old Man of Coniston. You've crossed at least 450 million years of history, reading some of its story for yourself. Even so, standing here, it's quite hard to imagine that everywhere all around you was covered in a thick ice sheet as little as 15,000 years ago. But you've seen the evidence so you know it to be true. Now for that drink . . .

ROCKY RAMBLE 4:
THE LANGDALE PIKES

How to get to the start of the ramble

The quickest and easiest way to get to the start of this ramble is along the
B5343 through Skelwith Bridge and Chapel Stile. There is a convenient
National Trust car park [294 063] on the right, just past the turning to the New
Dungeon Ghyll hotel (Fig. 4.1). There is an alternative route which goes through
Little Langdale, but this is definitely not recommended for motorists as the road
is both narrow and potentially dangerous. Incidentally, 'Dungeon', by the way,
doesn't refer to a prison; merely to the deep, gloomy, dungeon-like fissure of
Dungeon Ghyll itself.

The ramble: needs, distances and times

The ramble is around 10 kilometres (just over 6 miles) in total, involving about
700 metres (2,300 feet) of ascent. Since it is across rugged mountain country, be
prepared for bad weather and mist. It is definitely a fine weather walk and you
should allow a full day for it in order to appreciate all that you'll see. There are
several 'escape' routes if you want to cut the ramble short. In fine weather,
idyllic grassy platforms perched just below the summit of Pike of Stickle make
the best picnic spot in the area. And after the long slog up Troughton Beck,
you'll need that picnic.

The OS Outdoor Leisure map is Sheet 6, South Western area.

Introduction

If someone asked you to conjure up a Lake District scene, the chances are you'd
choose the justly famous Langdale Pikes. Most people have seen that timeless
view from Tarn Hows with Pike of Stickle, Loft Crag, Harrison Stickle and
Pavey Ark decorating the horizon. Maybe you've walked up some – or all – of
the Pikes, but you probably didn't notice the amazing rocks which you walked
over. Like those of the earlier rambles in this book, they have a story to tell.
This story is one of huge volcanic eruptions of thick *lavas, ignimbrites* and *tuffs*
followed by subsidence of the area below water level. The actual source for the
igneous rocks must have been very close indeed.

The rocks you see on this ramble are all part of the *Borrowdale Volcanic
Group* which glaciers chiselled into the craggy silhouettes we all know so well
today.

Figure 4.1: *New Dungeon Ghyll Hotel, Stickle Ghyll, Pavey Ark and Harrison Stickle.*

To Mickleden: the start of the ramble

A path leaves the car park at its northwest end, passing up through a group of larches. A sign states: 'Path to Dungeon Ghyll and Mickleden'. Follow this path up the hillside for a short distance until it joins the main walking track which connects the two hotels. **Turn left (southwest) towards the Old Hotel, being sure not to take the path to Dungeon Ghyll Force and Harrison Stickle (one of several alternative routes for descending if you want to abandon the ramble early). As you pass by the Old Hotel and Middle Fell Farm on your left,** look up to Raven Crag on your right, much favoured by climbers. Cones of *scree* emerge from the deep gullies in the crag to be lost under bracken and grass lower down in the intake ('intake' meaning enclosed by a wall and improved) land. In the little beck below the farm – if you care to make the diversion – monkey flowers (*Mimulus*) grow.

The beautiful yellow monkey flowers, members of the snapdragon family, are native to the Aleutian Islands, Alaska, and were brought to Britain in the 19th century. They have since become naturalized (= escaped).

A broad track continues on towards Mickleden (Old English for 'large valley') **with intake fields still above you to the right.** Spreading out to your left is the broad, gentle *alluvial cone* from Oxendale Beck, a powerful stream which drains from Crinkle Crags, dropping nearly 700 metres in 2 kilometres, a fall of 1 in 2.8 (35% gradient). The *alluvial cone* has developed because of the abrupt change from steep to nearly flat. The water loses its energy and ability to carry sediment and so dumps it. This simple, 'living' illustration of the linkage of energy with gradient is of immense importance in understanding some earth science processes. It applies not only to rivers but to *mass flows* of all types including certain types of volcanic eruptions.

You'll notice that these large becks are now mostly confined within artificial dykes to prevent them flooding their natural *flood plains* – the reason that the valley floor is flat.

After a while, you come to a gate. Go through and bear left through a second gate along the main track into Mickleden. Above you to your right is Pike of Stickle (from 'sticel': a steep slope) and Loft Crag. *Screes* fan out from the base of their crags and are now largely inactive and so covered with bracken. To your left is Mickleden Beck, snaking its way through its *flood plain* with a set of *river terraces*: these terraces are the eroding edges of an older flood plain at a higher level which the river is now slowly removing as it cuts lower in its course (see notes on *rejuvenation*, p. 210).

The walls hereabouts are often very thick and you see many piles of stones, all witness to the back breaking labour of stone-clearing from the grazing land in past centuries. I know just how hard this work is, having done a good deal of it myself on my own land.

The Pike of Stickle Neolithic axe factory

You can't fail to notice the great streak of pale scree which descends from a deep gully at the east end of Pike of Stickle. It was around the outlet of this gully that in 1947, a number of roughly shaped stone axes were found. Since then, the Pike of Stickle axe factory has become well known. The roughed-out axes have been found all along the base of the Pike of Stickle crags; below Harrison Stickle, around Martcrag Moor and again at Scafell. There's little doubt that the Neolithic people who fashioned them did so out of suitable fallen blocks which are abundant at the top of the *screes*. The finished Pike of Stickle axes – made of a distinctive *BVG tuff* – turn up as far away as Bournemouth, Gloucester, Yorkshire, Scotland and the Isle of Man, telling us just how well-established trade routes were, even in those far off times.

The rock from which the axes were formed by human hands over five thousand years ago – nearly halfway back to the last glaciers – is a fine-grained,

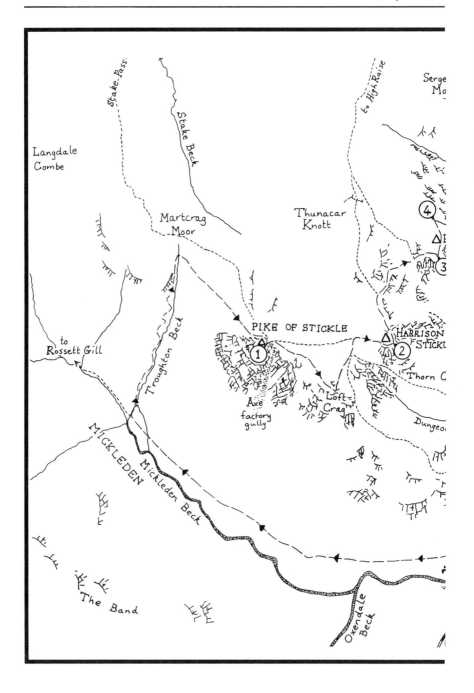

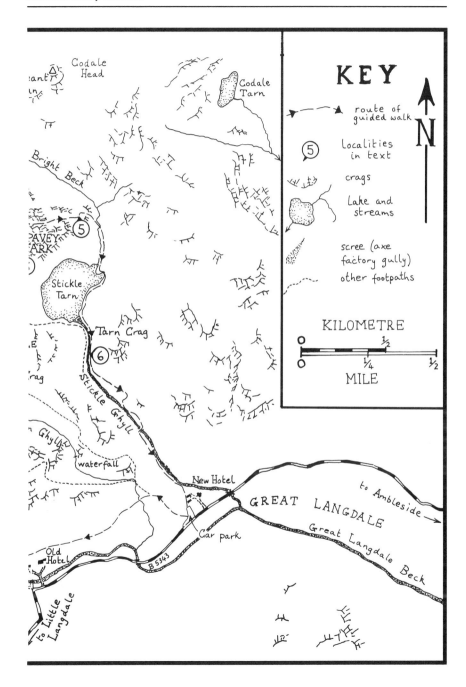

KEY

➤---➤ route of guided walk

⑤ localities in text

crags

Lake and streams

scree (axe factory gully)

.... other footpaths

N

KILOMETRE

0 ——————————— ½

0 ——— ¼ ——— ½

MILE

green *tuff*, part of the well bedded sequence which forms Pike of Stickle and Loft Crag which you'll see later on the ramble. The *tuff* was rich in *silica* when it was laid down and so is extremely hard – a tough *tuff* – quite like flint in its properties.

Mickleden: humps and hollows everywhere

As you continue, the wall on the left stops and you find yourself on a broad, recently made track up the valley. Ahead are many curious, bracken-covered humps contrasting with the smooth, gently sloping foreground. The backdrop to these is the rugged outline of Rossett Pike with the gash of Rossett Gill on the left followed by the path to Angle Tarn.

The humps are glacial *moraines* and are justly famous, looking as if they were made yesterday. In fact, they formed at the end of the *Younger Dryas* cold period some 11,500 years ago (see Appendix: Timescale, Column D). The head of Mickleden would have been occupied by ice descending from the extensive steep, east and northeast facing slopes of Bow Fell and The Band. The direction is important because of the warmth of the sun. The coldest direction is always northeast which is why almost all the corries of the Lake District face that way. As you see, the *moraines* begin quite abruptly, telling us where the glacier snout must have been at its maximum advance.

Moraines are characteristic of ice whose source 'dries up'. As the climate warms, the ice melts dropping the load of rocky rubbish it contains in these irregular mounds. Some glacier snouts are so covered by rocky rubbish that you'd hardly know that there was ice underneath. A modern example is Glacier Noir in the Ecrins Alps of France. If and when Glacier Noir finally melts it will doubtless leave humpy *moraine* just like this.

As you approach the *moraines*, the track runs close to the beck on an older *terrace*, the *flood plain* of the present day stream being about 3 metres lower. After heavy rain, the whole of this network of braided streams becomes inundated by a powerful torrent of sediment-laden water which can roll surprisingly large boulders.

Troughton Beck to Martcrag Moor: a steep ascent but soon over

Towering above you on your right is Pike of Stickle. Just before the main track enters the Mickleden *moraines*, it bridges Troughton Beck and you take a faint track off to the right up Troughton Beck's boulder-strewn

alluvial cone, crossing to its northwest side and ascending through the bracken a few paces west of the stream; the left (west) side of Troughton Beck. The track zigzags up the west shoulder of the gill as the slope steepens up towards Martcrag Moor and you have a fairly vigorous climb ahead of you. There are good reasons for stopping to look around you on the way up and the track, though not marked on the O.S. map, is reasonably clear higher up. Like all such tracks, it is easy to see looking down from above but often quite difficult as you approach from below.

In the steeper parts of Troughton Beck's *alluvial cone,* just before solid rock outcrops begin, you'll find parsley fern (Fig. 4.2) and stonecrop (Fig. 4.3).

Figure 4.2: *Parsley fern, a member of the Polypody (Fern) Family like bracken and maidenhair fern.*

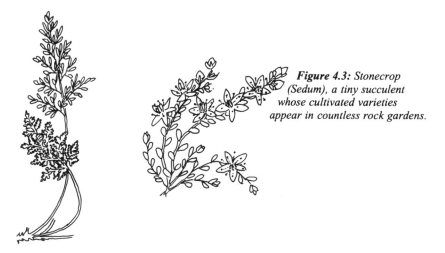

Figure 4.3: *Stonecrop (Sedum), a tiny succulent whose cultivated varieties appear in countless rock gardens.*

Continue zigzagging up with the stream on your right and at the point where the track is only two or three paces from the beck – before it zags away over the shoulder of the gully higher up, you'll find outcrops both in and beside the stream of grey, streaky rock. The details are easier to see if the rock is wet. It is an *ignimbrite,* a *welded tuff* with large *fiamme,* flattened discs of *pumice* the thickness of a pencil and many times longer, giving the highly characteristic *eutaxitic foliation.* A scatter of white *feldspar* crystals the size of grape pips give a pepper-and-salt appearance to the rock and red iron oxides coat the *joints* which cut it.

Now continue your climb. About half way up, stop again (if you haven't

before!) where you see a large rowan tree about 8-10 paces west of the beck. Here are mossy boulders and grassy hollows which make an attractive place to rest and have 'a little something', whilst admiring the view. Opposite are (left to right) Pike of Blisco, Crinkle Crags and Bow Fell. Below are the braided channels of Mickleden Beck and the *morainic* hummocks of Mickleden, thrown into relief by the bracken which prefers their drier slopes. Close to the beck where you are now, you should find foxgloves and parsley fern; ling heather also grows here, a glorious purple in August.

Rejoin the main track – an old drovers' track – which runs up above the shoulder of the stream gully, and continue on up the zigzags. As you gain height, look over to Rossett Pike which forms the head of Mickleden. Between Rossett Gill, Little Gill (middle) and Stake Gill (right), you can see clear horizontal 'ledges' of rock – *bedding* in the *BVG* sediment sequence – picked out by erosion. To the left is Bow Fell where bedding (dipping from upper left to lower right at 20-25°) is very clear both below the summit and below the north end of the Bow Fell ridge, closer to Rossett Gill (Fig. 4.4). The bed surfaces below Bow Fell summit are spectacular with football-field-size single *bedding planes* tilted to the northwest. If you could see them close up (and you will at Locality 5, Bow Fell ramble), you'd find many bed surfaces are covered in wave ripple marks, a sure sign that the beds were laid down under water. Looking from where you are now, practically all the rocks you can see are well bedded and dip quite uniformly to the northwest. The flat ledges on Rossett Pike – if you could see them close up – are also dipping in this way, but because the section you see is oriented at almost 90° to the dip direction (i.e. the Rossett Pike ridge trends southwest to northeast which is the *strike* direction of the beds), you cannot readily see that they too are dipping northwest. This is an example of *apparent dip* which can sometimes be confusing (see Fig. 4.4 Inset).

At the top of the zigzags, you begin to be able to see the whole range of Crinkle Crags, Bow Fell, Esk Pike and Great End, the wild heart of the Lake District unsullied by any road. You can also see that the bedding in Rossett Pike is indeed dipping northwest at about 20°. Looking the other way to Pike of Stickle, notice that the entire rock mass of the Pike is likewise bedded with the gentle dips towards the north.

Now look down Mickleden where you can easily see its shallow 'U'-shape. Remember that the *rock* valley sides are actually steeper than you can see now because all the lower slopes are cloaked in thick *screes*. The *rock* floor of the valley is buried much deeper than you'd imagine because of thick washed-out glacial debris and stream flood deposits. Look across to the low pass over to Little Langdale, with Blea Tarn nestling within it. An ice tongue must certainly have carved its way over the divide between the two valleys at this point, exploiting some weakness in the underlying rocks as do all processes of erosion.

The Mickleden glacier must have been pretty powerful having a great reservoir of thick ice flowing down from some of the highest peaks in the Lake District. By contrast, Little Langdale as its name tells us, is a diminutive valley with a small source area for its glacier.

Now continue on the track which emerges onto the bleak Martcrag Moor. At the top of Troughton Beck, you'll notice neat bonsai-like dwarf juniper trees.

The pollen counts from the kettleholes in Langdale Combe, less than one kilometre northwest of here, tell us that these junipers were amongst the first trees to colonize the uplands (along with Arctic birch – see after Locality 5) after the ice finally vanished. We can make the reasonable guess that these little trees are their living descendants, having existed here continuously for nearly 11,000 years.

Now you have two choices: either continue northwards along the diminishing Troughton Beck until you intercept and turn right (southeast) onto the main walking track from Stake Pass to the north, or follow the other small track around to the right, crossing the headwaters of the beck and heading for Pike of Stickle which, beacon like, is always in sight ahead. The first option is slightly longer and inclined to be muddy because the path is much used, but it is easy. The second option is indistinct, though since Pike of Stickle is always visible to guide you, you shouldn't have problems.

Almost all the outcrops you see on the ascent to Pike of Stickle are coarse fragmental (*volcaniclastic*) rocks with golfball-sized fragments of *lavas* which being harder than the enclosing matrix of finer ashy material, give the rock a knobbly appearance. As you climb, you may notice that the fragments increase in size indicating an increase˙ in the energy of the eruption processes that produced them. Some of the *volcaniclasts* are the size of a large teapot.

Pike of Stickle: Locality 1

When you reach the base of the rocky summit of Pike of Stickle, you'll see that there are several easy scrambling routes up to the summit. One such route along the northwest side overlooks a deep chasm excavated by erosion along a line of *faulting*. This *fault* apparently cuts off the coarse fragmental rocks you've seen on the ascent to this point, but now you find yourself climbing up very fine grained *bedded tuffs*, cut here and there by milky *quartz* veins. Rocks such as these are almost flinty in their fracture and so can result in hard, sharp edges when chipped. These flinty *tuffs*, sometimes called 'hornstones', were the type generally favoured by the Neolithic axe makers.

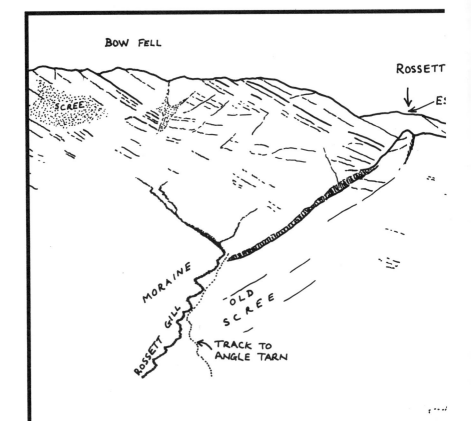

Figure 4.4: *Bedding form lines on Bow Fell and Rosset Pike which I have picked out in outline. The entire rock sequence dips to the northwest. The Inset attempts to show you the difference between apparent dip (the visible face of Rosset Pike) and true dip (the mountain 'sliced through' to give the third dimension and show the true geometry.*

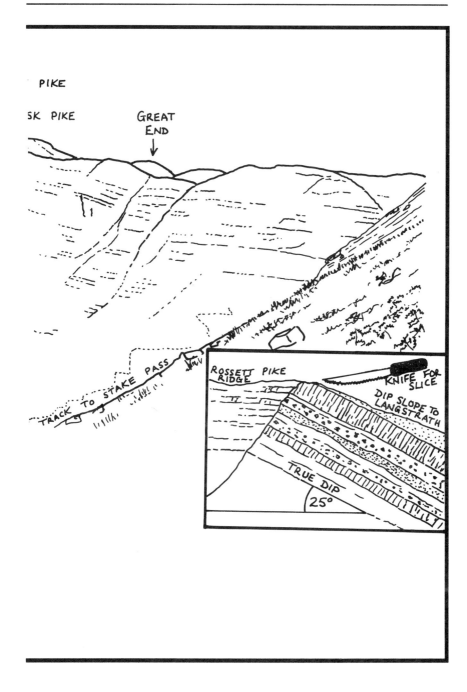

PIKE

SK PIKE   GREAT
            END

TRACK TO STAKE PASS

ROSSETT PIKE
RIDGE

KNIFE FOR
SLICE

DIP SLOPE TO
LANGSTRATH

TRUE DIP
25°

The view from the summit of the Pike is – or should be if the weather is kind to you – superb. Below is the lush green of Great Langdale with Pike of Blisco and the Coniston ranges to the south. Close by to the southeast is Loft Crag (Fig. 4.5) whose higher parts, you'll notice, are well bedded, creamy white *tuffs*. Far away are Windermere, Ingleborough and Morecambe Bay. To the east is Harrison Stickle, the next sector of the ramble whilst further afield are St Sunday Crag, Fairfield, Dove and Hart crags and Loughrigg Fell. To the north is the bleak High Raise, whilst to the west are the great ranges of Scafell, Great Gable and the complete panorama of those you saw earlier from Troughton Beck. As I mentioned at the beginning, the grassy platforms just below the summit – above the axe factory gully – make wonderful places to picnic or simply sit and contemplate. Most of the climbing is now over and from here onwards, the rocks become really exciting.

Figure 4.5: *Loft Crag with steep rocky buttresses showing the well bedded tuffs dipping gently from right to left – to the northeast. The lower crags are not obviously bedded and show prominent columnar jointing. These may be ignimbrite flows. Windermere stretches out far away in the distance.*

Drop down to the east side of Pike of Stickle by whichever route seems easiest to you and cross the top of the great 'axe factory' gully which you looked up into from Mickleden, far below. The National Trust have erected

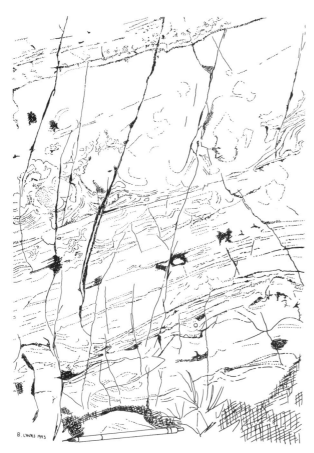

B. LWAS 1993

Figure 4.6: *Water escape structures such as these make it certain that these beds were laid down in water. These curious looking structures form when wet, sloppy sediment becomes so overloaded by fresh material deposited above it that something has to give, like someone stomping on a tube of toothpaste. It does, often triggered by earthquake shock, and the excess water suddenly erupts from the lower beds, disrupting all the delicate primary bed forms and blasting its way through the upper layers towards the seafloor (or lakefloor) whence it came. You can find these beds at the top of a steep scree gully [2767 0720] at the beginning of the short climb to Loft Crag.*

a sign here asking people not to enter the gully because of the damage they do on the steep, unstable slopes. The gully has developed along a line of weakness caused by a small *fault* and many of the rocks hereabouts are stained red with iron oxides which have percolated along the fault.

Continue along the path towards Loft Crag. The rocks are pale grey to white flinty 'hornstones' interbedded with knobbly-looking *lapilli tuffs* with golfball-sized fragments. These beds are beautifully exposed **to the right of the path about 200 metres southeast of Pike of Stickle.** Other beds show small scale disruption due to water ejection from once sloppy wet sediments, weighed down by later sediments deposited on top of them (Fig. 4.6).

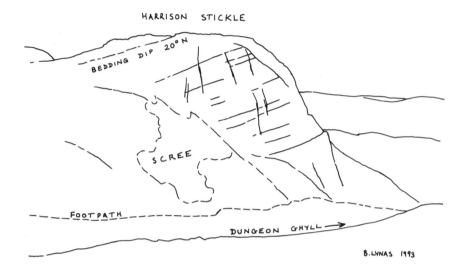

Figure 4.7: *Sketch outline of Harrison Stickle showing how the beds dip from right to left, about 20° northwards.*

From the top of Loft Crag, you have a fine view of the southwest face of Harrison Stickle where the rocks again show quite clear bedding (Fig. 4.7). They are all *tuffs* of various sorts: beds laid down in water with wave ripples and *slumps*, crystal-rich rather *massive* beds and *lapilli tuffs*. Looking back to Pike of Stickle and Great Gable (just to the left), you can see the bedding even more clearly, again dipping fairly gently to the north.

Now descend towards Harrison Stickle and cross the headwaters of Dungeon Ghyll to start the climb to the highest point of the ramble, Harrison Stickle summit (736 metres). Note that two good tracks run directly down to the New Dungeon Ghyll Hotel if you wish to cut short your ramble. One via Mark Gate and Dungeon Ghyll, starting from Loft Crag; the other running along the north flank of Dungeon Ghyll via Thorn Crag and Pike Howe. The lower part of the second track has been carefully rebuilt with cobbles of *ignimbrite* and *lapilli tuffs* so that it is like a staircase. From the Mark Gate track, you can peer into the dank and gloomy recesses of Dungeon Ghyll and see why it was so named.

Cross the headwater of the ghyll to join the main track up to the summit of Harrison Stickle.

You'll find the rocks easy to identify by now as you stump up the track. They are alternating beds of coarse and fine grained *tuffs* dipping north at 20°.

Harrison Stickle: Locality 2

I used to tell my younger son, who accompanied me on many of these rambles, that this mountain was really named 'Harrison's Tickle'. A man named Harrison, my story went, climbed this mountain with an overexuberant friend who, whilst Harrison was resting at the summit, discovered he was very ticklish and set about exploiting this weakness. Poor Harrison was 'tickled to death' and so from that day to this, I'd say, the mountain has been called 'Harrison's Tickle'. The spelling on the map is wrong, I told him. Maybe there's truth in it? Okay, so there isn't but it made an amusing story.

Naturally the view from the summit is grand. Below to the east is Stickle Tarn and, brooding over it impressively is the great crag of Pavey Ark (Locality 3), completing a splendid example of a glacial corrie. Once, this entire hollow, now occupied by the tarn, was filled with ice (p. 83). Hop into your time machine and imagine yourself here 18,000 years ago; you'd have been freezing cold for a start. And you could have stepped out onto the thick ice to the northeast of Harrison Stickle where today there is only air. Actually, if you had tried stepping out onto the ice, you'd probably have fallen down the *bergschrund*, a deep crevasse which forms between the ice and rock face of the corrie back wall – and that would have been the end of you.

But let us go back much further in time to the prodigious volcanic eruptions which produced the rocks you're standing on, here made up of a jumble of chunks of greenish white *lavas,* some the size of a small rugby ball, though most are golfball or marble size. All these were literally blasted out of a huge volcanic vent which cannot have been more than a kilometre or so away from here (though in which direction, we cannot say). Bedding is much harder to see because of the jumbled and unsorted material, so we don't even know if the chunks fell into water or whether they formed part of the flank of an actual volcanic cone.

Continue on northwards, towards Pavey Ark but keeping to the highest parts of the curving ridge which connects it with Harrison Stickle. If you prefer, you can miss out Pavey Ark altogether and drop down to Stickle Tarn, but I'd recommend you keep going since the rocks you'll be seeing shortly are spectacular and exceedingly odd.

As you walk, you continue to cross outcrops of the coarse fragmental rocks you started to see on Harrison Stickle (Fig. 4.8). We can be fairly sure that such rocks were formed as some sort of avalanching *mass flow* or represent part of an actual *pyroclastic flow* eruption (p. 88).

Figure 4.8: *This outcrop is about 220 paces north of Harrison Stickle. Note the extraordinary range in size of the consituents, from pea-size or less to cake-size. Remember the beautifully bedded rocks you were looking at near Pike of Stickle? These could hardly be more different for they show no sign whatever of bedding. They are a completely unsorted jumble of shattered lumps of lava.*

Continue walking north towards Thunacar Knott and then more to the northeast directly to Pavey Ark. Your route takes you close to small peaty pools a little to the left of the main track. Some of these pools have small clusters of bogbean growing in them indicating that these plants must be pretty tolerant of the highly acid conditions typical of such pools. **Continue over and around the large outcrops to where a drystone wall ends a short distance southwest of Pavey Ark summit. This is Locality 3.**

Pavey Ark, Jack's Rake and amoeba rock: Locality 3 [2843 0787]

Have you ever seen anything like this rock? I thought immediately of Amoeba when I saw it first. You remember the little protozoan organism that everyone studies at school? Of course the strange shapes in the rocks here have nothing whatsoever to do with amoebae, except that the analogy describes well the extraordinary shapes which the volcanic *blocks* possess in this odd-looking outcrop (Fig. 4.9). But why are they like this? Most of the *blocks* or *bombs* you've seen so far have been fairly unornamented; angular but not with the deep embayments that these have.

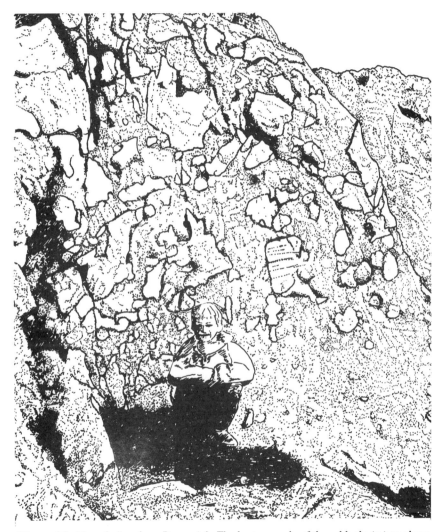

Figure 4.9: *'Amoeba' rock on Pavey Ark. The best example of these blocks is just above my son's head. How could such extraordinary deeply embayed shapes be preserved amid the presumably violent eruptive event which produced it?*

The 'amoeba' blocks continue south down towards the top end of Jack's Rake, the diagonal ledge which forms a rather scary scramble right up the precipice of Pavey Ark and, if you walk around this locality a little, you'll find that the blocks tend to occur in one or two distinct bands, indicating some sort of temporary and unusual volcanic event – which was both preceded and followed by the more normal *block lapilli tuff* you've seen all the way from Locality 2. The 'amoeba' blocks themselves are, as you can see, pale-weathering *lavas*. That much we can be sure of. And now, thinking caps on please . . . for at this point, we enter the realm of conjecture. I'll suggest several possible explanations for what you see here. You can take them or leave them; or add ideas of your own.

The extraordinary shapes suggest to me that the *blocks* may have been at least plastic (nearly molten) until quite late in the eruption that produced them. Maybe they were violently splattered out of a foaming (de-gassing) mass of *magma,* becoming partially solidified as *bombs,* so re-entering the main *pyroclastic flow* mass which may have produced this rock. Such flows are characterized by their heat, speed and gas content, the expanding gas being capable of keeping the lumpy material of the flow completely *fluidised*. This gives the flows their extraordinary mobility and also means that the fragments do not bash into each other. The 'amoeba' blocks are obviously delicate forms. They would normally break up into more rounded shapes.

Another possibility for their formation also assumes great internal heat. The large *blocks* – note that most of the rock consists of *lapilli*-sizes or smaller – would retain their heat better. After the flow settled, because the blocks were plastic and non-gassy (unlike *pumice*), they were squeezed by the weight of the material above them. The squeezing forced parts of them to extrude like the pseudopods (= 'false legs') of real amoebae, so giving the deeply embayed shapes you can see now, frozen for 450 million years.

A third possibility is that this rock was originally a *lava,* but one that flowed out under water, perhaps in a volcanic crater or *caldera* lake (see my notes about this for the next locality). *Lava* which erupts underwater often forms structures like pillows (hence *pillow lavas*) but certain types of *lava,* because of the intense chilling effect of the water in direct contact with molten rock at, say, 900°C, fragment into glassy chips and lumps. Volcanic glass forms when the *lava* is instantaneously quenched. The resulting rock contains no crystals at all, unlike normal volcanic rocks, because crystals have no time to grow from the liquid. Glass, as we all know, is tough but cannot stand big temperature changes. If you put a piece of hot glass in water, it shatters. The same thing happens when the hot glassy lava is quenched: it breaks up into fragments of all shapes and sizes. Geologists call it *hyaloclastite* (from 'hyalo' = glassy, 'clast' = fragment, '-ite' = rock made of hyaloclasts). This amoeba rock may be a type of *hyaloclastite*.

Of the three explanations I've offered, I'm inclined to favour the last. But what do you think?

Scramble up to the summit of Pavey Ark, noticing the car-sized block perched some 30 metres southwest of the top. The presence of this block tells us that at some time during the glaciations, the summit was completely submerged by ice. How else could the block have got into its present position? **Now walk northwest towards High Raise for 150-200 metres, noting but not following the cairned track which leads down into a steep gully on the north side of Pavey Ark. This will be your descent route after visiting the next locality. Don't walk in a straight line; look about at the outcrops around you.** You're walking up the rock sequence, for the dip of the rock formations is to the northwest (another way of saying the rocks become younger in that direction). You should soon see clear bedding in the outcrops as the volcanic fragments, mostly *lapilli* and smaller, are sorted into beds, a fairly clear indication of water activity. These beds are almost certainly the lowest part of that same sequence you saw around Loft Crag and Pike of Stickle.

Bedded tuffs again tell us of sealevel rise: Locality 4 [284081 area]

Figure 4.10 shows one set of outcrops in which you can see how the fragment size diminishes from the lower to the higher beds. This tells you that the volcanic source of the coarse *lapilli* and *block tuffs* was waning, or had stopped altogether leaving slower and gentler water erosion and deposition processes to operate. It is the presence of *bedding* and the diminishing grain size, becoming clearer the higher you go (northwest) that tells us that violent volcanic eruptions had ceased and probably the area had subsided again, and had become submerged. But by what? Sea or lake? And why should this happen? This is an important question, for we see this elevation and submergence of the land surface over and over again in volcanic areas such as this once was.

The sinking, or deflation, of the land surface is commonly associated with the ending of major eruptions. But usually, prior to eruption, the surface inflates, just as a tyre expands when you pump air into it, resulting in a rise of the land surface and consequent retreat of the sea. This inflation is due to 'pumping in' to the upper crust of *magma*, which originates well below the relatively thin crust in the Earth's *mantle*. When a large body of *magma*, high in the Earth's crust breaks through to the surface, it erupts as a volcano (or several volcanoes). If the *magma* is both gassy and *silica*-rich, the eruptions are normally exceedingly violent and very rapid. If you shake a bottle of champagne vigorously, having first released the wire which holds the cork in, the cork blasts out followed by a stream of frothing liquid. By the time the eruption dies down, because the champagne has lost most of its pressurized gas, only half may be left in the bottle. (I don't recommend the experiment. Better to carefully open your champagne, pour yourself a glass or two, sit back and imagine the experiment whilst savouring the drink.) Similarly, the space once occupied by the *magma* after it has given rise to volcanic eruptions is only partially filled. So in certain extreme cases, the roof caves in, often accompanied by cataclysmal eruptions, and a *caldera* forms. The new *caldera* often becomes filled with rainwater to form a lake, or is flooded by the sea for it is just a very large hole in the ground. Geologists working in the *BVG* rocks have begun to piece together a coherent story of a very large caldera collapse with many of the later *BVG* rocks being laid down in the huge crater lake (see p. 171).

Inflation and deflation of volcanoes is so marked that geologists can use devices called tiltmeters and laser surveying instruments to measure the change in angle of the slope of a volcano which can help predict eruptions. The United States Geological Survey continually monitors the active volcanoes in Hawaii in this and other ways. Inflation of one of these huge volcanoes' flanks almost always indicates the injection of *magma* at shallow depth, always accompanied by swarms of small earth tremors. This phase is usually followed by the opening of a fissure and an eruption. Fortunately the Hawaiian volcanoes erupt *basalt* in mostly slow-moving lava flows with little or no violent activity.

Figure 4.10: *Bedded lapilli tuffs to the northwest of Pavey Ark ridge [284 081]. The appearance of bedding in these rocks tells us that they were probably laid down in water. Water currents have sorted the different fragment sizes into coarser and finer grades.*

Before leaving this locality, look north across the headwaters of Bright Beck towards Sergeant Man. You should be able to see that the rock formations which form Codale Head, Sergeant Man and the entire sequence north of Bright Beck are all dipping the same way: gently to the northwest – the same direction as all the rocks you have seen on this ramble (Bow Fell, Rossett Pike, Pike of Stickle, Harrison Stickle and right here). So the rock formations become younger as you walk northwest. Yet we know that further northwest the rocks are older for on Ramble 1 (Haystacks), we saw the oldest parts of the *BVG* resting upon the even older *Skiddaw Slates*. How can this be?

The clue is in the direction of dip of the rocks. Everything you saw on the Haystacks ramble dipped in the opposite direction – southeast – to the rocks hereabouts, so they were becoming younger to the southeast. This tells us that there must be a huge fold affecting the entire *BVG* sequence whose axis lies between this area and the Haystacks area. This is a downfold, a *syncline*, called by geologists the Scafell Syncline. Similarly, the youngest *BVG* rocks you saw on the Coniston ramble all dip southeast again, telling us that between this area and Coniston, there must be a complementary upfold – an *anticline*: the so-called Wrynose-Nan Bield Anticline. These huge folds (and many smaller ones) and the *cleavage* which goes with them apparently began to form before the *Coniston Limestone* was laid down, thus accounting for the *unconformity* between the *limestone* and the *BVG,* but then were squeezed tighter during the main *Caledonian* earth movements around 390-400 million years ago.

Now partially retrace your steps to the cairned track which you crossed on the way to Locality 4, and head east along it towards Bright Beck far below, directly into and down the steep gully (North Rake Gully) on the north side of Pavey Ark.

The gully has almost certainly developed along a line of relative weakness caused by injection of a *dyke*. The walls of the gully are the familiar *block tuff* of Locality 3, but if you look carefully underfoot within the gully, you should find outcrops of a green-grey rock which are all you can see of the *dyke*.

About half way down to Bright Beck, the gully opens out and is joined by a grassy bench from the right. Look across to the opposite slopes of Bright Beck towards Codale Head. The slopes are covered by hummocky *moraines* reminding us again how this high valley and the hollow now holding Stickle Tarn were so recently – in geological terms – occupied by ice. **Turn off right at this point and walk about 30 paces along a grassy hollow to a fine viewpoint.** From here, you can see Stickle Tarn and the Coniston ranges framed by the two sides of Easy Gully which descends to intersect the start of Jack's Rake at the bottom of Pavey Ark. Here you will spot a few rowan trees, dwarf juniper, bilberries, parsley fern and heather growing in cracks in the crags, safe from nibbling sheep. **Now return to the main track and continue on down**

(east). Although the gully has widened, the *dyke*, you will notice, is still there, around 5 metres thick, often riddled by white *quartz* veins and crushed by *fault* movements along which it is reddened by iron staining.

Further down, the gully stops abruptly at a flat grassy patch, and the track kinks to the left before continuing down. This is Locality 5.

The mysterious ring rock: Locality 5 [2878 0810]

The abrupt cessation of the gully – and its *dyke* – indicate that a *fault* must cut the sequence here, displacing both *dyke* and the Pavey Ark *tuffs* into which the *dyke* was injected. And quite suddenly, we are confronted with some of the oddest looking rocks (Fig. 4.11) in the Lake District. So put your thinking cap on again. And before reading further, have a good look at these strange structures and find out what you can about them. Once you have some idea of their sizes, shapes and how and where they occur, you are then equipped to start thinking about why they formed.

The evidence: you are confronted by concentric circular shapes, mostly a little larger than a long playing record though some are over one metre in diameter. Some are almost perfectly circular; others less so. Some seem to a have a nucleus; others don't. Some show distinct concentric rings right through from the edge to the centre; again, others don't. They adorn rather rough bed surfaces (*strike* 015°, *dip* 55°). And importantly, they are not flat pancakes. They seem to have three dimensions; they are spherical. The rock in which they occur appears to be fragmental – a variety of *tuff*. That completes the description. Now for the speculation.

We can account for the variability (some with nuclei, others without) by assuming, reasonably enough, that many of the spheres have not been 'cut away' by erosion through the centre.

If you have whole boiled eggs cooked in a meatloaf and you cut your loaf into slices before eating it, you will slice some of the eggs almost exactly in half so they will have obvious nuclei – the yolk. But in some slices, you'll miss the yolk and only cut through the white, so they would seem to have no yolk or nucleus.

So we can probably assume here that each of the spheres has a nucleus, either cut away by erosion or still buried in the rock. And at this point, I have to confess that when I first puzzled over these rocks, I assumed that they were *pillow lavas*, for they share certain characteristics. But I quickly trashed this theory when I continued on down towards the beck, for lower down is new and significant evidence that these rocks cannot be *lavas* of any sort.

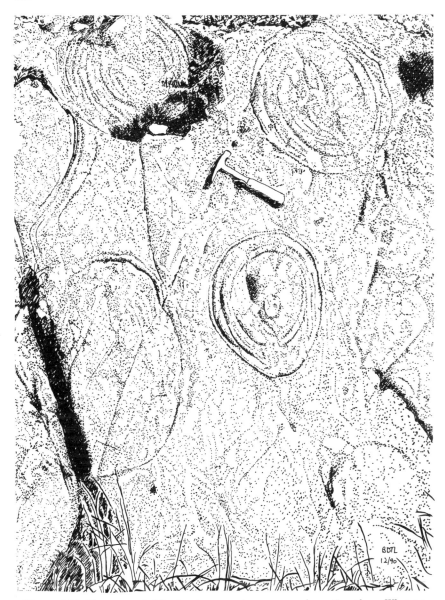

Figure 4.11: *These remarkable structures puzzle everyone who notices them. What are they? Fossil jellyfish? Rock pancakes? The answer appears to be much more prosaic: they are oddball concretions (see text).*

Continue on down the main track towards the beck, but observing the rock sections on either side of the track.

Further down, you'll spot distinct *bedding* and at the base of the crags, bedding is everywhere to be seen and very clear. Yet, our sphere structures, though poorly developed, still exist, with the *planes* of the *bedding* passing through them unaffected. This destroys the 'lava' theory unequivocally. *Lavas* are not bedded, though they may be *foliated*, but *pillow lavas* are not even that. In any case, the fragmental and sedimentary origin of these beds is beyond dispute here. Which leaves us with the $64,000 question: what are these spherical structures which cut through the beds? The point I made earlier about the nucleus now enters the discussion. Because we have seen that the *bedding* — a primary structure which develops as the sediment falls out of suspension in water (or air) — is unaffected by the spheres. And we know that the spheres cannot have formed before the *bedding* since the rock didn't exist, so they must have formed afterwards. In fact, this is a common occurrence in water-saturated and unhardened — fresh — sediments. Geologists refer to the secondary alteration which takes place in sediments after deposition as they begin to harden into rock as *diagenesis*. These structures are clearly secondary and must be rather unusual concretions. Concretions are exceedingly common in mud and lime rocks like those of the Jurassic Period (Appendix: Timescale) which crop out on the north Yorkshire and Dorset coasts. Almost invariably, these secondary concretions (nodules) form around a nucleus which is usually a fossil, resulting in perfect preservation of certain types of fossil (ammonites) which have made these rock sequences widely famous. But here, the nucleus, as you have seen, is composed of a fragment of volcanic rock. It may be that the composition of the nuclei (usually a pale-weathering, *silica*-rich fragment of *lava*), somewhat different from the majority of darker ash material which makes up the bulk of this sequence, could have triggered the growth of secondary concentric shells of harder (*silica*-rich) minerals. What do you think?

One thing is certain: these structures are very unusual (though there are strange rocks of perhaps similar origin on the Coniston ramble, p. 93). I've never seen anything quite like them either in the Lake District or anywhere else for that matter.

Complete your descent to Bright Beck, cross it and follow the track to the right towards Stickle Tarn. Just after you cross, notice the thick black peat which is now being eroded. Near the base of the peat, you can make out pieces of tree root, well enough preserved in the acid peat to indicate that they were apparently birch. You may have noticed similar tree remains on other rambles. The Langdale *kettleholes* (p. 187) show birch (*Betula nana*, Arctic birch) pollen forming almost 100% of all tree pollen at the beginning of the *Boreal* period (Appendix: Timescale, Column D). This marked a rapid transition from near

Arctic to a warm, dry climate starting just after the *Younger Dryas* cold period. So we may safely assume that many areas of the bare mountains of today were once covered with small birch trees no more than waist high. Later, the climate became wetter (around 7,000 years ago), followed 4,500 years later by a marked cooling to give the notorious climate which characterizes the Lake District today.

As you walk on towards Stickle Tarn, you'll spot the familiar knobbly *lapilli tuffs* like those between Harrison Stickle and Pavey Ark. Many of the outcrops have been moulded by the passage of glaciers from Bright Beck combe to form *roches moutonées* and on some ice-polished surfaces, you should find *glacial striations*. Before entering the lake, the stream cuts down into the rock to form a small gorge, probably initially cut by powerful meltwaters as the decaying glacier receded, and since deepened along some line of weakness in the rock.

Continue on around Stickle Tarn, passing mounds of *moraine* on your left.

Stickle Tarn was dammed in 1838 to give an improved water supply to the Elterwater gunpowder factory. The factory, started in 1823, flourished until the early years of this century using cheap local labour, the abundant water and charcoal from the nearby forests.

You cannot fail to be impressed by the lowering crag of Pavey Ark which forms the backdrop to this beautiful mountain tarn. The hazardous-looking Jack's Rake path angles directly across the precipice which was once the backwall of a sizeable corrie glacier during the *Younger Dryas Stadial* (cold period).

Your descent continues along Stickle Ghyll. Though there is a track on either side of the beck, I recommend the east side where there is more to see. The prominent and well worn track descends rapidly past Tarn Crag on your left, with the continuous roar of the beck in your ears as it rushes down towards Great Langdale.

The banded lavas of lower Tarn Crag: Locality 6 [289 073]

As you descend though the lower parts of Tarn Crag, look at the rock outcrops which continue for some distance both in and beside the track. This rock is very different from the *lapilli tuffs* of Harrison Stickle and Pavey Ark, higher in the sequence. Here, it is pink to almost white, indicating the virtual absence of dark minerals characteristic of *basalt* or *andesite*. The component minerals of this rock are mainly *feldspar* and *quartz*, mostly so fine grained that you cannot make out individual crystals without a microscope, though if you look carefully, you'll see that some of the outcrops do contain recognizable larger crystals; they are *porphyritic.* You can't fail to notice too that much of the rock is *flow banded,* indicating clearly that these are *lavas.* The pale colour, presence of *quartz* and *feldspar,* the banding which shows us that the *lava* was thick and treacly, tells us that these *lavas* are of *dacite* or *rhyolite* composition. Because such *lavas* are viscous and sticky when they erupt, they seldom travel far from the vent, so we can also be sure that with this thick pile of *lavas* forming the entire mountainside below Stickle Tarn, the volcano producing them was probably within a kilometre or so.

At the top of the first main Stickle Ghyll waterfall, the track has been carefully cobbled to arrest further erosion by walkers' boots and opportunistic streamlets. The partly cobbled track drops down through a series of outcrops which you should have a look at. The rock type is apparently the same as the overlying lavas, but if you examine smooth outcrops close to the beck, wetting them if possible since it is always easier to see textures if the surface is wet, you'll recognize the familiar signs of *welded tuff* which you'll have seen both on the Coniston ramble and as you puffed up the steep slope by Troughton Beck at the start of this ramble. From here on, much of the track is cobbled with these *tuffs.* The polished and wetted cobbles show fine examples of *eutaxitic foliation,* but the best block of all, over a metre long, is at the entrance to the footbridge crossing Stickle Ghyll where the *fiamme* are large, pink and set in a green-grey matrix. Do wet this block (if it's not raining) to see the beautiful texture at its best.

Cross the footbridge and continue on down beside the west bank of the beck (ghyll). The slopes now become gentler and typical valley vegetation begins with hollies, rowans and other deciduous trees with lush grass beneath along the banks of the vigorous beck. Outcrops of the *welded tuff* continue both in and around the track for another 150 paces or so before disappearing beneath the glacial and *scree* deposits of the lower valley sides.

Return via the New Hotel buildings to the carpark. So ends one of the finest walks in the Lake District. You have seen two principal rock formations, one overlying – and therefore younger than – the other. The older formation, called by geologists the Airy's Bridge Formation, consists entirely of *dacitic* or *rhyolitic lavas* and *welded tuffs.* It forms the lower steep slopes of Great Langdale valley. You crossed it at Troughton Beck and again below Stickle Tarn. Overlying this, indicating a change in eruption style from *lavas* and *ignimbrites* to *pyroclastic flows* and *lapilli tuffs* is the sequence you saw on Harrison Stickle and Pavey Ark. As the initially powerful eruptions waned, so the *clasts* became smaller and smaller, the land surface subsided and was flooded by a lake or the sea. Currents in these waters caused the *tuffs* to became sorted into different sizes, eventually being laid down as the fine grained, delicately bedded rocks you saw around Pike of Stickle and Loft Crag. Some geologists regard these *bedded tuffs* as the equivalent of the *Tilberthwaite Tuffs*: the much quarried 'vein' of grey and green slates which you should have seen already (p. 85).

Jumping forward in time a few hundred million years, you've seen the effects of the great rivers of moving ice which once filled Great Langdale, whilst a smaller glacier scooped out the rocky basin of Stickle Tarn. You've seen the *morainic* mounds left by the last remnants of the decaying ice in Mickleden. And you've seen the site of the first definite human activity in the district – the famous stone axe factory at Pike of Stickle. It's a little like a huge, natural museum full of stunning exhibits which lack labels. So most of the time, we don't know what they are – or have only vague ideas. I hope that you'll have found that this guided ramble – a museum explanation – has helped you to appreciate and enjoy the Langdale Pikes.

ROCKY RAMBLE 5:
TROUTBECK AND WANSFELL

How to get to the start of the ramble

This ramble actually starts and finishes in Ambleside. Car parking is easy at the Rothay Bridge park [373040] though there are others equally convenient.

The ramble: needs, distances and times

Although the distance is just over 10 kilometres ($6^1/_2$ miles), it only involves climbing about 450 metres (1500 feet). Most of it is easy underfoot though the descent from Wansfell Pike is quite steep, so I'd recommend normal mountain walking clothing and boots. You may wish to include a visit to Town End, in Troutbeck (National Trust, so check opening times beforehand) in which case you'd be wise to allow for a full day, especially if you also fancy a leisurely lunch in a Troutbeck tea shop or pub.

Town End is the only unaltered yeoman's house surviving in the Lake District. It was built in 1623 and (for me) typifies all that is best in Lakeland architecture. You could imagine any of Beatrix Potter's characters living here – especially country mouse Timmy Willy.

You'll need OS Outdoor Leisure sheet 7, South Eastern area.

Introduction

This is a less-ambitious ramble than the previous ones without high mountains to scale. You might like to do it when the weather is not too good in the high fells though if the weather is fair, you'll be rewarded with fine views of the southern Lakeland mountains and the beautiful Lake Windermere. And Troutbeck village is one of the prettiest in the area. At the end of the ramble as you return towards Ambleside, you'll see a fine waterfall.

The rocks you cross are the top layers – the youngest – of the *Borrowdale Volcanic Group (BVG)* overlying which you'll spot the familiar *Coniston Limestone* (p. 70). You'll be able to trace this important change in the rocks for some distance and see just how much it influences the scenery.

To Jenkin Crag

If you're parked at Rothay Bridge, walk round the triangle of one-way

roads for around 200 metres to start off on the public footpath southeast of the bridge. Follow this east towards Wansfell Pike. The fence on your left is made of huge cleaved slabs of *BVG*, almost certainly from the Loughrigg Fell quarries (p. 163). Rocks of the *BVG* also crop out in the track and nearby in the field, smoothed and rounded by the passage of thick ice sheets which once filled this valley. So powerful was the ice that less than a kilometre to the south, it gouged deep into the bedrock to excavate England's longest lake: Windermere.

Windermere (40 metres above sealevel) is now up to 67 metres deep, but echo sounding techniques show that the glaciers actually cut it to about 35 metres *below* sea-level (making the rock basin at least 80 metres below the surface of its quiet waters). When the ice sheets melted, large quantities of debris carried by powerful rivers of meltwater, partly filled the lake. Today, these and later sediments – collected by 5-inch-diameter cores from the lake bed – give geologists a detailed record of climate since the end of the main ice melt around 14,500 years ago.

Yet here, the valley floor is solid rock. Why should this be so? The answer is simple: the rock type changes between here and the north tip of the lake from the tough, craggy *BVG* to the much softer and younger sediments which you'll see something of later on this ramble. The softer rocks were easy prey for the gouging action of the heavy glaciers, by then stuffed with lumps of hard abrasive *BVG* which cut the great overdeepened trough which would become Windermere. Yet today, walking along this path with main roads, traffic and houses nearby, it's hard to imagine that around 20,000 years ago, you'd have been buried under hundreds of metres of ice here.

Continue east through the houses, turn south (right) to walk along the main Windermere road for just over 100 metres before turning east to pass a small carpark with public toilets, and begin the ascent on the bridleway to Skelghyll Wood and Troutbeck. As you ascend, you almost immediately begin to have views of the Coniston Fells. **Pass by various private houses off to both left and right, but the right-of-way is clearly signposted up to Skelghyll Wood which is owned and managed on everyone's behalf by the National Trust.**

The wood is a delightful mix of broadleafed and coniferous trees. As most people know, broadleafed trees lose their leaves in winter and conifers don't. As usual, there are exceptions to this rule. Larches which are conifers, do lose their leaves and there are many broadleafed trees which do not (such as holly). Of the broadleafs, you should spot ashes, oaks, sycamores, birches, holly and hazel trees in this wood. The conifers include larches, douglas firs and true firs (Fig. 5.1).

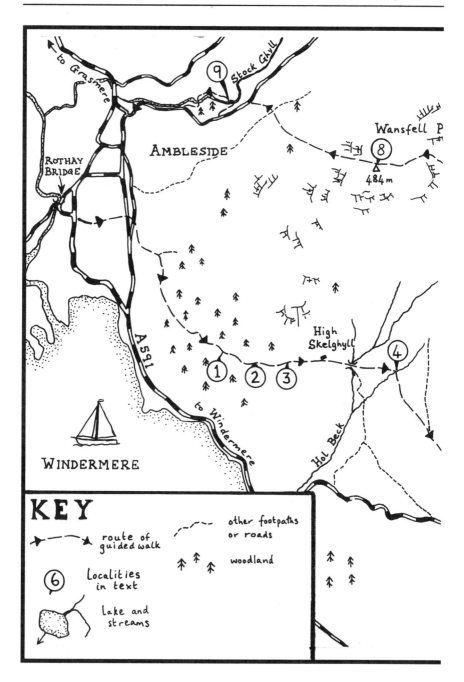

KEY

- ↦ route of guided walk
- ⑥ localities in text
- ⬛ lake and streams
- - - other footpaths or roads
- ⋀ ⋀ ⋀ woodland

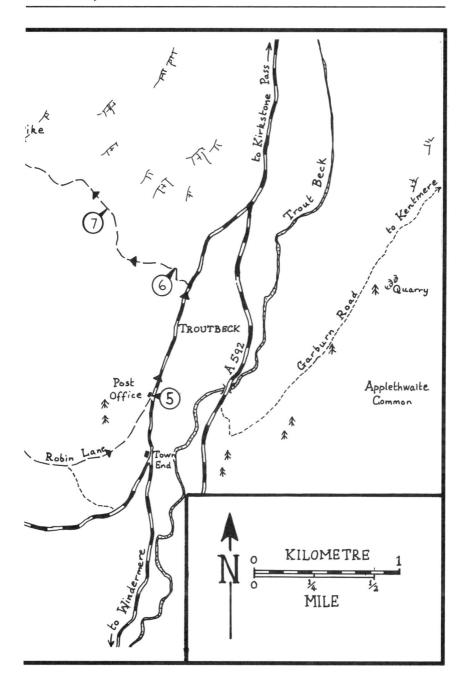

Figure 5.1: *This sketch shows you the differences between true firs (Abies), douglas firs (Pseudotsuga) and spruces (Picea). The leaves of true firs attach to their branches with sucker-like bases. Those of douglas firs have a slender 'waist' (petiole) just above the attachment. Spruces, 'Christmas trees', the commonest and least attractive of the conifers so beloved of forestry plantations owners and no one else, are different again for their spiky leaves are mounted on small woody pegs, quite unlike the sucker-like base of the true fir leaves. The cones of each type are also highly distinctive.*

Have you ever found a fir cone? Most people may think they have, but are they *really* fir cones? Probably not, for the cones of true firs disintegrate whilst they are attached to the branch leaving nothing more than a central spire. Other conifers shed their cones complete once they have opened to free their winged seeds. Some of these are the cones commonly – and wrongly – called 'fir cones'. A.A. Milne's Winnie the Pooh invented a game called Pooh-sticks using fircones . . . but they weren't; they were pine cones. Pooh didn't know his trees very well, being a Bear of Very Little Brain. Squirrel Nutkin and his botanically-knowing creator, Beatrix Potter, *did* know. Being a squirrel, he was able to snap off green fir cones from the trees on Owl Island (Derwentwater) to play ninepins outside Old Brown's house.

Cross Stencher Beck, noting the profusion of mosses, liverworts and ferns growing on the damp and shady *BVG* outcrops around the stream. **About 300 metres further on, a sign indicates 'Jenkin Crag' off to the right through a gap in the wall, some 50 metres southwest of the track. Walk out onto the top of the crag.**

Jenkin Crag: Locality 1

Although you are only about 170 metres above sealevel here, the view is quite striking for you can not only see the upper part of Windermere but also the Coniston Fells, the central fells and the Langdale Pikes. As for the rock, it is very obviously fragmental (Fig. 5.2), the *volcaniclasts* being mostly quite angular and mostly around fist-size or smaller, ranging down to almost microscopic. The passage of many feet has worn some of the rocks almost smooth, so it's worth wandering a little farther afield. In 1990, a tree fell here in a gale, its upended roots leaving a fresh and clear outcrop of this rock (Fig. 5.2). It's always worth searching about for fresh outcrops such as this. Rocks are not always easy to make sense of, but it helps if you can see the best evidence on offer. What, then, do you make of these? The fragments all seem to be identical and softer than the paler matrix which encloses them, which is why they tend to weather faster, leaving the shallow hollows you can see now. This is probably because they contain less *silica* than the matrix. We could name the rock a *volcaniclastic breccia* (which is rather like calling a heart attack a myocardial infarction: it sounds great but it doesn't tell us what to do about it!) but how did it form?

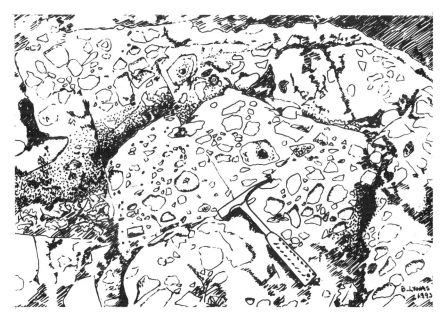

Figure 5.2: Fragmental BVG outcrop (hammer for scale) at Jenkin Crag.

You may have noticed that here and there, there are rather rough *bedding planes*, dipping quite steeply (50º) towards the southeast. If there were no *bedding* (if that is what these surfaces are), then we could assume that the rock was some sort of *pyroclastic flow* or a *brecciated lava* which broke up into fragments as it flowed. Also the fragments all seem to be similar which argues against a normal *sedimentary* origin since in most *sedimentary* rocks, the fragments (*clasts*) tend to be mixed up and from more than one source. And so the arguments for and against go on. I favour – though only marginally – a *pyroclastic flow* origin. How about you?

Return to the main track and continue on towards Troutbeck, noticing as you walk that *BVG* outcrops continue in and beside the track. This is important because shortly, there is going to be a complete change. **The track climbs a little, then flattens out, swinging round to the left where a drystone wall meets it from the right.**

A change in the rocks: Locality 2

Did you spot the change? It's not easy or obvious, but it's happened. Suddenly the rocks beneath your feet are limy *siltstones* with a strong vertical *cleavage* which cuts across the track from 4 o'clock to 10 o'clock (*strike* 230º). These beds are the younger sediments (*Ashgillian* in age; highest of the *Ordovician Period*) which overlie the *BVG*. You'll see the familiar *Coniston Limestone* again near High Skelghyll and from here until well beyond Troutbeck, we leave the *BVG* buried beneath these younger sediments, waiting for more millennia to pass before they too become exposed to the air as erosion relentlessly removes what is now the land surface. The actual change – the contact, which we know to be an *unconformity* (p. 79) – occurred about 10-15 paces back down the track before its leftward swing and the right-hand wall. If you look carefully, you should see these slaty rocks cropping out in the track and the mossy wall on the left is built of them too.

Drystone walls often give away something of the geology even though you may not be able to see the rock outcrops. The builders of these wonderful walls always quarried the rock for building from as close as possible to the site of the wall – for obvious reasons. So if there's a major change in the rock type, you often spot it in the walls first.

Grey slate fragments abound in the debris by the track and from now on, all the walls are made of this rock.

As you continue on, the wood ceases on the right, giving good views of Windermere again. Pass an iron gate on the right with neat, tombstone-like

red sandstone gateposts. This *sandstone* is obviously not from around here for there are no such rocks for many miles. **Just past the gate is a wooden seat, kindly provided for the likes of us to sit and enjoy the view. Just 25-30 paces after the wooden seat and before the gate at the end of the wood is the next locality.**

The Coniston Limestone and fossils: Locality 3

To the left side of the track, you can see the first definite *Coniston Limestone.* It is strongly *cleaved* but you should be able to spot the *bedding* (which dips at about 45º to the southeast). The *cleavage* is itself 'kinked' by a later fold structure. The rough bed surfaces at chest height show casts of fossil shells, like those near Timley Knott and Boo Tarn (p. 71). **Walk on, through the gate, and on the left in the field** are more outcrops of the *limestone* under several hawthorn trees. Blocks of the rock lie about on the grassy slopes to the left of the track and most of these contain small fossils: *brachiopods, trilobites* and other animal remains (p. 74). If you have a hand lens, now is the time to use it. If you look carefully, you'll see that all the fossils are casts: their original shell material has been dissolved away by acidic waters leaving imprints on the enclosing *siltstone* matrix. The *limestone* is identical with that at Coniston (p. 70) and has a near vertical *cleavage*. The gentler-dipping *bedding* is picked out by rows of elliptical hollows which give the rock its unmistakeable appearance.

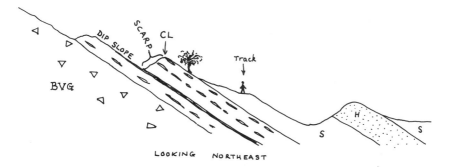

Figure 5.3: Sketch showing an imaginary section (the track is in the centre) through the dip slope here, looking north east, and showing how the harder formations form small scarps and the softer beds remain only as hollows at the bottom of each dip slope. BVG (triangles) = Borrowdale Volcanic Group; CL = Coniston Limestone; S = soft beds; H = harder beds.

The grassy slope along the left side of the track is a true *dip slope*, which closely mirrors the dip of the beds just below the grass (Fig. 5.3). In fact the beds dip at about 30° and most of the slope is closer to 20° (Fig. 5.3) which means that as you walk down the slope, you are actually walking *up* the beds! Now turn your eyes to the right, down this near-*dip slope,* to a pronounced hollow (well below the track). Indeed, these humps and hollows dominate all the landscape ahead of you, and all are due to the orderly succession of hard and soft *sedimentary* rocks in and above the *Coniston Limestone.* This type of scenery is very obviously different from that created by the hard *BVG* so the change from the one to the other is easy to detect, even from miles away as you'll see later on in this ramble.

Walk on through High Skelghyll onto the tarmac road which ends at the farm and continue on down towards the bridge. The *Coniston Limestone* continues to *strike* towards the northeast behind the farm until it reaches a cluster of oak and ash trees from which a small stream emerges to run down across the field on your left to the bridge. On the other side of these trees, you'd expect to see the *limestone* again, but you don't. It has disappeared. Why? The answer is almost certainly a small *fault* which has dropped the rocks downwards on its northeast side so that the *limestone* (if you were to look for it) would be further up the hillside to the northwest. If this doesn't seem to make sense to you, try this simple experiment: stand facing the stream and the group of trees. Hold both your hands extended but touching so that their backs 'dip' towards you just like the limestone *dip slopes.* Your fingertips represent the *scarps* such as you saw before the farm. Now, whilst keeping the 'dips' of your two hands constant, let your right hand drop vertically down a little. What happens? The right hand 'scarp' drops down and to be able to find it cropping out again on this hill which slopes towards you, you'd have to move your right hand up the 'dip' (keep the same dip orientation remember) until the left hand's fingertips are on a line with your right hand's knuckles, say. The *fault* lies between your two hands.

Cross Hol Beck at the cattle grid and bridge and take the lefthand path through a gate, marked 'Troutbeck'. As you walk up the path, look behind again for a clear view of the faulted *Coniston Limestone* outcrop.

The Skelgill Beds and flowers: Locality 4

Pass a ruined barn and stop at a small beck where the path turns abruptly south. Growing along the marshy stream banks you should see butterworts, bright yellow lesser spearworts (Fig. 5.4), the attractive and attractively-named, white-flowered grass of Parnassus (Fig. 5.5), mint and Devil's bit scabious. Harebells are common everywhere around here.

Figure 5.4: *Lesser spearwort.*

Figure 5.5: *Grass of Parnassus... not
really a grass at all.*

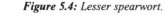

Both above and below the flat stone bridge, you'll notice outcrops of dark grey *siltstones* with a strong vertical *cleavage*, but with well developed *bedding planes* (dip 50° to the southeast). It is these bed surfaces which constrain the stream which runs along one of them beneath the alder trees just above the stone slab bridge. The rocks are the lowest representatives of the *Silurian Period*, known to geologists as the *Skelgill Beds*. These form part of the *Stockdale Shales* and lie between the older *Coniston Limestone* and the younger *Brathay Flags* which you'll see later (see Appendix: Timescale, Column C). The *Skelgill Beds* hereabouts are full of *graptolites* and one particularly patient geologist collected over 20,000 specimens of these from the nearby Skelghyll .

Why, you may justly ask, does he spell 'Skelghyll' two different ways? It's clear (High and Low Skelghyll) on the OS map after all. Placename spellings are often revised back to the traditional forms on modern maps. 'Skelgill' was an 'easier' form which prevailed for a while – and became thoroughly established in the geological literature. To avoid confusion (!), geologists agree to stick with the version of the spelling which happens to have been used for a formal rock name. Otherwise you might think that 'Skelgill Beds' and 'Skelghyll Beds' were two different rock formations. So 'Skelgill Beds' remain. Confusing, isn't it? But you can see why geologists do this for there are many examples, especially in Wales where many names were once Anglicised.

Continue past the junction with Hundreds Road, a farm track which angles in from the left about half a kilometre after the stream. Note the wealth of outcrops of *Silurian* sediments, off to the left in the higher pastures. They are all *cleaved* but all show small-scale *scarps* and *dip slopes*. **The track, now called Robin Lane, continues round the flank of the hill to descend gently to Troutbeck. If you wish to visit Townend (owned by the National Trust), you can turn off to the right from Robin Lane down to a 'T'-junction where you turn left along a narrow motor road to find Townend about half a kilometre on the left at the start of Troutbeck village. Otherwise, continue along Robin Lane, a track sunk between high drystone walls** which are built almost entirely of the *Silurian* beds, as you'd expect. Towards the village, the trees become increasingly varied: sycamores, ashes and a huge gnarled holly all of which suggest that this track is very old.

Shortly, you pass the first delightful cottages (Rose Cottage and Robin Lane Cottages), stone built with traditional round stone chimney stacks and beautiful gardens on steep slopes.

Troutbeck Post Office and a view: Locality 5

Why not stop and sit on the wooden bench outside the Post Office underneath the flowering cherry tree? If you picnic or snack here, an enterprising hen may visit, as well as a robin (from Robin Lane?) and chaffinches.

Whilst sitting, look east across the Trout Beck valley to Applethwaite Common whose top is once again dominated by small *scarps* and short *dip slopes* in the *Silurian* sedimentary rocks (Fig. 5.6 and Inset). Some of these were once quarried for building stone above the Garburn Road, a track which angles up Applethwaite Common from lower right to upper left, crossing Garburn Pass to descend eventually to Kentmere. The quarries (in the *Brathay Flags*) are now partially hidden in a triangular conifer plantation just below a prominent northwest-trending wall.

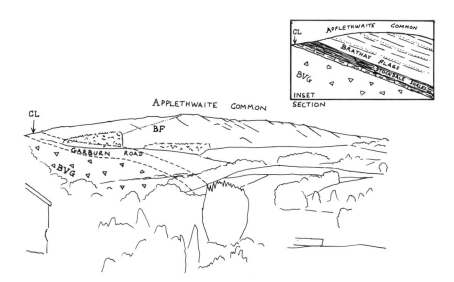

Figure 5.6: *Outline sketch, slightly exaggerated for emphasis, of scarp and dip topography on Applethwaite Common which you can see from Troutbeck, Locality 5. CL marks the approximate position of the Coniston Limestone on the hillside (between dashed lines) with BVG (triangles) below and Brathay Flags (BF) above. The smaller scale Inset shows an imaginary cross section: a vertical slice through Applethwaite Common taken along the skyline with each of the various formations which we've seen earlier on this or the Coniston rambles. You'll see the Brathay Flags at the next locality.*

Continue on north through upper Troutbeck, passing several little wells in the lefthand wall, towards High Green (some 800 metres). Look for the left turn onto the bridlepath up Nanny Lane to Wansfell and Ambleside. This is indicated by a wooden signpost on the righthand side of the road. Nanny Lane is at first quite steep, flanked by walls, and becomes something of a stream in wet weather. Grey *Silurian siltstones* (*Brathay Flags*) form the surface of much of the track, the *bedding* dipping at around 30º towards the southeast as you've seen earlier. As you climb up, you're actually walking *down* the rock sequence: the rocks become progressively older again as you cross back towards Wansfell Pike and the *BVG.*

At first, the bridleway doglegs about, but after you have climbed a little way, it turns sharply left (west), leaves the trees behind and heads towards Wansfell Pike.

Brathay Flags and the *BVG* contact: Locality 6

Just after the final dog-leg, the right side of the track becomes a continuous *bedding plane* in strongly *cleaved Brathay Flags*: mostly *siltstones* (Fig. 5.7).

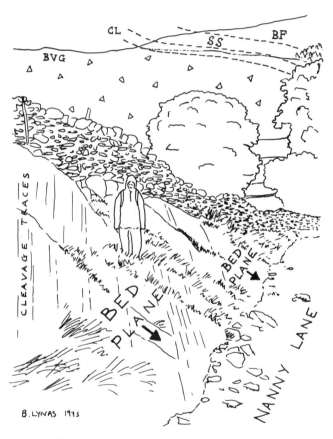

Figure 5.7: *Brathay Flags in Nanny Lane, looking east; stongly cleaved siltstones. The bedding plane actually forms the left side of the track, dipping at about 40° to the southeast. The vertical cleavage cuts this, striking northeast (labelled 'cleavage traces'). The hillside in the distance shows the Garburn Road and Pass which marks the contact between the BVG and later sedimentary rocks. CL – Coniston Limestone; SS -Stockdale Shales; BF – Brathay Flags. I emphasize that you can't actually see these beds – only bits of them. The dotted lines I've sketched on are approximately where they would be if a giant with a huge hosepipe were to expose them all by swilling off all the soils and glacial deposits from Applethwaite Common, leaving the rocks bare.*

How were these rocks formed? Whilst the *Coniston Limestone* tells us that when it was laid down, the sea was shallow and full of shelly life, the *Brathay Flags* tell a rather more subdued story of much deeper seas with no nearby land. The flags – an alternation of mud and silt rocks which readily break up to form flat slabs (flagstones) – contain many *graptolites* and are remarkably widespread, occurring as far away as Wales. This tells us that the *Silurian* sea in which these rocks were laid down was of considerable extent and depth. So the whole area must have subsided substantially towards the end of the *Ordovician*, the subsidence continuing into the *Silurian*.

The *Brathay Flags* were laid down by two processes: a slow but continual fallout of mud particles in suspension in the seawater which provided a 'background rain' of material (probably many centuries per millimetre). This was irregularly interrupted by low energy *turbidity currents* washing in slightly coarser grained sediment to give the characteristic *siltstone laminae*, some of which show *grading*. The *turbidites* would have been triggered by some major distant event in shallower water such as an earthquake or a storm whose huge waves stirred up the shallower seafloor sediments, triggering the temporarily *fluidised* sediments to flow down into deeper water. In shallower parts, the 'stirring up' would also bring the slightly coarser silty fraction of the seafloor sediments back into suspension, and ocean currents would spread this turbid water far afield before the silt particles had time to settle again. This is the likely origin of the finer *laminae*. Remember the *Skiddaw Slates* of the first ramble? Those were laid down in similar conditions to these much younger rocks. Indeed, we can be sure that similar sediments are being laid down today in the deeper seas of the world, but not too remote from land, for the really deep ocean basins receive no sediment at all from that source.

Whilst at this locality, look back across the valley to the Garburn Road and Pass. This upper part of the bridleway almost exactly defines the gently southeast-dipping junction (contact) between the ordered *scarps* and *dip slopes* of the *Coniston Limestone* and overlying *Silurian* beds (above and right of the bridleway), and the older underlying *BVG* which forms all the ground below the track and to the north. This is the same contact that you crossed earlier in Skelghyll Wood (Locality 2).

As you walk on up the bridlepath, the *Brathay Flags* continue to crop out beneath your feet with clear *bedding planes* which the track follows almost exactly. This means that for a time, you are walking *along* the sequence of rocks rather than crossing it. **Then the track swings round to the north (right) passing a large sycamore on the right. Beyond this, outcrops cease but you are now walking *down* the rock sequence again.** This means that shortly, you should cross the *Coniston Limestone* again. **The track runs flat for a while up to a second sycamore tree, also on the right, just past a stile and a gate.**

Making contact – meet the *BVG* again: Locality 7 (second sycamore tree)

In the adjoining fields, small outcrops of *bedded* sediments, good quality grass as well as the drystone walls (a good part of which are still built of *sedimentary* rocks), tell you that you still haven't crossed back into the *BVG*. But past the sycamore tree, the scenery changes abruptly to rough mountain grasses, sedges and peat bogs and you'll see the familiar knobbly outcrops of the *BVG* not far away to the north. So it's clear that the contact you've been more or less following from Ambleside is somewhere about here, but is not actually exposed (or hardly so; see below). It is these indirect lines of evidence which allow geologists to make maps of the rocks even when they cannot see them. Behind you, the same contact is very clear below Applethwaite Common, though again, there is little actual rock outcrop. In fact, there *is* a small outcrop of *Coniston Limestone* here: head for a lone hawthorn tree on the right side of the track, some 50 paces on from the sycamore. Twenty five paces beyond it are a few very small outcrops on the right, by a ruined wall. The *limestone* is strongly *cleaved*, but contains many fossil *brachiopods* and beyond it, the abrupt change from lush grass to yellow, acid moorland occurs. That's our contact! From now on, everything is *BVG* again. It crops out where a second drystone wall meets the left side of the track just a few metres after the last *Coniston Limestone*.

Ahead now is Wansfell ridge and Nanny Lane bears round to the right after about 200 paces. At this point, a footpath passes through an iron gate to the left, signposted to 'Ambleside via Wansfell'. This is your route across rather dreary peaty moorland, punctuated by outcrops of unexciting *BVG*. The cairned track is clear because much of it has been rebuilt with cobbles to prevent erosion damage. The summit is the next locality.

Wansfell Pike; a fine view and a last word on contacts: Locality 8

The view from Wansfell Pike is as fine on a good day as from many nobler peaks. From here, you can see Windermere, Grasmere, Rydal Water, the Coniston fells, the Langdales, the Scafell ranges, Fairfield, St. Sunday Crag, Red Screes, Angle Tarn Pikes and Ill Bell to name the most prominent only.

Below you to the southeast, the upper intake wall (which separates rough mountain grazing from the improved hill pastures on the lowland side) defines the line of contact between the *BVG* and the *Coniston Limestone* and later beds, quite well – until it turns northwestward to run up to Wansfell ridge. Here and there you can pick out small quarries in the *Coniston Limestone* which would have been used for wall-building. The *BVG* rocks at the summit are rather decayed fragmental volcanics.

The descent towards Ambleside is initially steep and somewhat slippery but not otherwise dangerous. At the bottom of the steep grassy slope, you continue straight on over stiles, crossing a track. There are *BVG* outcrops at the bottom of the stream gully to your right, buried under thick glacial *till*. **Continue straight down the hill until you reach a stile and iron ladder which will bring you to the tarmac road down to Ambleside. After about 300 metres, you have the choice of returning directly to Ambleside (continue straight on down the hill) or visiting Stockghyll Force (waterfalls). If you choose the waterfall, take the footpath off to the right through an old iron turnstile opposite Charlotte Mason College, to 'Stockghyll Park and waterfalls'. Keep right and ascend a little to cross the upper falls at a footbridge.**

Stockghyll Force and gorge: Locality 9

The waterfall exists because of a bed of hard *BVG tuffs* (difficult to see here in the shady woodland with all rock surfaces covered with luxurious growths of mosses and lichens) and would have only begun to develop after the final melting of the glaciers for below the grinding ice, the rock would have been smoothed of all former irregularities. You need running water and a hard rock bar (across the valley floor) to form a waterfall and gorge like Stockghyll Force.

Now walk down the paths to recross the beck at another footbridge. Finally walk back into the pretty market town of Ambleside and so to where you started this ramble.

ROCKY RAMBLE 6:
LOUGHRIGG FELL – Small Is Beautiful

How to get to the start of the ramble

The ramble starts at the church in Ambleside town, from wherever suits you best.

The ramble: needs, distances and times

As with the Troutbeck and Wansfell ramble, this could be done on a less than perfect day though you'd probably lose some of the better long-distance views. The overall distance (starting at Ambleside Church) is around 9.5 kilometres (under 6 miles) during which you'll be climbing, perhaps surprisingly, 435 metres (around 1430 feet). Obviously this is not a full day trip but you should allow a good half day; more if the weather is fair for there are many delightful spots to sit – either in the bracken or on benches on Loughrigg Terrace. The walking is in places quite rough and the weather as fickle as anywhere else so I'd recommend the usual mountain garb.

Do take a picnic if you can, for Loughrigg Fell abounds in delightful comfortable spots from which you can admire many different views.

The OS Outdoor Leisure map is Sheet 7, South Eastern area.

Introduction

Although the highest point on Loughrigg Fell reaches only 335 metres (1,099 feet), less than half the height of Pike of Stickle, this ramble has a special quality of its own. The views are outstanding in all directions, precisely because the fell is not very high; the ramble rewards you well for little effort. If you head for the highest summit in an area, you often find that the surrounding mountains and hills – which may look superb from lower down – become somehow much less impressive. Loughrigg Fell has that strange quality whereby you feel as if you are in the mountains, surrounded by craggy outcrops and little tarns just as at much higher levels. You could easily get lost on this little fell even though parts are only a few minutes walk from the centre of bustling Ambleside. If you follow this route, I hope you won't get lost, but you should be able to make sense of the meaning of some of the classic scenery. You'll also see three underground slate quarries, one of which is readily accessible and is quite spectacular – as are the views from it across Rydal Water to Fairfield.

Ambleside Church: start of the ramble

Set off from wherever you are parked or are staying and head for the church, opposite the school. Continue on through Rothay Park (with its *roches moutonnées*) to the delightful hump-backed bridge over the River Rothay (Fig. 6.1). Turn right onto the narrow tarmac road (to Rydal) and cross a cattle grid. Then turn almost immediately left through a kissing gate (or by crossing the adjacent cattle grid), to head up the public bridleway to Loughrigg Fell. The tarmac road climbs to Browhead and towards Pine Rigg and almost immediately you begin to have views to your right of the Fairfield range and (behind you) Wansfell Pike. The road passes through pretty mixed woodlands where you should spot ashes, oaks, alder, yews, rhododendrons, willows and hazels.

Figure 6.1: *Hump-backed bridge over the River Rothay.*

Rhododendrons (from the Greek 'rhodon', a rose and 'dendron', a tree) are not native to Europe, originating in the Himalayan regions. They were brought in by enthusiasts in the 19th Century and some kinds have now become something of a menace, since they spread fast and the damp and cool British climate suits them. They regenerate well from seed, regrow vigorously after cutting back, tolerate poor soils and rapidly form secondary woodland. But they do put on a pretty display of pink, red, purple and white flowers in spring.

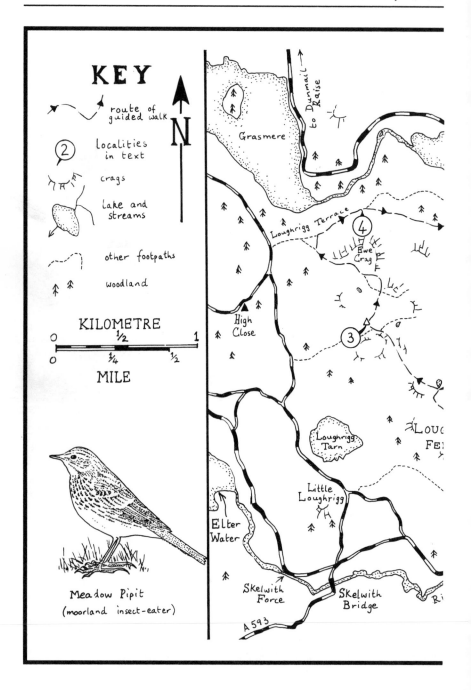

KEY

N

- route of guided walk
- ② localities in text
- crags
- lake and streams
- other footpaths
- woodland

KILOMETRE
0 ½ 1
0 ¼ ½
MILE

Meadow Pipit
(moorland insect-eater)

Grasmere

to Dunmail Raise

Loughrigg Terrace

④ Bwe Crag

High Close

③

Loughrigg Tarn

Lough Fell

Little Loughrigg

Elter Water

Skelwith Force

Skelwith Bridge

A 593

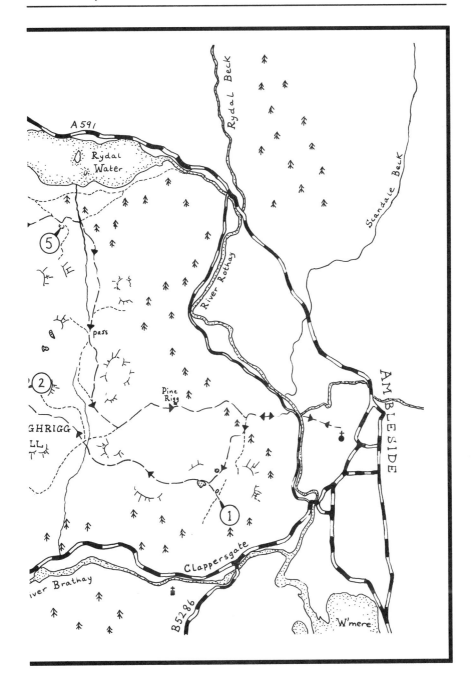

At the sharp bend after three cottage conversions, turn off the road over a stile to follow the footpath to Clappersgate. Immediately after the stile, a huge Scots pine (Fig. 6.2) grows right in the middle of the track. **The path climbs through the woodland for a short way,** and although there are many *BVG* outcrops, they're all covered with lush growths of moss, so you can't see anything of them. **After less than 100 metres, you cross another stile and a stream, leaving the wood behind. Head to the right up the bracken-covered fellside, keeping close to the little beck to your right.** You should spot insect-eating butterworts (Fig. 1.9, p. 22) in the boggy patches beside the beck. **There are several tracks which head up towards the southeast end of Loughrigg Fell. The principal of these makes for a ladder stile over a drystone wall which you cross.** You'll notice plenty of *BVG* outcrops and you'll also notice that they are all smooth and rounded. This is the work of ice once again and the entire area of Loughrigg Fell is like this, showing us that it must have once been deeply buried under thick ice sheets. When you reach Locality 3, you'll see just why this should have occurred.

Figure 6.2: Scots pine with cone and branch (left), a leaf and general form of this tree which is a true native of the central and western Highlands of Scotland.

Continue on past a tiny tarn. This little tarn has masses of sphagnum moss, sundews (Fig. 1.4, p. 16), yellow spearwort (Fig. 5.4, p. 135) of the buttercup family, and bog cotton growing in and around it. This last plant, also called

cotton grass (Fig. 6.3), often covers the boggy shores of tarns or former tarns with its white cottony powder puffs.

Figure 6.3: Bog cotton is a member of the Sedge Family. These generally rather unexciting and little-noticed plants differ from grasses in that their stems are three-sided (not round) and the leaves are not jointed where they join the stem). The white cottony threads grow from the fruits and we can assume that they are, like dandelion 'umbrellas', of help in seed distribution.

At the large tarn, the largest on Loughrigg Fell, you have your first views of Crinkle Crags, Bow Fell and the Langdale Pikes. Turn left along one of the many tracks to make your way to the southeast end of the fell. This whole area is a delight for picnicking and for children to play about by the several little tarns. The grass is close-cropped by the sheep and the bracken makes comfortable lying-down places or cover for hide-and-seek games.

Lying in bracken is unlikely to harm you but remember that it is poisonous. The plant contains shikimic acid which is both cancer-causing (carcinogenic) and damages the chromosomes in animal cells (mutagenic). As if that weren't enough, it is also *allelopathic*: the toxins it produces can prevent other plants' seeds from germinating. It is now thought that inhaling the russet-brown spores which it sheds in the autumn might occasionally trigger cancers, so it's really best to avoid it. And you can do because of the numerous paths hereabouts. Bracken (*Pteridium*), now an invasive pest like Rhododendron can be, is a member of the Polypody (Fern) Family. Despite its modern toxic reputation, the North American Indians and Japanese regularly eat the young fronds (fiddle-heads) without harm. Various eradication techniques have been tried. The most effective seem to be regular cutting whilst the plant is growing vigorously or allowing cattle to trample the young fronds. Unfortunately, some animals will eat it at this stage and because it is poisonous, it can make them ill or even kill them. But without bracken, the fells – especially in the autumn when the dying fronds turn whole hillsides to a rich brown colour – would be much less colourful than they are. It was once even considered useful: as bedding for animals and, when burnt, as a source of potash alkali for soap making. The soap was made by burning green bracken in kilns. The potash-rich ash from this was then leached with lime, tallow and water to make lye, the basis of soap. The lye was then used in 'fulling,' a process in which yarn or cloth is made heavier and more compact by shrinking, beating and pressing. Back in Tudor times, fulling mills formed an important minor industry in Lakeland. To make soap from lye, you mix it with fat, either vegetable or animal. Bracken was even used by the Scots as a dye (dark yellow) in some tartans.

Loughrigg Fell southeast: Locality 1 [3657 0388]

You reach the locality after about 150 paces of ups and downs, southeast of the large tarn. There are two rocky hummocks which form the highest point (about 200 metres above sealevel) at the southeast end of Loughrigg Fell. The right hand one of these is the locality.

Figure 6.4: *Windermere, excavated by the glaciers in softer Silurian rocks which contrast with the hard ice-smoothed BVG in the left foreground.*

The first thing that strikes you here is not the *cleaved*, rather indeterminate fragmental *BVG* beneath your feet, but the view. Ambleside is so close that, like Beatrix Potter's Little Lucy of Littletown in 'The Tale of Mrs Tiggy Winkle', you could almost drop pebbles down the chimneys. Below to the south is Windermere (Fig. 6.4). Further to the right is Clappersgate and its unusual and isolated church. ('Clappersgate' is Old Norse meaning 'the road over the rough bridge'.) Further afield are Wetherlam and the Coniston fells, Pike of Blisco, Crinkle Crags, Bow Fell, Esk Pike, Great End, the Langdale Pikes, west Loughrigg Fell, Fairfield, Red Screes, Ill Bell, Froswick and Wansfell Pike.

You'll have noticed that there are several tiny tarns around here. One such just a short distance to the southwest of this locality is now almost wholly overgrown with sphagnum moss and lilies. This, on a minute scale, is the inevitable fate of all lakes. They fill up to become just marshy hollows and as humus from decaying plants builds up, trees become established so that finally, they would (if Nature took its course) become wooded. You'd never know they'd been there. This process is nearly complete at Blind Moss Tarn, Easedale. Elter Water, best seen from Locality 3, is another example of this and even Windermere will one day be filled in.

Figure 6.5: *White water lily (Nymphaea). This has large white, fragrant flowers with bright yellow stamens. The flowers open when the sun shines and you can see them between June and August. The fruit ripens underwater and then splits to release the seeds which have air in them so that they float and disperse. The frog is admiring the flower too; I drew him just for fun.*

Return now to the large tarn. This has myriads of sundews along its marshy sphagnum banks. Bogbeans (Fig. 3.10, p. 81) and white water lilies (Fig. 6.5) abound in parts of this tarn which, like Windermere, owes its existence to the gouging action of glaciers. **Walk on west with the lake on your left (south) along a broad grass track which shortly runs along near to a drystone wall. You keep this wall fairly close on your left for a time. I mention this because there are dozens of paths on Loughrigg Fell and they can be confusing, for not all are marked on the OS map.**

As you walk, you have fine views over towards Wrynose Pass and Little Langdale. Bracken is everywhere and harebells are common too, scattered amongst the golfcourse-quality nibbled grass. The *BVG* outcrops are rather unexciting, being fine grained, *cleaved tuffs*, without any of the obvious *bedding* structures you've seen on earlier walks (or will see on later ones, especially Bow Fell). All the rock exposures have been ground by the ice sheets into the rounded hummocks so typical of ice action. If you look carefully, you should be able to pick out *glacial striations* where rock chunks, like cutting tools in the glacier base, gouged and scored grooves into the solid rock below.

Head on gently downhill and through a kissing gate (and feel free to kiss if you want to, and there's someone appropriate) **still keeping the wall on your left. After you cross a beck, fork away from the wall to head northwest towards Black Mire and the next locality. Cross a major walking track (Ambleside to Loughrigg Tarn) and continue northwest up to the right of some small** *screes* **and past a pile of stones. Then there's a short scramble.** But now, the rocks have changed: Both the stone pile and the rocks on the scramble are *porphyritic andesites*, quite unlike the indeterminate *tuffs* which have formed all the outcrops so far. They are probably *lavas* and are similar to those you saw (p. 20) on the Haystacks ramble.

Continue up the side of a shallow valley until you come to a small tarn with a prominent stone cairn close by on the hilltop to your left. Walk north (effectively making a right turn off the track) along this shallow valley for about 100 paces, passing another small tarn, until you come to a third, the largest tarn.

Glacial meltwaters: Locality 2 [3522 0471]

Even the largest of these tarns is very shallow and with the passage of a little more time (a few centuries perhaps at most), the bog bean and sedge tussocks (which now form tiny islands) will aid the shallowing process, turning the tarn into a peat bog. The silting-up of lakes doesn't have to be only sands, gravels and silts from inflowing streams, it can be purely organic in origin. Such plants as grow in places like this (especially now with acid rain) tend to decay only slightly to acid fibrous material: humus and peat (p. 62). Here, bits of heather, sedge or sphagnum mosses blow or fall into the peaty tarns and sink to the bottom, forming an oozy layer of black peat. It doesn't rot away and so sooner rather than later, the tarn disappears and becomes a bog.

But why is this little chain of tarns here in the first place? You'll know now that they are likely to have something to do with the glaciers that forced their way over Loughrigg Fell just 18,000 years ago.

Remember that when I say things that might seem preposterous like 'just 18,000 years ago' as if it were yesterday, I'm comparing the glaciation timescale with the actual age of the *BVG* rocks underfoot. You'll recall that these are around 450 million years old: 250 times older than the final big pulse of glaciation that we call the Ice Age! And the age of the Earth is 4,600,000,000 years; 255,000 times older. Yet of course if you're 46 like me as I write this, the last glacier in the Lake District melted 11,500 years or 250 lifetimes ago! Perspectives (see Appendix: Timescale).

But why should there be several tarnlets in a row along the bottom of an obvious shallow valley? The answer is certainly glacial. The crushing weight of the moving ice tends to exploit any weakness in the underlying rocks (as you'll see at Locality 3) and presumably did so here also. But I think that this short yet prominent valley (Fig. 6.6) was probably formed not so much by ice, but by water.

Figure 6.6: *The north end of the glacial channel at Locality 3, near Black Mire. Dove Crag, High Pike and Low Pike are in the background; the east side of the Fairfield horseshoe. 'A' is where the meltwaters would have started running through this shallow channel, presumably southwards along the valley's axis which is now occupied by the little tarns. Note how this one is already partially silted up with peaty flats, formerly submerged but still wet, and thick growths of bog beans as well as the tussock islets.*

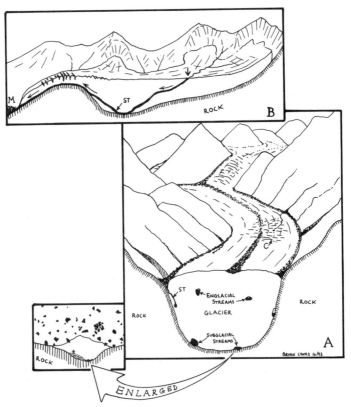

Figure 6.7 A: *Imaginary cross section of a glacier. The dark bands on its surface are –
or will become – moraines. They originate mostly from rock falls onto the glacier edges
and when two glaciers merge, their two side, or lateral moraines unite to form a central
one. Like any other running water, the streams in or below the ice carry lumps of rock,
gravel and finer sediments from the mountainsides above. This means that they can
erode their ice or rock beds – just as streams in flood do. 'C' on this figure shows a
cluster of crevasses where one stream disappears down into the ice. Streams which
remain in the ice are called englacial whereas those which run between the ice and
bedrock are subglacial, one of which I've shown running at the side of the glacier (right)
as commonly happens. Another stream ('ST') plunges from a gully on the left, through
the lateral moraine, into an englacial tunnel. I've enlarged one subglacial stream to give
an idea of scale. A tiny figure stands on a bank of cobbles which are rolled along every
day as the stream power increases. Remember, this tunnel is completely full of water
under immense hydrostatic pressure. Note too that the ice is full of lumps of rock, some
acting as cutting tools at its base. The rocks are not evenly distributed because they
mostly arise from rock falls from steep mountain slopes, but much earlier in the glacier's
history.*

Figure 6.7 B: In certain cases, subglacial streams can actually run uphill under the ice. This diagram shows how hydraulic pressure can drive water up and over an ice-covered watershed, provided the inlet to the submerged system of flowing water is at a higher level (a little like a siphon). Similar up-hill flows may take place in limestone cave systems for the same reason. The vertical arrow shows where the stream, after running across the glacier's surface for a while, sinks into the ice. The stream (ST) is first englacial, then subglacial before emerging at the glacier's snout where the ice is retreating, and dumping its loads of moraine (M). Note the crevasses where the ice is bent as it flexes over the submerged hill top.

Aside from the polar glaciers where temperatures rarely exceed freezing point, those in mountains like the Alps, Himalayas or Andes melt rapidly during the warm days of summer. If you walk on any such glacier on a summer afternoon, you'll often find the surface is slushy and wet and that there are quite large streams running across it. But that's just on the surface. You'll also often find that these streams suddenly vanish down a 'pothole' or a crevasse. The water doesn't then refreeze inside the glacier, but continues running either in a cave inside the glacier itself or between the base of the glacier and its rock bed (Fig. 6.7 A & B). In some cases, the stream may be in contact with the rock valley side or floor (buried by the ice) and then may retreat back into the glacier. This can leave puzzling features after the ice has melted: little bits of water-cut valley which don't seem to connect up or odd mounds of obvious stream gravels in an unexpected place like the edge of a valley.

Here, we can be sure that the hillside was covered with thick ice which shaped it into the characteristic humps and hollows which you see everywhere. The ice sheet would have had to force its way from the narrow, restricted and kinked main valley to the north, now occupied by Rydal Water, to ramp up and over Loughrigg Fell. But once the ice started to melt, there would have been millions and millions of tons of raging meltwaters surging and seething on, within and under this great decaying mass. What has probably happened here is that one such powerful but temporary *subglacial* stream hollowed out this shallow valley across Loughrigg Fell.

If you doubt the power of such streams, be sure to visit the snout of a real glacier and see for yourself. The flow varies according to the season and time of day, being at its greatest late on a warm summer afternoon for obvious reasons. Then you see surging masses of chocolate-brown or grey, sediment-laden water foaming out from the huge ice cave at the glacier's snout, rolling quite large boulders and chunks of ice before it. (The most convenient glacier snout I know of, both safe and easy to get at, is that at Glacier Blanc in the Ecrins Alps of France, a superb place for looking at glacial landforms as they are actually being made).

But we cannot assume that this meltwater channel was *subglacial*. It could have formed because the decaying ice sheet to the north continued to block other exits for meltwaters which cascaded off the ice at this point (just at the north end of the channel you see today). The ice-damming effect may even have formed a short-lived lake on the north side of the fell which overflowed at this point. This sort of meltwater channel – an overflow from an ice-dammed lake – is very common in glaciated areas. Some are long and deep and obviously continued to be active for many years (for example Newtondale in the North Yorkshire Moors). Whether it was *subglacial* or a true overflow channel, this tiddler here – one of many on Loughrigg Fell – could have formed in a year or so.

Make your way up to the stone cairn. Here, once again, is the classic view of the Langdale Pikes and Great Langdale and underfoot are the cleaved *BVG tuffs*. **Continue northwest towards the trig point up another shallow valley with small** *screes* **cloaking its sides.** This valley too is certain to have been formed by ice and meltwater action, the *screes* having covered up the steep sides since the end of the glaciation. Along the track in this valley are regular stone piles. Pick up a piece or two and you'll see that we're back in *porphyritic andesite lavas* again. This time, the *lava* has an additional feature of interest: it is *vesicular*, full of small cavities.

These cavities – *vesicles* – are formed in the same way as those in Aero chocolate (which I am not being paid to advertise): by gas. *Magma* can contain enormous amounts of gas, dissolved within it due to the intense pressure within the *magma* chamber. Very gassy magma, when it erupts (which releases the pressure), does so violently just as a shaken champagne bottle pops its cork and gushes everywhere. Imagine the frothing champagne becoming instantly frozen into a solid. It would be full of bubbles, like the chocolate, and like this rock. For *lava* does 'freeze' fast, especially if it is in thin flows or erupts under water. The extreme example of frothy, *vesicular lava* is *pumice*. Any further expansion means that the bubble walls shatter and the eruption no longer produces *lava* but becomes an *ignimbrite*-type.

Finally, climb out of the *lava* **valley to the trig point (335 metres and the highest point of the walk) and the next locality.**

Deltas, faults and glaciers: Locality 3 (trig station)

I don't have to tell you about the view. You can see that for yourself. You can also see prominent *bedding* features in the distant *BVG* below Sergeant Man (northwest) and above Codale Tarn (which you can't see from here). Beneath your feet are *BVG tuffs*, not very exciting rocks when they're weathered like this because you can see nothing of their subtle character. But don't give them up: you'll see them in a much fresher state at the two abandoned slate quarries you'll be visiting shortly.

Now take a seat facing, first, to the southwest so that you have a good view of Elter Water. Sitting at a vantage point such as this is the next best thing to being airborne.

From the air, you can see all kinds of features and structures in the landscape and rocks that are hard to make out or make sense of on the ground. Nowadays, almost all geological maps (and many other kinds of maps including those produced by the Ordnance Survey) are made using vertical air photographs. And increasingly, scientists use other techniques known as remote sensing to detect anything from the temperature of the ocean surface to the rate of destruction of the Brazilian rain forest. Most of this imagery comes from satellites such as the American LANDSAT and French SPOT. But we only want to look at and consider Elter Water and for that, this locality does fine.

The end is nigh for Elter Water

Elter Water is a dying lake. I don't mean that it's polluted, but that it is rapidly filling in. It formed originally, as usual, because of a glacier: that from Great Langdale. If you look at the OS Outdoor Leisure map, you'll see that below (east of) the lake, the valley becomes very restricted just west of Skelwith Bridge. Rocky hill spurs protrude from both north (Little Loughrigg) and south (Park Fell). The Langdale glacier obviously had some difficulty gouging its way through this hard *BVG* rock despite help from the much smaller ice tongue from Little Langdale at this point. It managed to scoop out the rock basin which would become Elter Water but couldn't make much impression on the rocky barrier to the east. The iceflow may even have split at this point with a tongue forcing its way round the north side of Little Loughrigg where it may have met a similar tongue heading south from the Grasmere valley. Between them, they carved out the rock basin for Loughrigg Tarn, just below you to the southwest.

When the ice finally melted, it left the remains of this tussle between the Irresistible Force and the Immovable Object in the form of a rock bar (simply a valley-floor bar of hard rock) about 300 metres west of Skelwith Bridge. Rock bars (nothing to do with disco-pubs) such as this are very common in formerly-glaciated areas and greatly influence the nature of the valleys in which they occur. They impound lakes (Elter Water in this case); they also create rapids or waterfalls (as at Skelwith Force) which result in the river, if powerful enough, cutting its way slowly backwards to leave a gorge (p. 141).

But Elter Water itself is much diminished in size. Looking again at the OS map, you can see from the absence of contours (and you can see directly by looking from your vantage point) that the lake must once have stretched from near Elterwater village practically to Skelwith Force. The reason for its rapid demise is obvious: not only Great Langdale Beck but also the stream from Little Langdale outpour into this lake. Because they lose their power to carry sediment when they enter a lake, the sediment falls out of suspension to build deltas. You can see the two deltas both directly and on the map. Not many more centuries will pass before the deltas merge to cut the dwindling lake in half and then fill it completely.

The Dunmail-Grasmere glacier

I suggest that now you move yourself to another vantage point giving you a good view to the north and west: you should then be able to see Dunmail Raise, part of Grasmere and Helm Crag at the entrance to Easedale. Now for a flight of fancy: Imagine that you are a time traveller, properly dressed in survival clothing and that you'd arrived here at the peak of the last ice age. Your time machine would have to be able to adjust automatically for height differences, because if you were here at this height 22,000 years ago, you'd have been crushed under hundreds of metres of ice. So travel back in time and upwards in height!

Here you are in the late-*Devensian* ice age (say 22,000 years ago), the last of several which go back almost 2 million years (Appendix: Timescale, Columns C (top) and D). It's a clear day and the sun is shining. The temperature is -30°C and there's a steady northerly wind whipping up a little spindrift just on the snow surface. The wind chill factor means that the temperature is -45°C so far as you're concerned, so you're glad of your layers of warm and windproof clothing. There are only two things to see: the white of the snow surface and the blue of the clear sky. Silence reigns with just the rustle of the wind in your insulated hood. There is no sign of life anywhere; nor has there been or will there be for thousands of years. But wait: there is something a long way off. Something black. Several things. You screw up your eyes to counteract the blinding brightness of the glistening snow surface. Over to the west you can make out what seem to be projections of rock through the icy waste. You can't tell how far away they are because you have nothing to give you an idea of scale. In fact the rocks you are looking at are the very tips of Bow Fell and Scafell, the only clearly visible signs of the underlying mountains and valleys. These are 'nunataks,' an Eskimo word for ice-bound peak. Sometimes, not even these would have been visible, for with climate fluctuations, even they were buried by the ice.

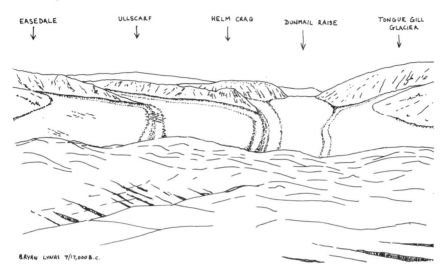

EASEDALE ↓ ULLSCARF ↓ HELM CRAG ↓ DUNMAIL RAISE ↓ TONGUE GILL GLACIER ↓

BRYAN LYNAS 7/17,000 B.C.

Figure 6.8: My attempt at reconstructing what you would have seen had you been here about 15,000 years ago on a sunny day in summer (so that the winter's snow would have melted, revealing the details of the ice – and the rocky ridges). Most of what you see is ice of course, but I've named some of the hills and valleys. At Dunmail Raise, the ice sheets on the Thirlmere side were connected to this one. The bands on the ice surface are moraines (see Fig. 6.7A for explanation). The foreground – Loughrigg Fell – consists mostly of pressure ridges in the ice which is being forced upwards again by the huge constricted glacier further to the north (over Grasmere). As it flexes over the top, crevasses open. There are several just close by (near right) so be careful where you walk.

Now jump forward in your time machine to about 15,000 years ago. You drop down with a bump because everything has changed. Much of the ice has gone and now you can see recognisable mountains and ridges all around. In Figure 6.8, I've attempted to show you what I think you would have seen at around this time. The ice still fills the valleys right up to Dunmail, but now the lower ridges are exposed. The ice surface is smooth for the most part because it descends gently from the higher valleys, carrying only *moraine* material which has fallen onto it higher up the valley side. When two glaciers merge, as they do here (Easedale and Dunmail), the *moraines* which each ice stream has along its edges merge together in the centre of the united glacier to form *medial moraines*. You can see these in any of the world's valley glaciers of today.

What you cannot readily see on my reconstruction is the heavy crevassing of part of the ice which continues to force its way up over Loughrigg Fell, which is still submerged in ice. But as you stand by your time machine, you can hear occasional creaks, rumbles and sharp snapping noises as the ice bends and breaks as it is inexorably forced up over the hard *BVG* below.

Travel forward another 500 years (these figures are my guesses for we cannot be sure of the exact dates involved). Bump: you're on the summit of Loughrigg Fell again. The temperature is +15°C and the sun beats down from a cloudless sky. The glacier in what will soon become Grasmere valley is much shrunken and covered in piles of boulders and mud. And listen, you can hear the sound of running water; lots of it. For the ice surface is alive with rushing torrents of meltwaters. The mountains all around are covered in splashing streams pouring out of decaying ice masses stranded in various parts. Along the edge of the main valley glacier, ponded up by both submerged ice and *moraine* are several dirty-looking lakes. Wherever they can, these lakes overflow or drain down under the ice to become *subglacial* torrents. One overflow is pouring out over Loughrigg Fell, actively cutting the channel which 14,500 years later will become my Locality 2.

In the lower country, just a short distance to the south are the gnawed bones of a reindeer which wolves brought down last night. The reindeer, confused by the rapid changes of the landscape which affected its instinctive migration route, had become separated from the rest of the herd. It had been nibbling at the lichens growing on the rocks and a few blades of grasses which are beginning to shoot up now between the chaos of floodwaters, piles of *moraine* and ice-polished and grooved rock. Here and there, profusions of tiny flowers form cushions or mats between the rocks. Life is returning to the land.

Fault lines and strike-slip

Enough of these imaginary time travels for now, but we'll be using our time machine again later in this book. But for now, back to the rocks themselves. Why, for example, did this great valley from Grasmere form? The answer is that erosion (water and ice) exploited a major weakness in the rocks. This was caused by one of the largest *faults* in the Lake District: the Coniston Fault. Coniston Water was excavated by the glaciers along this *fault* line, and from there it is easy to follow north, for it forms the valley now occupied by the A593 to Coniston, crosses Loughrigg at the low pass near High Close Youth Hostel and then runs straight up to Dunmail Raise, over to Thirlmere, then St. John's Beck towards Threlkeld (Blencathra). This makes it at least 30 kilometres long. It is interesting that this *fault* is not of the type we've seen before (pp. 77 and 134) where one side has simply dropped down relative to the other.

For the Coniston Fault is a *strike-slip fault*, a type of fault (such as today's San Andreas Fault in California) where the movement along the line of the fault is horizontal.

Try this experiment using your hands as before. Place both your open hands together, touching along the line of your thumbs, and level them so that they are horizontal. Now move your left hand away from you slowly, but keeping it horizontal and in contact with your right hand. This movement imitates that of the Coniston Fault. It is actually *right-lateral* movement, for obviously, *strike-slip faults* can move either way. To know your left from your right in this, imagine yourself standing on one side of the *right-lateral* Coniston Fault. While you are watching it, an earthquake begins (for *fault* movements always cause ground shaking) and it starts to move — and the ground on the other side of the *fault* appears to you to be moving to the right. That's all there is to it: so you can have *left-lateral strike-slip faults* and *right-lateral strike-slip faults*. Both good mouthfuls, but not hard to understand. Incidentally, the San Andreas Fault (really a system of faults) is a *right-lateral strike-slip fault* so one day, Los Angeles (built on the Pacific crustal plate which moves north) will pass by San Francisco (on the North American continent crustal plate, heading south).

The Coniston *strike-slip fault*, as I said, is *right-lateral*. It has, over a long period, shifted the rocks on its west side towards the north by almost 2 kilometres. It's not surprising then – given that you have a vertical gash in the Earth's crust along which you know an enormous amount of movement has taken place – that the rocks along the line of the *fault* were somewhat smashed up and thus weakened by the relentless grinding of the two sides, one against the other. And so the forces of erosion have exploited this line of weakness, giving us the great valley you see in front of you.

Dunmail Raise is the site of a legendary battle over a millennium ago in which King Dunmail of Cumberland was killed. Stones were piled on his body, goes the story, and this stone pile is still to be seen at the summit of the pass.

Time to move on down towards Grasmere on an obvious track, again with piles of stones, the same *porphyritic lavas* you saw just before the last locality. The green specks you may be able to see are *chlorite* crystals. Under the influence of deep burial, heat and circulating fluids (probably at the time of the mountain-building episode during which the *cleavage* formed), these *chlorite* crystals grew, thus replacing the original mineral which was probably *pyroxene*. This is why it is uncommon to find in rocks of this age, fresh crystals of the more unstable mineral species such as *pyroxene*. *Feldspars*, on the other hand, are more resistant to alteration and *quartz* is almost totally resistant. Some of the *lava* outcrops you pass as the track drops down towards Ewe Crag are full of gas cavities – *vesicles* – and have a strong, steep-dipping *cleavage*.

If you walk out onto the top of Ewe Crag, you'll be rewarded by a marvellous view of Grasmere. Descend more steeply now to Loughrigg Terrace on the cobbled track with steps. Amidst the cropped grass and bracken, you'll also see parsley fern and foxgloves (Fig. 6.9). **Take the right fork of the track to join Loughrigg Terrace just before the mixed woodland to the northwest. Turn right onto the terrace and walk northeast along this flat, easy track with its famous views. After around 350 metres, you come to unmistakable signs of quarrying: a rock tip above the track.**

Figure 6.9: Foxglove

Slate quarry below Ewe Crag: Locality 4 [347058]

This small slate quarry, marked 'level' on the OS map, is really a mine since it was largely underground. If you wish, you can scramble up into the tree-filled entrance of the mine, duck under the vegetation and walk in. It is not large or especially interesting (Fig. 6.10A) from a geological viewpoint since most of the rocks are stained by trickles of mineral-rich water and covered in a layer of algae, obscuring the structures they contain. You'll find several clumps of ferns, lots of mosses and liverworts, all of which flourish in the damp, low-light conditions here. Even so, there are one or two places on the right hand wall near the entrance (looking inwards) where you can make out clear rippled *laminations* in the fine grained grey, strongly *cleaved tuff* (Fig. 6.10B). These are delicate structures which do not show up on the weathered surfaces you've seen so far on the walk. In fact most of the *tuffs* right from the start have probably been of this sort. They are almost certainly the northeasterly continuation of the *Tilberthwaite Tuffs* we saw on the Coniston ramble (p. 85). The *bedding* here dips at 20-30° southeast, the *cleavage* cutting this at almost 90° and so dipping steeply northwest.

Figure 6.10 (a): a view looking from the back of the mine to the entrance. No trolls here; not enough room! *Figure 6.10 (b):* Delicate ripple forms in the tuffs just inside the entrance to the mine. These beds tell us that the tuff was laid down in shallow water with occasionally vigorous, scouring currents. In parts (e.g. centre right), the tops of older ripples were scoured off by later currents, making tiny unconformities. The humpy bed forms are sections through ripples which have been 'tightened' or steepened up by the compressional effect of the deformation process (mountain building). This created the cleavage which cuts across the rock from top left to bottom right. The piece I've sketched is about the height of a hammer.

But you can find the best samples of the delicate *bedding* structures outside the mine on the dump (Fig. 6.11). Some of these are exquisite and you can easily see why this particular rock has been so much quarried wherever it crops out. The *cleavage*, which is almost perpendicular to the *bedding* means that the rock splits easily into slabs which display to perfection the *bedding* structures. These show up even better on wet or polished surfaces and many people buy 'Lake District *objets d'art*' made of this rock without knowing what it is or why it is like it is. But you don't have to buy your piece: help yourself from the tip. There's plenty for everyone. *And* by the time you've walked through the remaining pages of this book, I feel sure you'll be able to amaze your friends and expound at length on the angular relationships between *bedding* and *cleavage* and so on, won't you?

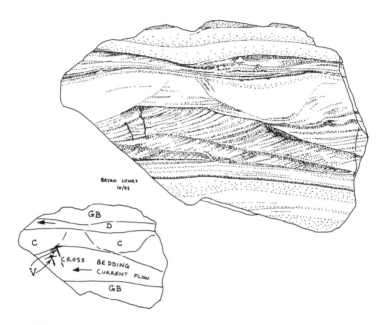

Figure 6.11: *Beautiful bedding structures on a slab about the size of an outstretched hand. I've drawn a smaller 'index' slab (below left) with abbreviations to illustrate what's going on in the larger drawing. See text for details.*

As for the slab I've sketched in Fig. 6.11, it has quite a tale to tell, particularly of vigorous water currents building out thin deltas of *cross bedded tuff*.

You can see this sort of thing happening on any sandy beach at low tide, where a stream crosses the beach and builds out deltas of sand at about this scale.

This slab is a cross section (the third − depth − dimension which you almost always see in rocks but not on the beach) of several superimposed delta-like beds. The currents moving the grains of volcanic *ash*, from which the *tuff* is made, streamed from right to left (this sector is labelled 'cross bedding' on the index sketch). The two little structures 'V' are probably tiny sand volcanoes, formed by water-saturated muddy sand forcing its way up to 'erupt' and build a miniature cone. You can see the volcanoes' necks and the source layer from which the 'eruption' came (the equivalent of a *magma chamber*). Such sand volcanoes are common structures in sediments like these and are yet another form of *dewatering structure*. There are incipient ones at 'D' in a higher bed but they aren't so clear. Finally, some of the beds are *graded* ('GB'). After the *cross bedded* 'deltas' in the lower middle sector of the block, stronger currents prevailed for a while, actually scouring into the *cross bedded* sediments beneath to form two distinct channels (labelled 'C'). Then followed more *cross bedded* ripples (with the 'D' *dewatering structures*), again with currents from right to left. Each lump beneath your feet has its own story to tell and there's more to be said about this one still. Try seeing if you can 'read' a few of these for yourself.

If the slab (Fig. 6.11) had been part of an outcrop – attached to its neighbours as it had been since it was deposited – you can see now that we could actually measure the direction of the ancient currents which formed it. Many such measurements mean that geologists can build up a picture of currents which operated hundreds of millions of years ago, which will also tell us the source of the sediment. This is one approach to understanding the ancient environment.

Incidentally, the active Pets Quarry, near Kirkstone Pass and just 4.5 kilometres away to the east, is almost certainly exploiting this same *tuff* as have the quarries at Elterwater, Tilberthwaite (source of the name *Tilberthwaite Tuff*) and Coniston.

Onward now to one of the largest accessible man-made caverns in the entire district. Continue east along Loughrigg Terrace, taking the first right-hand path and so cutting off a corner. Rydal Water is now to your left and the path contours round above a wood to the next locality, crossing several streamlets as it does so with the familiar assortment of water-loving plants like butterworts and lesser spearwort. You'll also notice dwarf juniper shrubs, ancient hawthorns and ash trees scattered about on the slopes. Above on your right are craggy *BVG* outcrops and *scree* patches whilst lower down, ice-smoothed *roches moutonnées* prevail. **After the wood, the track climbs slightly,** crossing ice-grooved rock outcrops as it does so, **and around the corner is our locality.**

Loughrigg quarry, a huge cavern: Locality 5

Quite a surprise – and quite a sight (Fig. 6.12a), isn't it? As you go in, try the cathedral-like echo. Whilst I am not guaranteeing that this chamber is safe to enter – how could I? – people do so all the time and so far as I know, no accident has occurred. There's not much to see inside except the view (Fig. 6.12b). You can see the *cleavage* which dips steeply northeast, and it was this structure which made these *tuffs* worth quarrying, because they would split into the parallel slabs so useful in building. But if you look about on the stonecrop-covered tips, you'll find fresh slabs a few of which show good, clear bedding. The *tuff* is on the whole somewhat coarser grained than that you have just seen at Locality 4, but in every other aspect, it is identical: *Tilberthwaite Tuff* again. Cast your mind back to localities 3 and 7 on the Coniston ramble: the *tuffs* were very similar to these and bedding structures tended to be rather uncommon. So this *tuff* was a thick and widespread 'event' in the *BVG*'s history. Wherever we can see bedding developed, the *tuff* always seems to have been water-lain. The parts with no bedding presumably were too, but being even in both composition and grain size, the bedding simply doesn't show up.

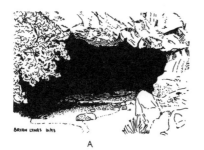

A

B

Figure 6.12: Views from (a) the outside in and (b) from the inside out (Nab Scar is outside).

Now follow the broad track which doubles back down below the tips, through larch trees and pass a second quarry chamber, less readily accessible than the first. The track crosses a beck under a group of larches, and your path turns off immediately afterwards to the right. Alternatively, you can continue along the track to Rydal and so back to Ambleside but I think my suggested route is pleasanter, though you have to climb a little again. The path ascends steadily heading almost due south most of the time. Keep to the right where other paths go off, keeping the beck on your right. Higher up, you'll find several possible paths and it's not important which you take provided you keep south, up the shallow valley, to cross a low pass. This is another glacial meltwater cut-through, formed in the same way as Locality 2 earlier on this walk. **Keep on south over the pass, with a ridge on your left and boggy area on the right.** This mire, presumably the Black Mire mentioned on the OS map, was certainly once a small tarn, now completely filled in.

Soon, you curve round to the left (southeast) to join other paths and cross some boggy patches (stepping stones provided) to meet with, and turn left onto, the main track between Ambleside and Loughrigg Tarn. You crossed this earlier just a little to the southwest of here, on the way up to Locality 2. From here it's downhill all the way back to Ambleside, past Pine Rigg, a small house with a beautiful garden, tucked away in the hills. Beyond Pine Rigg, the track is broad, dropping down through a marshy valley with mixed woodland and juniper bushes. Soon you pass the footpath (on the right) where you headed off to Locality 1 earlier in the day. And in another ten minutes, you should be back in Ambleside.

So you see there's more to Loughrigg Fell than the obvious admirable views. And even though the rocks aren't quite as spectacular as those on Pavey Ark (p. 115) or Bow Fell (p. 173), they still have a story to tell.

ROCKY RAMBLE 7:
BOW FELL AND ESK PIKE
-Rugged Heart Of The District

How to get to the start of the ramble

You can park at the National Trust car park [294 063] in Great Langdale, just
after the New Dungeon Ghyll hotel, or at the Old Hotel. The latter means 2
kilometres (1$^1/_4$ miles) less walking but the former will more likely have space.
The distances I've given below assume that you'll start from the National Trust
car park, so knock off 2 kilometres if you leave from the Old Hotel. There's a
convenient camp site [288 058] just south of the Old Hotel which makes an
ideal place both to stay and set off for this ramble.

The ramble: needs, distances and times

This is the toughest ramble in the book at 18 kilometres (11 miles) and about
1,030 metres (3,380 feet) of ascent for the complete circuit. But there are other
options: you can cut out Esk Pike and/or Rossett Pike. Cutting out both of these
reduces the ramble to 14 kilometres (just under 9 miles) and 850 metres (2,800
feet) of climbing. The going is all on clear tracks but is very rough underfoot in
parts. Remember too that temperatures in the valleys have no bearing on those
of the high, windswept summits where the wind chill factor can rapidly cool
you down if you aren't properly equipped for both wind and rain. So be
prepared – and that includes gear like a compass, the OS Outdoor Leisure map
(Sheet 6, South Western area) and the usual survival aids.
As for time, this ramble obviously demands a full day. So take plenty to eat.

Introduction

Bow Fell is one of the most distinctive of all Lakeland peaks. At 904 metres
(2,965 feet), it is also one of the highest (Scafell Pike is only 74 metres higher;
Skiddaw 27 metres higher). This ramble – a long one – is one of the most
spectacular you can do in the area, both from a scenic and geological viewpoint.
The rocks you'll see on Bow Fell almost scream to be noticed and should amaze
you with their strange and beautiful structures. All are varied *BVG*. Later, you'll
have fine views down onto the classic glacial *moraines* both in Mickleden and
Langdale Combe.

This fellow is obsessed with food and picnic sites, you might think. I ascribe it to an early 'event' in my married life when I forgot the lunch on a particularly foul day in the Cuillin hills in Skye. My wife has never quite forgiven me, having just about died of hunger and cold. And I've never forgotten the lunch since . . .

Oxendale Beck

Regardless of your starting point, you have to make your way to Stool End Farm [277 057] from which you have a choice of routes. The aim is to get to Three Tarns col [248 061], Locality 2. You can go the dull way via The Band which is slightly quicker and easier, or you can head up along Oxendale Beck, past Whorneyside Force and Hell Gill (Locality 1) which is what I recommend. Both paths are clearly signposted just after Stool End.

At first, the Oxendale track is broad and easy as it gently makes its way up the beck's *alluvial fan* (a powerful stream which drops 700 metres in 2 kilometres, p. 101). **The track becomes rocky as you leave the top of the fan and begin to cross some** *moraines*, **passing** *BVG* **outcrops and small** *scree* **patches. It crosses the beck at a footbridge to follow a** *moraine* **ridge on the south side and from here, the climb steepens. Shortly, you come to the fine set of waterfalls known as Whorneyside Force.** In the steep banks of the beck, you'll see various types of ferns, ling heather and foxgloves growing. Whorneyside Force is an impressive waterfall with a deep plunge pool at its base, all clearly visible on your right as you climb. **Now the ascent really becomes steep as you puff your way up the newly-cobbled track on the south side of Hell Gill.** Half way up this steep sector, you pass several outcrops of *porphyritic lavas*, *bedded coarse tuffs* and a scatter of *welded tuff* boulders. The *welded tuff* comes from Crinkle Crags where major flows of this rock crop out as you will see.

Hell Gill: Locality 1 [258 055]

As the steep ascent slackens, take a break and peer cautiously down into the great chasm of Hell Gill. This inaccessible gulch, worn down by the curiously named Buskoe Sike is cut through *BVG* rocks weakened by minor *faults* which accounts for its near-straight course.

'Sike' is from the Old Norse 'sik', a ditch or gully; 'buskoe' may refer to a 'bower', 'bosk' or 'bosket', meaning a shady, leafy place or thicket, derived from the Old Norse 'buask'. Shakespeare used 'bosky' meaning covered with underwood or bushes.

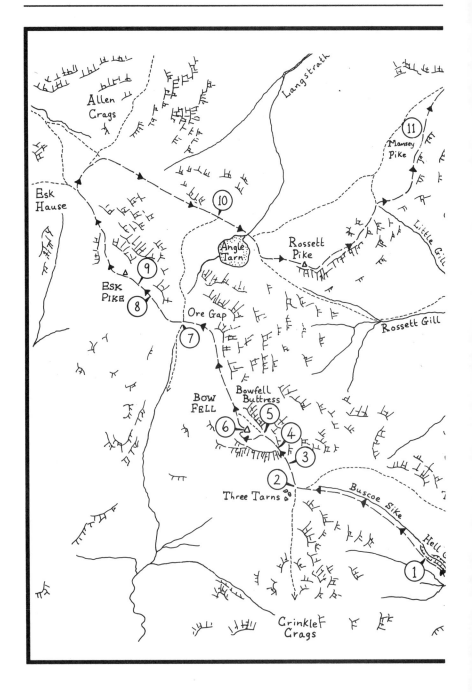

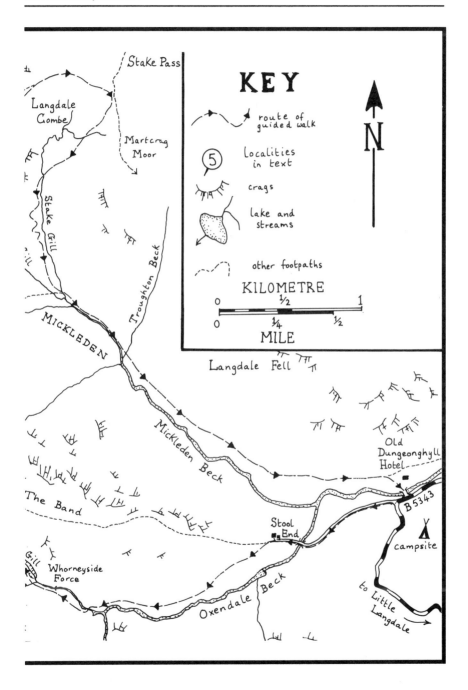

KEY

route of guided walk

⑤ localities in text

crags

lake and streams

other footpaths

N

KILOMETRE

0   ½   1

0   ¾   ½

MILE

Stake Pass

Langdale Combe

Martcrag Moor

Stake Gill

Troughton Beck

MICKLEDEN

Langdale Fell

Mickleden Beck

Old Dungeonghyll Hotel

B 5343

The Band

Stool End

campsite

Whorneyside Force

Oxendale Beck

to Little Langdale

Buskoe Sike is a small stream though and you'd think it unlikely that such a tiddler could tear this great gully out of the mountainside. But this was probably the site of a powerful *subglacial* stream (p. 158) through which water surged for a time as the last glaciers melted. Since then, the little stream has continued the downcutting process, though not so fast.

There's actually a danger here, as elsewhere, of making assumptions about the power of a stream. If it's a sunny day and there has been no rain for a week or so, a stream may indeed be small – and you tend to think of it always being so. But after days of rain, the tiddler can become a torrent with enormously increased downcutting power giving a very different impression. This is why people, who for obvious reasons generally only visit mountainous areas in fine weather, find it hard to believe that the clear, tinkling becks they see could ever erode the hard rock beds they run over. They never see these same becks in flood, chocolate-brown with sediment, surging and roaring downwards, bursting their banks and, because of their suspended loads of gravel and cobbles, bashing lumps off the rocky stream bed.

Continue on up towards the Three Tarns pass. To the left of the path, you'll see small 'cliffs' of peat where blanket bogs are slowly eroding (p. 62). The ice sheets have also carved *roches moutonnées* and have scattered *BVG* boulders haphazardly about. **Parts of the path can be quite damp underfoot as you continue the upwards slog. The broader Band track joins yours just a short way before the pass.**

Three Tarns pass: Locality 2

Now the grand views begin. From here you can see the sea away to the south and west, and even the Isle of Man on a clear day. The outcrops of ice-smoothed rocks – for the ice sheets clearly buried this col although it was at nearly 800 metres above sealevel – are white-weathering *silica*-rich *welded tuffs*, the highest part of what geologists call the *Airy's Bridge* Formation (Appendix: Timescale, Column C). In fact, these rocks were so thick and hot when they settled from the *ignimbrite* flow which produced them that they didn't just weld; they actually started to move just like *lava,* in some cases even buckling into *flow folds* (as in the true *lavas* you saw on the Haystacks ramble). Small wonder that earlier geologists thought that many of these *welded tuffs* were actually *lavas* in their own right.

When you leave this locality to begin the ascent of Bow Fell, you'll notice an immediate change in the rocks from *welded tuffs* to water-lain sediments. This tells us that some big event occurred: sudden major subsidence which caused the local area to become submerged. Geologists have begun to work out the confusing and difficult rocks in this area and their work points clearly to a huge collapse of part of the volcano from which the *welded tuffs* (which form most of Crinkle Crags) were so violently erupted.

It's hard to believe, but geologists have shown that if *ignimbrite* flows into water, it can continue right on below the waves and still be hot enough to weld. This is not what you'd expect, and no one did until it was proved beyond doubt in North Wales a few years ago. Previously, everyone thought that you could only find *welded tuffs* on land.

This collapse, due to the emptying of the underlying *magma chamber* would have produced a *caldera* and like any large depression (and these are often many kilometres wide), it filled with water. This is why everything you see from now on as you climb Bow Fell shows evidence of being laid down in water. But be warned: the rocks you are about to see are mind-blowing! So hold on tight and set off.

Scramble up the steepening gully which contains the main Bow Fell path. Keep your eyes peeled for the next locality, to the right of the gully about half way up.

Sloppy slumps: Convoluted beds at Locality 3 [2484 0627]

As you see, the *tuffs* here are all beautifully bedded, but there's one bed which almost takes your breath away. Okay, your breath has already been taken away by the climb, but this particular *slumped* and folded bed (Figs 7.1 and 7.2) is really striking in the midst of all this neat, parallel-bedded uniformity, both below and above. Without doubt, all these sediments came from *ash* eruptions as direct fallout from the eruption clouds. This explains why the beds are so uniform, parallel and delicate. They show neither ripples nor any other signs of currents, save for the planing-off of the top of the *slumped* bed (Fig. 7.2). The pale green-white colour of the beds here tells us that the eruptions were quite *silica*-rich, like the *welded tuffs* below, and so were probably still quite violent with huge clouds of steam and *ash* being blasted into the sky by successive bursts of explosive activity. The more violent eruption pulses would have given the showers of *lapilli* which you can see forming some of the beds.

Since there was a lot of water around, as these sediments tell us, some of it probably came in direct contact with the red hot *magma* which was awaiting eruption below the volcano. This regularly happens in present-day volcanoes and gives rise to *phreatomagmatic* eruptions which are violent and dangerous.

Figure 7.1: *General view of the well bedded, northwest-dipping sequence which includes the dramatic slumped bed. My wife, who is far more beautiful than my rough sketch of her suggests, is standing on the inclined top surface of this bed.*

'Phreatic' is from the Greek, a water well, and means 'water which occurs underground'.

It's a potent formula: Water + Molten Magma + Confining Pressure = Massive Explosion! The largest and most famous of such eruptions in modern times was that at Krakatoa (Indonesia) in 1883.

For the *slumped* bed to have formed, we can tell that there must have been a slight slope on which these *caldera*-lake beds were deposited. Obviously, the beds closer to the eruption centres would have been thicker than those further away so, as successive beds built up, a sloping cone would have formed. This is why volcanoes build up into the classic Mount Fujiyama shape. Water is also a vital ingredient, for if the beds had been above water they would have slid and avalanched if the slope had been steep enough. The third ingredient would be a triggering earthquake shock. All active volcanoes cause earthquakes in the surrounding area, mostly small but some quite large. The *slumped* bed here must have formed because of a much larger than normal quake which caused the soft bed to partly liquify – *fluidise* – and so slip and *slump* down the gentle slope. If you look closely at its base, you can see that most of the bed hasn't moved far – only a few centimetres – whereas some of its middle parts must have slipped much further, forming the folds you see today.

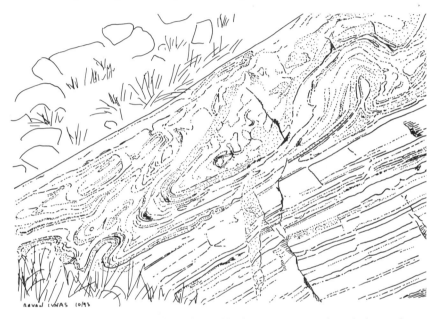

Figure 7.2: *Details of part of the slumped bed contrasting greatly with the neatly uniform tuff beds below, which show only small faults. The slumps you can see here have overturned from left to right which indicates that the downslope movement of these soft, sloppy sediments was also from left to right. (This is opposite to the direction you'd somehow expect because since then, the whole sequence of beds has been tilted to dip northwest.) You can see how the tops of these folds have been planed off by erosional currents before the next set of evenly-bedded tuffs (Fig. 7. 1, upper left) were laid down.*

Continue on up the steep and stony track for a few metres. To the right, you can see beautiful examples of sediment *fluidisation* structures in the *tuff* beds due to earthquake shock (Fig. 7.3) with some beds completely broken up into globs and blobs 'floating' in finer material. This is because some of the slightly denser beds *load casted* down into the underlying temporarily liquefied fine grained *tuffs*. Do these beds remind you of anything you've seen before on these rambles? How about the Coniston ramble, Locality 5 (p. 90)? I described those as 'geological custard' and they were an extreme example of what was beginning to happen here.

Figure 7.3: *More evidence of earthquake-induced fluidisation. Some of the thicker coarser beds have, being denser, load casted down into the material below. In parts, the process has only just started, with a lobe of material projecting down but in other parts, the lobes have detached completely from their source beds to leave the 'floating' globs you see here. The less dense beds have also tended to squirt up through the denser ones.*

Keep to the right side of the track to walk up past magnificent exposures of white-weathering, beautifully bedded *tuffs* which pass up into flinty, very fine grained *tuffs* with little evidence of bedding apart from bands of coarser material. **At the top of the steep gully ascent**, the rocks change to well bedded *lapilli tuffs*. **Walk about 60 paces to the right of the track to the next locality**.

More rocky custard? Locality 4 [2478 0636]

At this locality, you'll find a vertical wall of rock up to 3 metres high which gives you an excellent section through the gently northwest-dipping beds (Fig. 7.4). This is similar in origin to the honeycomb rock you saw on the Coniston ramble (p. 90) and has the same origin: earthquake *fluidisation*. Some of the *fluidised* beds have squirted upwards through the overlying beds for quite some distance, almost reorienting themselves to vertical. I've tried to show these on Figure 7.4. But wait, there's something odd about all this.

Figure 7.4: *Outcrops at Locality 4. Some beds are quite even but the majority have been affected by fluidisation giving both load casting and injection structures which have largely destroyed the original bedding.*

Because these injection and *load casting* pro-cesses are ultimately dri-ven by gravity (lighter material moves up; hea-vier material down, as we have seen at Locality 3), you'd expect that the channels up which the injected sediment had moved would have been vertical -perpendicular to the original beds. Look-ing here, you see that they are not. The injec-tions are nearly vertical in this rock face right now, but the beds them-selves dip northwest at around 25º. This means that when the sloppy sediment beds squirted (injected) upwards, causing all this fossilised disruption before you, either the injections weren't vertical when they occurred (most unlikely) or the bedded sequence of *tuffs* weren't flat-lying; they already had a dip of about 15º.

This is the dip angle you get for these beds if you, in your imagination (though you can sketch this for yourself too, after measuring the various angles), 'tilt' this outcrop clockwise until the injections are truly vertical.

Thus we can be sure that these *ash* and *lapilli* beds were indeed deposited on a slope, as we were led to suspect by the *slumps* at Locality 3. This dip angle should tell us roughly in which direction the eruption vent lay (I say 'roughly' because we aren't allowing for *apparent dip* (p. 108): because the beds get thicker as you approach a volcano's vent, you'd have to walk uphill to reach it – in this case, *up* the dip. The updip direction you can see from this outcrop would place the original vent somewhere to the southeast of here. This Sherlock Holmes sleuthing is part of the excitement of geology and of science as a whole. But of course my interpretation could be wrong! What do you think?

Rejoin the main walking track and continue northwest towards Bow Fell summit for about 150 metres. Then branch off just a few paces to the right until you arrive at the edge of the plateau area.

The Great Slab: Locality 5 [2468 0645]

'The Great Slab' was Wainwright's name for this extraordinary place where *bedded tuffs* form perfectly smooth planes dipping northwest at around 25°. You can see these *bedding planes* from afar (Troughton Beck, Langdale ramble, for example) and each plane gives you a unique opportunity to see all of the three dimensions at once -length, breadth and depth. Normally, you only see length and breadth.

Think about it: if you're standing on a flat plain – a beach for example – you can see in all directions, but only in those two dimensions. You cannot see anything of the third – depth – dimension, unless you dig a hole.

Here, you can stand at the edge of the Great Slab (Fig. 7.5) which has length and breadth, and also look at the depth dimension to see what materials (*tuff*) and structures make up this unique huge bed surface. You can walk on this inclined plane if your boots have a good grip. If you do, remember that you're actually walking about on a 450-million-year lake (or sea) floor. And if you look carefully near the top of the slab, you'll even see a patch of quite good ripples, just as you might if you were snorkelling in shallow water above a sandy seafloor. These are wave ripples and they tell us the water was quite shallow, perhaps only a few metres at most.

One reason to think that *BVG* water-lain sediments such as these were laid down in fresh water, not sea water, is the total absence of fossils. The seas of that time teemed with life just as they do today. You've seen this for yourself in the *Coniston Limestone* (Rambles 3 & 5). If the sea had invaded the volcanic landscape, we should expect to find some evidence of fossils on huge bedding planes like the Great Slab. But nothing has ever been found, neither here nor anywhere else; not even humble worm burrows or tracks left by scurrying animals, both of which are common in almost all marine sediments. However, at one place in the outlying southwestern fells near Ulpha, microscopic fossils called acritarchs have been found in a mudstone interbedded with the *BVG*. Since acritarchs were marine planktonic creatures, this tells us that at this one place, the sea did briefly invade.

Figure 7.5: *The Great Slab, an enormous tilted bedding plane, once the floor of a either a shallow lake or the sea; we can't be sure which.*

Have a good look at the wonderful outcrops around this locality. There's a great deal on offer here – if you look for it and keep your eyes open. This part of the summit plateau area is a mass of small replicas of the Great Slab; small *scarps* and *dip slopes* (Ramble 5, p. 133). All these rocks are telling you a story. Their language is quite simple and you know enough now to make sense of it. You should find more ripple marks, *slumps* and many beautiful examples of *fluidisation* structures (Fig. 7.6). You'll also, no doubt, find some outcrops which defy explanation. Don't worry, so have I! Have a crack at some kind of explanation anyway . . . there has to be one and you might be right.

Now make your final bid for the summit which, at 902 metres, is the highest point on the walk. If you skip Esk Pike, it's almost all downhill from here.

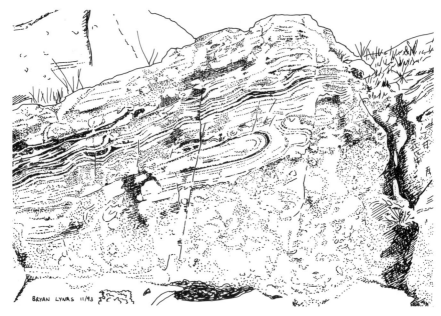

Figure 7.6: *Examples of some of the structures you can see in the third (depth) dimension: slumped beds, ripples and indications of fluidisation due to earthquake shocks.*

Bow Fell summit: Locality 6

First there's the panorama about which I need to say little since it's obvious enough and has all been said before by Wainwright. But I do think that the views of the wild and craggy splendour of the Scafell range from here and Esk Pike are unsurpassed.

Bow Fell's summit is a *tor*-like lump sticking up out of a rough, boulder-strewn plateau area. The rocks are now quite different from the delicately bedded *tuffs* you've seen all the way from Locality 2. They are crystal *tuffs*, but without any traces of bedding or internal structures. They have been noticeably affected by *cleavage* which dips fairly steeply northwest and has broken the rock up into close-spaced *joints*. It is along these *joints* that this otherwise hard rock (it must be since it caps the top of one of the district's highest mountains) has been broken up by frost action. This summit area was probably exposed throughout much of the ice age and so the freeze-thaw action of ice and water (when it became warm enough, for remember that even today, the climate up here is very definitely near-Arctic) prised apart the unbedded *tuffs*, breaking them up into the splintered *tors* (somewhat like those of Dartmoor) and *blockfield* you see around you. This is typical of the *periglacial* conditions which you find in the Canadian or Russian Arctic of today.

If you doubt the ability of water freezing to ice to prise rocks such as these apart, try this experiment next winter: Fill a glass bottle or jar with water right to the top and screw down the lid *tightly*. Place your bottle or jar outside during a period of severe frost and see what happens. When water changes from its liquid phase to solid ice, it undergoes a volume change; it expands. If it can't escape from the vessel (or a crack in rock) which contains it, it still expands, smashing the bottle – or prising out the rock. So maybe you should put your bottle in a plastic bag so that glass shards don't get everywhere.

Drop down towards Ore Gap, passing the spectacular Bow Fell Buttress to the right of the track. From the col at the top of the Buttress, you have a fine view of Great Langdale.

It was here that I once met a group of about 20 Japanese walkers, all carrying video cameras and other bulky photographic gear – and nothing else. They were most enthusiastic about the view, seemingly unaware that evening was approaching fast, as was a squall. I was okay since I was backpacking and could stop anywhere I chose, but where they ended up that night I have no idea.

As you lose height, notice that you're back in well *bedded tuffs* again, almost certainly exactly the same sequence – now in reverse – to that which you climbed through to Bow Fell summit. Look across to Esk Pike and notice how the lower two thirds of the ascent from Ore Gap crosses grey rock, but that nearer the top there's a marked colour change to pale grey-white. As you'd expect, this is a change in rock type as you'll see at Localities 6 and 7.

Before you reach Ore Gap, the track crosses another *blockfield*. This streaky-looking fragmental rock is probably of *ignimbrite* origin, but it wasn't hot enough to weld properly so that only the more fragile *volcaniclasts* (presumably *pumice*) collapsed to form the characteristic *fiamme*. This *pyroclastic flow* rock may be the continuation of the *welded tuff* you saw briefly at Locality 2. Or it may not be! Only geological map-making – actually following the distinctive rocks wherever they go and locating them precisely on a map – can show this one way or the other. So far as I know, this has not yet been done here.

Ore Gap: Locality 7

Ore Gap is a bit of a mystery. For here is good quality *hematite* iron ore which seems to have been mined, colouring the ground red under the grassy col and staining the adjacent rocks bright pink.

As so often elsewhere in the southern Lake District, this mining was probably done by the monks of Furness Abbey who may have carried the ore down to a bloomery (an iron-smelting hearth usually located close to a good supply of charcoal) at Greenup Gill in Langstrathdale.

The dense *hematite* chunks, red to grey in colour and scattered everywhere here, are all quite small and broken up, suggesting some sort of simple ore processing before transport by packhorses. And yet there's none of the usual signs of mining: no shafts or entrances, no ditches; nothing suggesting any serious attempts to get at this ore. All we know is that in 1242, Furness Abbey acquired some 14,000 acres of upper Eskdale which was bounded by Bow Fell and Scafell. So maybe this mining attempt dates back to that time over 700 years ago.

I once visited an ore processing plant such as the one that might have operated here. The one I saw was in the Peruvian Andes where labour, especially female labour, is cheap. The 'processing plant' was an old woman with a lump hammer and a basket. She broke up the lead ore that the two miners (the other members of this enterprise) had brought out of the mine and separated by hand the rich *galena* ore into her basket. Then she poured the 'concentrates' into a sack for transport by donkey to be sold.

As for the ore itself, *hematite* is a simple iron oxide (Fe_2O_3) containing about 70% iron and is the most important source of that metal. Its colour varies from steel-grey when crystalline to red when in its 'earthy' form. 'Kidney ore' is one common form (Fig. 7.7). Both here and in many other parts of the Lake District, *hematite* occurs in veins along *faults*. Geologists believe that these ores came from an enormous *granite intrusion* which probably lies beneath all Lakeland, though it was largely intruded long after all the rocks had been laid down, probably about 400 million years ago. Parts of this *granite* do actually crop out: at Eskdale, Ennerdale and Shap as well as in smaller amounts (pp. 33 and 248). The rest is conjecture based mostly on study with sensitive instruments called *gravimeters* of variations in gravity around the district. The iron, and other metals such as lead, copper and zinc too, are supposed to have been 'sweated off' by the cooling *granite* and carried upwards, dissolved in hot watery liquids which forced their way through any convenient crack or fracture (*fault*) into the cold overlying rocks (in this case the *BVG*). When these hot fluids cooled sufficiently, the iron or other metals they contained precipitated as oxides or sulphides onto the walls of the fractures, leaving the minerals we see today (here we have *hematite*; copper at Locality 6, Coniston ramble and lead in the Greenside Mine area ramble, for example).

Figure 7.7: *Kidney ore variety of hematite.*

Rumour has it that compasses go awry at Ore Gap because of the 'magnetic' ore. But *hematite* is not magnetic and I have tried in vain to get my compass to show any effects whatsoever of this vein of iron ore beneath your feet here. Try it yourself.

Ore Gap, like Three Tarns col, is a cross roads. You have a choice of routes from here. You can continue on the full walk up Esk Pike and down to Esk Hause or you can head straight down from here towards Angle Tarn and the return route. If you do this, you skip the next two localities.

Now for the ascent of Esk Pike, a mountain which, perhaps surprisingly, was nameless until Clifton Ward of the Geological Survey named it in his memoir on the geology of the northern Lake District in 1876.

Block tuffs, Esk Pike's foundation: Locality 8 [2386 0737]

Half way up Esk Pike, you encounter large outcrops of frost-shattered coarse *tuffs* which include angular *blocks* up to football-size with occasional ones much larger than this. The *blocks* are not all of the same rock type and there is no trace of *bedding*. So this material was probably a *pyroclastic flow*. Its darker grey-green colour suggests that it is not especially *silica*-rich and so is probably an *andesite.*

Continue on up the track and when the slope slackens for the remaining third of the ascent, you'll notice that the dark coloured *pyroclastic flow* rock is quite abruptly superseded by a much paler, grey-white rock which forms most of the summit area. This is the colour change you saw from Bow Fell as you were walking down towards Ore Gap. The white-weathering rock is hard and flinty, a fine grained crystal-rich *tuff,* devoid of any bedding or other structures.

A little further on, you can see that the flinty pale rocks are *bedded,* though many of them are contorted and convoluted like those you saw during the ascent of Bow Fell. So we know for sure that they were waterlain *tuffs.* The absence of bedding in parts may well be due to a secondary process, a form of *diagenesis,* in which the fine *ash* became hardened by *silicification.*

This means what you'd guess it to mean: *silica*-rich fluids permeated the rock, dissolving some constituents and replacing them with *silica. Silicification* is very common in all *quartz*-rich rocks and has the effect of making them extremely hard, but also brittle. It also tends to blur or even destroy the evidence of primary structures such as *bedding.*

Another change in the rock: Locality 9 [2378 0743]

After the path has levelled out, not far from the summit cairn, there's another abrupt change back to the same darker *pyroclastic flow* you saw at Locality 8, but here the flow has smaller *volcaniclasts.*

We know from modern volcanoes such as Unzen in Japan that *pyroclastic flows* are very common. Unzen volcano was spewing out up to 1,500 of them *per month* during part of 1992. Unfortunately, one flow took a different route and killed three volcano experts who were studying it at the time. I once examined one such flow, erupted by Mount Ngauruhoe in New Zealand just a couple of weeks previously. Wisps of steam rose from its surface, for it was still hot inside and the samples I collected were quite warm to my hands. It was a distinctly alarming place to be, just at the bottom of the great volcanic cone down which these flows roll with almost no warning.

After just a few metres, this dark-coloured flow stops and you find yourself back on the white-weathering flinty *tuffs,* some of which show well developed beds. The entire summit area is made of this flinty *tuff* which is speckled with tiny white *feldspar* crystals and shows rather vague *bedding,* dipping gently to the northwest like everything we have examined so far on this ramble. Like

Bow Fell, the summit rocks have suffered *periglacial* shattering by freezing and thawing, aided and abetted by the fairly strong *cleavage* which provided planes of weakness for the water to penetrate and the ice to force apart. This has formed a *blockfield* through which just a few outcrops of solid rock protrude like ruined castles after a great battle.

Begin your descent towards Esk Hause. The path is rather vague in places, keeping to the west side of the north-trending rocky ridge at first. Look back towards the summit after you've gone a little way, for the *bedding* in the flinty *tuffs* is much clearer viewed from the north side. By now, the bedding dips are minimal; some of the bed surfaces form almost horizontal ledges which you actually walk along as the track descends. This means that, once again, you are walking down the rock sequence and the rocks are becoming older. It should also mean that you see the same beds that you saw earlier as you went up Bow Fell and up Esk Pike, the succession being repeated but in reverse – unless the rocks have changed significantly in their sideways extension. **Look about you at the point where a ruined boundary wall intersects the track.** Here again is the grey *pyroclastic flow* you saw as you approached Ore Gap from Bow Fell. But note that the fragments it contains are smaller, meaning that the flow was probably further from its source, so having less energy to carry large *blocks*. You will continue to see this fragmental rock all around you most of the way to Esk Hause, but if you look carefully at some of the lower outcrops, you'll notice that there's a suspicion of welding once again, with flattened-looking fragments giving a streaky appearance which so characterises *welded tuffs*. The outcrops just before Ore Gap also showed signs of partial welding. So it's a reasonable guess that this is indeed the same flow though this could only be resolved by proper geological mapping.

Great End (which used to be called Long Pike) confronts you as you descend to Esk Hause. To the north of Great End is the beautiful Sprinkling Tarn. If you were to walk down to the rocks around the tarn, you'd find that they were all dipping southeast, yet everything between where you are now and Locality 2 dips in the opposite direction. This tells us that a major *synclinal* downfold must exist somewhere between the Bow Fell rocks and those at Sprinkling Tarn. In fact the axis of this fold probably runs more or less through Esk Hause, *striking* northeast to southwest. This is why the last rock outcrops you crossed were almost flat-lying. You've already been introduced to this fold: the Scafell *Syncline* (p. 119).

Esk Hause is another great meeting of the ways with no less than 5 tracks converging on this high col. It is not often a place to hang about, being devoid of sheltering rock outcrops and usually cold and windy. The rocky part of this ramble is now more or less complete though you have some interesting glacial treats ahead. But these don't need any great

thought or exertion to see. **Walk down northeast on the short track to the drystone shelter and turn right onto the main walkers' 'highway' to Angle Tarn.** Much of the track has been laboriously cobbled to try and prevent further erosional damage. After a little less than 1 kilometre of easy walking, you'll see the rather dark and gloomy corrie enclosing Angle Tarn directly below. Have a brief stop at this point.

Angle Tarn and its corrie: Locality 10

This is a fine example of a glacial corrie, complete with a rock lip (p. 83) and almost circular (certainly not angular as the name seems to suggest) lake. Like most corries, it faces northeast and its backwall is formed by the northern buttresses of Bow Fell. If you were to use your time machine again (as on p. 156) and zoom back just 12,000 years into the middle of the *Younger Dryas* cold snap, this corrie would be invisible, buried completely in snow and ice. Even in midsummer, this would be a barren and apparently dead landscape consisting only of black rock crags and the glistening whites and blues of snow and ice. But not quite dead, for as the snows melted off the ridges, you'd see that a few lichens encrusted the rocks underneath, and tiny clumps of alpine flowers would bring splashes of colour to the drabness for the few brief weeks of summer.

From the work of two international teams who collected ice cores by drilling down almost 3 kilometres through the Greenland ice cap, we now know a great deal more about temperature changes which occurred in the North Atlantic region during the last 250,000 years. We know, for example, that the brief warm period which preceded the *Younger Dryas*, ended suddenly. Temperatures plummeted by up to 10°C in less than 30 years for some reason we don't yet know. Consider that in terms of the degree or so of temperature change we are worried about with global warming. Until we know why the climate can flip at random from warm to cold and back to warm again so incredibly quickly, we can't take serious action to try and prevent it happening again. Indeed at this scale, we humans are still puny creatures and we are most unlikely to be able to do anything. Will your grandchildren see glaciers in Angle Tarn corrie again? Or will they see London engulfed in seawater? No one has any clear idea at present.

The decaying ice of Angle Tarn corrie left the usual mess which glaciers tend to do in the form of *moraine* humps and perched blocks which you'll see when you continue. **Drop down the eroded track to cross Angletarn Gill and ascend towards the pass over to Rossett Gill. This is positively the last serious climb of the day! When you reach the col, you have another choice** of routes. You can continue straight on to scramble rapidly down direct to Mickleden on the main Rossett Gill track or you can turn left up a faint path to the little summit of Rossett Pike just 200 metres and about 35 metres of climbing to the east. This is a much prettier route, little used and giving superb views of the Langdale fells and Great Langdale though it is, I admit, further to walk. It is almost all downhill though. The idea of this last sector of the walk is both to enjoy a pleasant, easy and little-used path down to Stake Gill and to view some of the best *moraines* in Lakeland: the Mickleden and Langdale Combe *moraines* (p. 104).

Walk up to Rossett Pike and take a few minutes to admire the fine view (Fig. 7.8).

Figure 7.8: *Mickleden and Pike of Stickle from Rossett Pike.*

I recently spent a night camping right on the edge of the easterly part of this summit as I wanted to take some early morning pictures of Langdale and the mountains. Unfortunately, the mist came down and I saw nothing whatsoever. Sod's Law is universal.

Pike of Stickle is easily the most prominent feature to the east. You can see very clearly that both this and Loft Pike behind are well *bedded* with the *tuff beds* (Langdale ramble, Locality 1) dipping northeast. To the south, the great precipices and gullies of Bow Fell loom and you have a fine view of the Great

Slab (Locality 5) *bedding plane* that you examined earlier. **Continue northeast along the crest of Rossett Pike – the path is faint in places – towards Mansey Pike and the final locality. You have to go down and up a little at the head of Little Gill.**

Mansey Pike and Langdale Combe moraines: Locality 11 [257 084]

Mansey Pike is something of a nonentity. Exactly where it is isn't important; the locality is only for looking more carefully at the Langdale Combe *moraines*, beautifully displayed below you (Fig. 7.9). This glacial corrie is unusual in that it faces south – most face northeast where they receive no warming sun's rays – but it is quite high at around 450 metres above sealevel. Most of the snow catchment which produced the small glacier, source of the *moraines* you see now, must have been on the east side of Mansey Pike and the bleak expanse of Martcrag Moor.

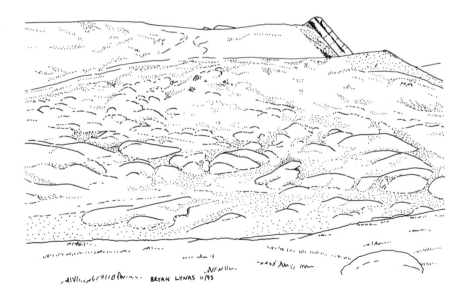

Figure 7.9: *Morainic humps and kettlehole hollows from Mansey Pike. Pike of Stickle to rear right.*

Here, a phenomenon called the 'helm wind' must have played a role. The 'helm wind' blows over mountain ridges (from the prevailing wind direction, usually the west in Lakeland) and on the ridge lee side, back eddies develop which cause drifting snow to settle. You can see this effect in winter when snow piles up on the lee side of drystone walls. The effect of the 'helm wind' and eddies is to remove snowfall from the exposed western slopes and summits and redeposit it on the upper lee side slopes. This explains rather well why most of Lakeland's corries face northeast: it's a combination of abundant snow drift and lack of sun. It also explains why rather unlikely places such as Langdale Combe should have become re-occupied by ice during the *Younger Dryas*. The combe is in the lee of both Mansey and Rossett Pikes. Similarly, Bow Fell itself would have redirected snow onto its lee slopes (now drained by Rossett Gill) to form ice thick enough to flow down into Mickleden and dump the moraines you have already seen and will shortly walk through.

The *moraines* continue over the north side of Stake Pass, so the ice must have been quite extensive for a period. Interestingly, both these and the Mickleden *moraines* include several *kettleholes* which, at the end of the final ice melting 11,500 years ago, contained deep ponds. As centuries passed, the ponds gradually became filled with muds and peat, preserving pollen grains from all the plant species which grew in the district. A few of these *kettlehole* ponds remain to this day, or are occupied by marshy ground. In the early 1960s, researchers took borehole cores up to 11 metres long from two *kettleholes*, and then painstakingly examined the samples and, using a powerful microscope, counted the proportions of pollen grains. This work tells us about the relative abundances of the different plants growing in the area at that time, and so about the prevailing climate. Importantly, it suggests a starting date for the Pike of Stickle stone axe factory (p. 101). Its development seems to be linked with a great decline in elm trees in the forest cover, and there are definite indications of forest clearances beginning around 5,700 years ago.

A few years ago at Thunacar Knott (about a kilometre west of Pavey Ark), another axe factory site was found. Here, small pieces of charcoal (from fires lit by cold axe-smiths?) gave *radiocarbon* dates of around 2,700 BC (actually about 5,400 years ago when corrected; see Appendix and Timescale), useful confirmation that we are about right in our ideas of when Lakeland's first industry started.

Now make your way around the head of Langdale Combe and join the major walking track – the Cumbria Way – at Stake Pass. Turn right onto this and head down towards Mickleden, passing the humpy *moraines* on your right. The track zig zags as it loses height, much of it being neatly

cobbled. The cobbling is mostly new but the track probably dates back many centuries or even millennia. As you drop down the steeper section, you have another fine view of the Mickleden *moraines* dead ahead. **The track joins that from Rossett Gill after the steep descent, and from here the return to the Old Dungeon Ghyll Hotel is a long, almost straight downhill plod.**

This ramble has taken you over some of Lakeland's finest mountain scenery -and over some of its most spectacular rocks. If I've done my job properly, it will have forged another link in the chain of understanding how to read the language in the rocks beneath your feet. Footsore, hungry and thirsty though you may be, I hope you've enjoyed the experience of this the most arduous of the ten rambles.

ROCKY RAMBLE 8:
CATSTYE CAM AND HELVELLYN

How to get to the start of the ramble

Glenridding (on the A592 at Ullswater) is the start point. The village has large and convenient carparks.

The ramble: needs, distances and times

This ramble is just under 16 kilometres (just under 10 miles) though, as usual, you can miss out parts – like the ascent of Catstye Cam or Raise. That would knock off a bit less than 2 kilometres ($1^1/_4$ miles). The total amount of climbing is about 960 metres (3,150 feet). The ramble is, like most of the others in this book, a full day excursion.

Introduction

Helvellyn, one of Lakeland's most popular mountains, owes its nature to glaciation. Without the carving effect of the ice, it would be a rather dull rounded hump – as it is today on its western side. Catstye Cam, which means rather romantically 'Wild cat path along the ridge' (from Old English), is a handsome peak from all sides. And the connecting ridge of Swirral Edge between the two mountains is one of the more exciting scrambles in the area, second only to Striding Edge. The rocks underfoot are all *BVG* showing its usual variability and you'll see several superb glacial corries, one occupied by Red Tarn.

Glenridding to Lanty's Tarn

Glenridding (Old English meaning 'bracken valley') owes its size to the once great Greenside lead mine (the remains of which you walk through at the end of this ramble, the mine itself being the subject of the next). This started on a large scale over two centuries ago. The rows of workers' cottages here date from the 1850s when the mine employed hundreds of people.

Walk west up the road past the miners' cottages until you reach a T junction (about 500 metres from the Glenridding carparks). Take the road to the left down over Rattlebeck Bridge (once the site of a powerhouse for Greenside Mine), passing a caravan and camping site at the side of Glenridding Beck. Continue up the road and take the clearly-signposted

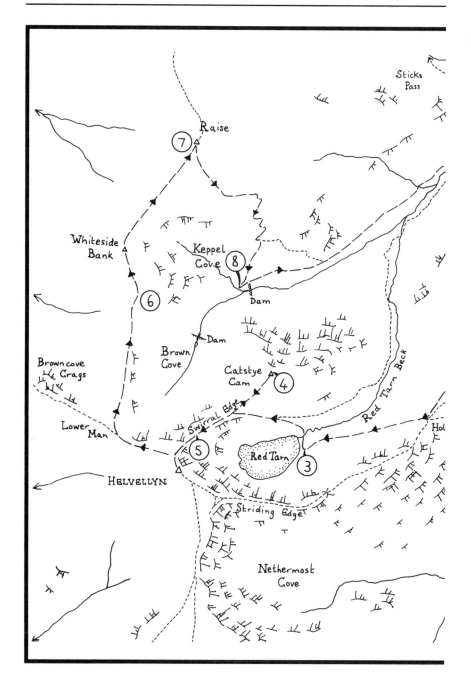

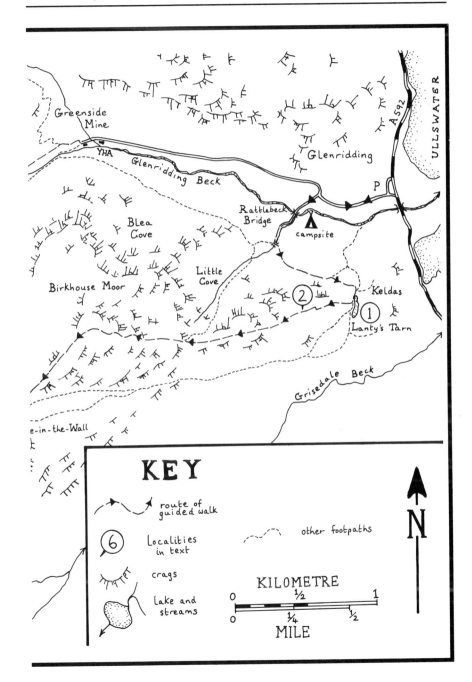

KEY

route of guided walk

6 Localities in text

crags

Lake and streams

other footpaths

N

KILOMETRE
0   ½   1

0   ¼   ½
MILE

footpath to Lanty's Tarn. At first, you climb gently through pastures and open woodland. The trees here are fine large oaks and ashes with holly and alders. The boulders dotted around the valley side were all left by the decaying *Devensian* ice sheet about 15,000 years ago. Although this is true *moraine* underfoot, the humps or ridges which fresh *moraines* always show have been destroyed by later processes such as *solifluction*; downslope mass movement of any unconsolidated material such as glacial rubbish, soil and so on. *Solifluction* is driven by gravity, but requires water and the regular freeze-thaw of heavy frosts to make it work. Behind you, further up Glenridding valley, are the largely reclaimed dumps from Greenside Mine.

The path flattens out and you pass through a kissing gate and turn right (a signpost indicates 'Striding Edge, Helvellyn'). There's a short climb and you go through another kissing gate to Lanty's Tarn.

Lanty's Tarn: Locality 1

This pretty little tarn, mostly surrounded by Scots pines, larches and birch trees, occupies a small hollow scooped out by a tongue of ice which at some time crossed between the Grisedale and Glenridding valley glaciers. Or was it? Could there be another equally good explanation? Yes, you've got it. It could have formed in the same way as those shallow valleys on Loughrigg Fell (p. 151): by glacial meltwater channelling. Which do you favour? I'm inclined to hedge my bets and favour both for undoubtedly this whole hillside was once deeply entombed by ice, as witnessed by nearby *roches moutonnées* on Keldas, a little hill just east of the tarn which overlooks Ullswater (Fig. 8.1). It's highly likely that any glacial gouging here would have been followed by meltwater downcutting too, probably from the very large Grisedale glacier which once occupied that valley to the southwest of this locality. If you wish, take the opportunity to walk up to Keldas for one of the great views Lakeland has to offer. Ice-smoothed *BVG*, bracken, scattered Scots pines and the sky frame a truly magnificent view of Ullswater (Fig. 8.1).

Now begins the main climb. Turn right onto the path which sets off uphill by the wood from half way around the tarn. At first, the wood (mostly spruces) is on your right and the grassy path heads due west. On your left, opposite the wood as you start your ascent, you'll notice several marshy hollows, now filled with soft rushes (Fig. 8.2) and surrounded by bracken. These were little tarns which have now become completely infilled.

Figure 8.1: *The famous view from Keldas, a roche moutonnée just above Lanty's Tarn.*

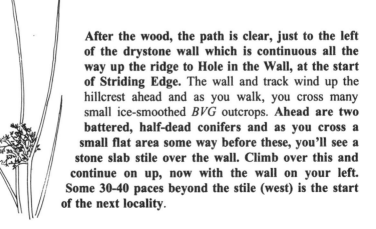

Figure 8.2: *Soft rush with its cluster of brown flowers. Rushes are similar to sedges, though their stems are often filled with white pith. Rushes, unlike grasses and sedges, have regularly-formed flowers, each with 6 petals. They are amongst the first plants to colonise infilled tarns such as these here.*

After the wood, the path is clear, just to the left of the drystone wall which is continuous all the way up the ridge to Hole in the Wall, at the start of Striding Edge. The wall and track wind up the hillcrest ahead and as you walk, you cross many small ice-smoothed *BVG* outcrops. **Ahead are two battered, half-dead conifers and as you cross a small flat area some way before these, you'll see a stone slab stile over the wall. Climb over this and continue on up, now with the wall on your left. Some 30-40 paces beyond the stile (west) is the start of the next locality.**

Roches moutonnées and old quarries: Locality 2 [3806 1627]

To the right of the track, *BVG* crops out in rounded humps of rock which have been ice-smoothed into the familiar *roche moutonnée* shapes. If you study them, you get the impression that the ice must have moved from the west to carve the shapes you see here. You'd hardly expect anything else since the two powerful glaciers which occupied both Glenridding valley and Grisedale would have coalesced in their lower parts to run east to Ullswater. Then they would have merged with other glaciers from the other dales to the south – Dovedale, Deepdale and the Hartsop valleys – to form one really massive glacier. It was this which carved out the deep rock basin which would later contain Ullswater.

Incidentally, the relentless process of lake infilling operates in Ullswater as in all the other lakes: streams like Glenridding Beck, Grisedale and Goldrill Becks are busily building out deltas of sediment into the lake. You can see this, both on the map and directly as you continue the walk. Ullswater originally would have stretched to well south of Patterdale. The growth of the Glenridding Beck delta greatly increased whilst Greenside Mine was operating. Much of the dumped mine material ended in the beck which then carried it down to Ullswater, building out its delta over ten feet forward each year during the last century.

Now climb up past the first *roches moutonnées* to find several small quarries a few metres higher up the ridge. The rock is a strongly *cleaved* fairly fine grained *tuff* which was exploited for building the sturdy drystone walls nearby. The *cleavage* made the easily-split rock good material for the slabs needed for these walls. Rock is heavy stuff to lug about, so naturally the wall-builders got their rock supplies from as close as possible to where they were building. You can usually find signs of small, temporary quarries such as these close to drystone walls. There were no excavators or 4-wheel drive vehicles in those days and everything had to be carried by hand or dragged on sledges (p. 22).

When were these walls built? Farming land was beginning to be enclosed from the pre-existing common fields or strips, by Tudor times. This enclosure was complete by the mid-19th century, having been speeded up by Parliamentary enclosure acts in the late 18th century. So all we can really say now is that most of these beautifully-crafted walls are at least 150 years old, and many may be much older. Will our steel-reinforced concrete structures of today still be around in two centuries? I suspect not.

Continue the ascent, keeping the wall close on your left. After a while, you join the popular walking track up from Little Cove and Mires Beck, and

start the steep climb up to Birkhouse Moor. This path too has suffered badly from erosion and a group of young men and women were cobbling it when I last went up it (late 1993). As you climb, take a breather to look at the ice-smoothed *BVG* by the track (which is still close to the wall). The rock is now clearly fragmental, with marble-sized *volcaniclasts*. Now follow the diverted path onto the Birkhouse Moor ridge and so along and slightly down to Hole in the Wall.

If you were to continue on straight ahead, you'd find yourself on Striding Edge. This is one of Lakeland's most famous *arêtes*, a knife-edge ridge formed by glaciers cutting it from both sides leaving a sharp edge (see also Blencathra ramble and the real Sharp Edge) with steep drops on either side. This is not your route today, though Swirral Edge (which is your route), is also an *arête* as you will shortly find out. Turn right at Hole in the Wall and walk towards Red Tarn on an almost horizontal path over patches of disintegrating hill peat and many erosion gullies.

The erosion is an inevitable consequence of many walkers, but there's more to it than that. Sheep play their part in preventing stabilising plants from growing by nibbling and trampling them. When these thin peats formed, much of Lakeland was forested up to this height (p. 122) and trees offer the best protection of all to thin soils, when they can grow large enough to survive browsing animals.

Red Tarn terminal moraines: Locality 3

As you approach the huge Red Tarn corrie with the crags of Helvellyn and Striding Edge looming over it, you'll notice right away that there are many quite large humps of *moraine* obscuring your view of the lake. The *moraines* (Fig. 8.3) contrast totally with the smooth slopes of the lower valley and, by their freshness, tell us that they certainly date from the last glacial cold snap: the *Younger Dryas*. Find yourself a convenient place near the stream outlet with a view of the tarn and all the striking features around you and enter your time machine again. Set the controls for 12,000 years ago. As usual for our glacial time travels, we arrive in summer so that the snows of winter have melted off the steep mountainsides as well as parts of the glaciers. The icefield-capped mountain to your west is Helvellyn. Can you make out the blue-green colour of the ice under the snow cornices? Right in front of you, like a huge mouth in the great sheet of ice which dominates the whole vista, is a cave out of which pours a dirty torrent of water. It's late afternoon on the mildest day of the year (though it still feels pretty cold to you if the sun isn't shining) and the *subglacial* river is in spate, rolling boulders along its bed as it surges and roars down what will one day be called Red Tarn Beck, when Homo sapiens comes on the scene and starts naming things. Most of the debris it carries will soon end up in Ullswater, building out the *alluvial fan* or delta on which Ullswater Hotel will be built in 11,900 years or so. Suddenly, you're aware of a roaring noise which drowns the surging river nearby. You look up towards Helvellyn ridge in time to see that a huge piece of the summit icefield has broken off and is crashing and smashing its way downwards onto the top of Red Tarn glacier, leaving a cloud of tiny ice particles to float gently away in the afternoon breeze. Nearer at hand, the blue of the ice in the glacier snout shows clear in the open crevasses. Everything is wet. The ice surface is covered in clumps of boulders and stones and every so often, some of these slither down the steep dirty ice slope to add to the pile of rocky debris at its foot, adding to its *terminal moraine*. This *moraine* shows us today the farthest point which this ice tongue reached.

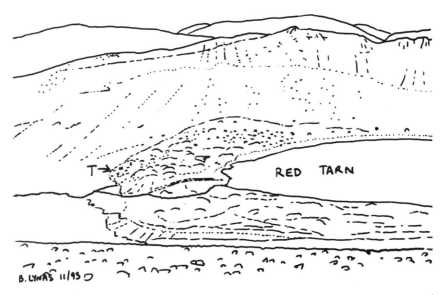

Figure 8.3: *Red Tarn with its terminal moraines. This sketch is a bird's-eye view of what you're standing in the middle of now, as seen from Catstye Cam. 'T' marks the eastward end of the terminal moraine.*

Now move forward in time by 500 years. Something has changed, hasn't it? You're still in the same place you were 500 years ago, and the *moraine* you saw being built then is just where it was too. But the ice has shrunk back quite some distance, leaving more recessional *terminal moraine* humps between you and it. In addition, you can now see the beginnings of a lake in front of it and the ice seems dirtier than ever, much of it being completely mantled in debris which as always is sliding down to build newer *moraine* piles. The *subglacial* river is still in spate, and has eroded away some of the earliest *moraine* ridges. The icefield on Helvellyn seems to have broken up into a few thin patches. Every so often, you hear sharp reports as rocks from high above the decaying glacier crash and tumble down, often to disappear again as they roll into the *bergschrund*. **If you now glide slowly forward decades at a time**, the seasons flash past scarcely noticed, but watch the glacier in front of you. It just melts like some giant dirty snowball in a thaw. At first, lumps of ice break off the main body to float about in the growing lake. Later, all the ice melts leaving nothing but mounds of debris which become drowned in the new lake that forms. The stream is not powerful enough to cut its way down to release the remaining waters because of the hard rock lip of the corrie basin. So now before your eyes, Red Tarn forms. **And so back to the present . . .**

Exciting stuff, don't you think? And made more poignant perhaps when I add that snow patches have often been recorded in the north-facing parts of this superb corrie until as late as July. It wouldn't have to get much colder for them to persist throughout the year. All you'd need is more snowfall in winter and a slight temperature fall to give you the beginnings of another glacier here.

The outlet of Red Tarn Beck over the rock lip was dammed and the level raised to provide a reliable water supply – one of several as you will see later – for Greenside Mine. The dam has long since been broken so that the water is now at its natural level again, though you can still see a sort of 'tide mark' which the enlarged lake once reached.

As you return to the track, look up a little to the north of Red Tarn where you can see clearly the repeated recessional *moraine* ridges still preserved on the steep valley side, not swamped in the later *screes* from Catstye Cam. In fact, the path runs parallel to the highest (i.e. oldest) of these for the first part of the ascent to Swirral Edge.

Start your climb, at first crossing *moraine*. About half way along, another path from Glenridding joins from the right. Glance back from time to time to get a changing perspective on the scene below of Red Tarn and its *moraines*. **When you reach Swirral Edge, turn right to head northeast up to Catstye Cam.**

Catstye Cam: Locality 4

Catstye Cam is a shapely pyramid 890 metres (2,920 feet) high. From here, you have a real bird's-eye view of Helvellyn, Striding Edge and Red Tarn and it is not hard to imagine the corrie filled with ice just a few thousand years ago. You can also see two other corries to the west and northwest: Brown Cove and Keppel Cove. Keppel Cove has a spectacular *moraine* ridge (Fig. 8.4) which you'll see close up later on this ramble (Locality 8). There's also a story of disastrous human interference with Nature which I'll relate later.

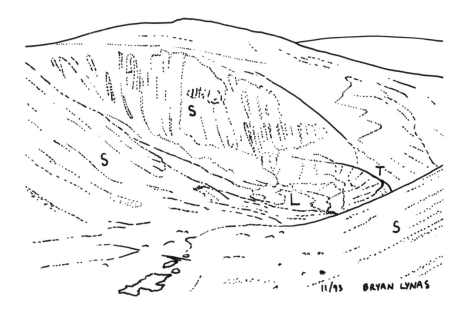

Figure 8.4: *Keppel Cove and its terminal moraine from Catstye Cam. Behind is Raise. 'S' is scree which masks most of the slopes; 'T' marks the crest of the Keppel Cove moraine. 'L' marks the site of the former lake.*

Both these corries were again the site of *Younger Dryas* glaciers. Now you can see why Swirral Edge has the shape that it does: it's an *arête*, like Striding Edge (Fig. 8.5), formed by two corrie glaciers gouging into it from either side (Fig. 8.6).

Figure 8.5: *Swirral Edge arête from Catstye Cam. Brown Cove is on the right, Red Tarn on the left and Helvellyn dominates the centre. The broken outcrops in the foreground are bedded BVG tuffs.*

The rocks of Catstye Cam are *BVG tuffs* which dip steeply southeast, so that the southeast side of the mountain is really a sort of *dip slope*; thus the *strike* and *dip* direction of these beds partially accounts for the shape of the mountain. The *tuffs* are all strongly *cleaved* and have been very much shattered by *periglacial* freezing and thawing so that actual outcrops are small and broken and most of the mountain is cloaked in a mantle of *scree* from top to bottom. The *tuffs* include scattered bands with marble-sized fragments but are mostly finer grained and, here and there (you have to search about a bit), are well *bedded* with familiar water-escape structures and micro-*faulting*. But parts of this rock sequence, particularly back down towards Swirral Edge, are of non-welded *pyroclastic flow* origin.

From the summit, you have fine views northeast to Ullswater.

Why should the lake be so kinked when other major lakes like Coniston and Windermere are relatively straight? Here are some ideas: obviously all river or glacier courses and the valleys they form are ultimately controlled by the relative softness of the rock. The rock may be naturally soft (like the *Silurian* sediments farther south) or they may be weakened by the smashing up effect of *faults,* or even by areas of strong *cleavage*. Coniston Water is dead straight

because of the great *fault* system which passes along most (or all) of its length
(p. 158). Ullswater is probably kinked precisely because there were no major
conspicuous lines of weakness so that river and, later, ice flows, tended to
meander about in their opportunistic way, searching for the easiest (= weakest
rock) route.

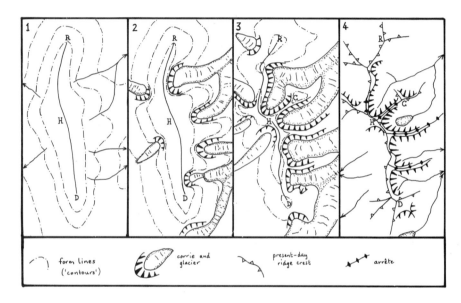

Figure 8.6: *How corries and arêtes form. This four-part drawing shows how corrie
glaciers form in favourable hollows or shallow valleys (mostly north- and east-facing)
originally cut by streams. 1: Helvellyn ridge as it may have appeared before the ice age.
Form lines (guessed 'contours') show the general aspect. R = Raise; H = Helvellyn and
D = Dolywaggon Pike. 2: An early stage in corrie formation with most of the glaciers
flowing down to join that which was actively cutting the Ullswater valley. 3: Continuation of the process. The corrie backwalls approach each other as their expanding
glaciers gouge and bite at the rock from opposite sides of developing arêtes like that
between Helvellyn and Catstye Cam ('C'). 4: The present day form of the Helvellyn
range with its corries, arêtes and tarns (Red Tarn and Grisedale Tarn). The steeper parts
of the corries are now often hidden by the sheets of scree which have formed since the
ice melted.*

From Catstye Cam, you have a good view of the upper parts of Greenside lead
mine (p. 213) to the northeast. Below Sheffield Pike, you can see the huge mine
dumps of the lower part of the mine, but higher up and to the left, you can also
see the funnel-like craters or 'gloryholes' of the caved-in upper workings. These

are marked on the OS map as 'Quarries, (dis).' This gives you some impression of the underground extent of this large mine.

It would be an unusual day if you didn't hear the familiar 'pruk pruk' of a raven hereabouts for this is just the sort of place they love. If you're lucky, you'll see two or three performing their remarkable aerobatics which even include flying upside down. They are the largest members of the crow family and are highly intelligent birds; real masters of the air (Fig. 8.7). They live off anything from bilberries to carrion. They'd be quite happy to eat your lunch if you left it for them.

Head back down to begin your ascent of Swirral Edge.

Figure 8.7: Ravens, one of which has found a tasty morsel.

Swirral Edge: Locality 5

By 'locality' here I mean the whole of Swirral Edge. The idea is that you should climb slowly, looking at the changing scene around you from time to time, watching your step carefully (because fatal accidents have happened here in bad weather) and noticing the rocks you are climbing or scrambling over. There are several different levels and grades of path up the Edge, though they all end up at the same place: about 120 paces from the summit trig point of Helvellyn. So choose whichever path you find most suitable and go for it!

First, look over to Keppel Cove to the north. Now you can really see the terminal *moraine* of the *Younger Dryas* corrie glacier (Fig. 8.8) which finally melted at about the same time as the Red Tarn ice.

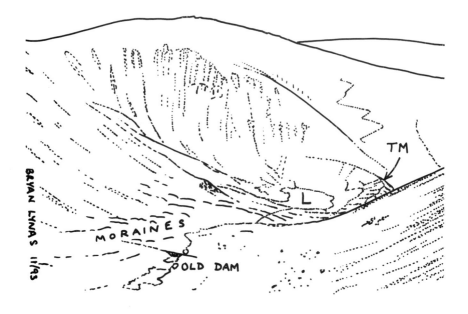

Figure 8.8: *Keppel Cove terminal moraine seen from Swirral Edge. 'TM' is the terminal moraine, 'L' the former lake. The floor of Brown Cove is covered with moraine hummocks. Note the old dam, relic of early attempts to regulate the water supply to Greenside Mine (see Locality 8).*

The rocks at first are the strongly *cleaved pyroclastic flow* which you probably saw on Catstye Cam. But then there is an abrupt change [3428 1538] (Fig. 8.9) which you can't miss after you've crossed the first part of the Edge: the rocks cease to be the dark grey *cleaved tuffs* you've seen up to now and abruptly become paler grey and blocky with large *joint* surfaces. If you look at the rock surfaces as you scramble upwards, you'll see no trace of bedding or any of the normal indicators of *BVG* sediments which, by now, you are quite used to looking for. In fact, this is probably not *BVG* at all but an *intrusion*, a rock which cooled from molten *magma* forced into the *BVG* rock pile at some later date. This particular rock is probably the *intrusive* equivalent of *basalt lava: dolerite*. Because it was *intruded* rather than *extruded*, it cooled much more slowly so that (as in *granites*) crystals had time to grow. The *dolerite intrusion* which forms the upper part of Swirral Edge is of no great size – it may be a *dyke,* or more likely a *sill* where the *magma* forced its way into the *BVG tuffs* more or less parallel with the bedding.

Figure 8.9: *View from Swirral Edge back to Catstye Cam. The slabby, blocky rock in the foreground is quite different from the strongly cleaved tuffs behind. You can just make out bedding in the outcrops in the centre of the figure, dipping to the right at about the same angle as the slope. The south (right hand) side of Catstye Cam has nearly the same inclination as the bedding in the tuffs and is a near dip slope.*

Or is this interpretation wrong? **As you scramble up the steepest bit of the final part of Swirral Edge**, you begin to get the sense of fairly flat-lying beds of *massive tuffs* again. Can you see any bedding structures? Or could it just be *flow banding* in the *dolerite*? What do you think?

Your guess may be better than mine because, to be honest, when I was here looking at these rocks for this ramble, a violent squall with large hailstones and thick mist overtook me on the Edge so my investigations were rather hurried. I was also aware that I could no longer see my wife who was somewhere in front of me before the cloud came down. I found her huddled behind a rock on the summit, none the worse for the lashings of hail and sleet. Swirral Edge is one of the least pleasant places to be in this sort of weather. So beware . . . !

The final steep scramble brings you quite quickly onto the broad and rather featureless flat top of Helvellyn. Now it's only a short walk to the trig station at 949 metres (3,116 feet). The view is magnificent in all directions since Helvellyn is the second highest mountain in the whole of the Lake District. But here's a curious contrast to the precipitous *arêtes*, corries and craggy lower slopes. Why should the summit of this mountain be flat; so flat that an aircraft once landed here?

The aircraft landing is commemorated by a plaque about 150 paces southeast of the trig point, near to the cross-shaped stone shelter. 'The first aeroplane to land on a mountain in Great Britain did so on this spot on December 22nd, 1926'. The plane was an Avro 586 Gosport.

The answer to my question is that this plateau, roughly the same height as others in the district (Blencathra, Bow Fell, Scafell, Grasmoor and so on) represents the remains of an old, pre-glacial erosion surface. Before the ice ages, the entire district was probably just a large, rather featureless dome, cut by relatively shallow valleys which did not resemble at all the deep valleys of today. The ice, as you know, changed all this for ever, carving the mountains into rugged peaks and *arêtes* and gouging out the deep valleys and lake basins which would later give Lakeland its outstanding character and beauty. These rather drab summit plateaux are the remains of this surface, scarcely affected by the ice which once encased them, for the ice only had serious erosive power lower down, where it was thicker and much heavier.

It's worth walking on to the southeast end of Helvellyn summit ridge – a matter of 300 metres and hardly any descent from the trig point – to get the famous view of Striding Ege, the classic *arête*, cloaked in *screes* and shaped like an upside-down 'V'.

You could reasonably say that glaciation gives you U-V landforms: 'U'-shaped valleys and 'V'-shaped ridges.

Where the Striding Edge path emerges onto the summit ridge is another larger stone memorial to Charles Gough who fell to his death from Striding Edge in 1803. When the poor man's body was found three months later, his dog was still guarding it.

From Helvellyn, most of the remaining walk is downhill, snaking its way along the northern ridges of the range: Whiteside Bank and Raise. The ridges are easy walking and give you fine and ever-changing views of most of the Lakeland mountains. **Head northwest towards Lower Man, turning north to drop down to the col between Lower Man and Whiteside – and the next locality.** The first part of the descent from Lower Man is a partially-formed *arête*. You can see clearly enough where the two corrie glaciers were: Brown Cove and in the corrie north of Lower Man. The col ahead of you between the two corries – just before Locality 6 – is quite flat, totally different in appearance from the knife-edge higher up. Probably, ice tongues crossed and recrossed this at various times, whilst *arêtes* tended to form at higher levels.

Whiteside Bank: lavas and blockfield at Locality 6 [339 163]

As you begin to climb Whiteside Bank, you'll notice that all the rocks underfoot are *lavas*, studded with small *feldspar* crystals and peppered with small gas cavities – *vesicles*. Some of the *vesicles* are filled with radiating crystals of *chlorite*. But you don't see any of this rock cropping out: it's all been smashed up by *periglacial* action (like the *blockfield* on the summit of Bow Fell) which was probably going on whilst the Brown Cove and Keppel Cove glaciers were grinding away below during the *Younger Dryas* cold period. Since these final glaciers melted, the entire west face of Catstye Cam has become covered in *screes*. This is mostly because the *cleaved tuffs* which form the mountain were unusually susceptible to break-up by freezing and thawing, the process which drives *scree* formation. On the opposite side, Browncove Crags (northwest of Lower Man and confusingly not in Brown Cove) have also produced several cones of *scree* which partly cover some of the rather vague *moraines* which you can see in this less well formed corrie. Also from here, you have a fine view of the Keppel Cove *moraine* and you can see clearly now where the lake used to be.

Continue your ascent to the top of Whiteside Bank. The *lavas* continue underfoot for most of the way until you're almost at the top when they are abruptly replaced by beautiful *welded tuffs*. The rounded grassy top of this mountain is entirely made up of this rock but you'll see that there are no outcrops of it. Just as at Locality 6, the rocks have been so broken up by *periglacial* action that only blocks remain.

Now you have the choice of continuing on to Raise, an easy walk with only about 50 metres of ascent, or of following the main track round to the east to descend straight to Locality 8, Keppel Cove. The col between Whiteside Bank and Raise is flat and not at all *arête*-like. It is only precipitous on the Keppel Cove side. **As soon as you start the gentle climb to Raise,** the familiar *vesicular lavas* reappear.

Raise summit and rubbly lavas: Locality 7

At the summit, you'll find plenty of outcrops of these *lavas,* much weathered and covered in lichens. Even so, you can clearly make out its rubbly appearance looking for all the world like a slag heap. It is full of gas cavities up to almost pingpong-ball size. *Lavas* are very variable in appearance.

You can see modern examples elsewhere in Europe such as the Puys d'Auvergne district in central France. These volcanoes erupted as recently as 7,500 years ago and the volcano craters are still perfectly preserved and well worth a visit. But one of the best places in Europe to look at modern lavas and volcanic landforms is Vesuvius which looms over the Bay of Naples and is theoretically well overdue for another outburst. The lavas from the great 1944 eruption are beautifully fresh – and utter hell to walk over. (My mother, who happened to be there with the RAF at the time, remembers them still being warm!) They are blocky lavas, broken up into jagged chunks and spikes by flow movement. This type of lava is exceedingly common in Hawaii where the Polynesian people named it 'aa'.

Here on the summit of Raise, you're standing on ancient flows of 'aa' *lava.* Another common type of *lava* is known as ropy *lava,* or 'pahoehoe' to the Polynesians (Fig. 8.10). Its surface is not broken at all, but covered in smooth rope-like swirls.

A quirk of lava flows is that they are often hollow, not solid as you might expect. When the outer part of a flow cools and solidifies, the inner part remains red hot and continues to flow downhill. When the eruption ceases, the lava source ceases also yet the molten lava in the hot core of the half-solidified flow continues to move. This results in the formation of often quite large open tunnels or tubes inside the lava flow – big enough to drive a bus into in some cases. And yes, you can see examples of these as well as 'pahoehoe' in the Lake District near Crinkle Crags. Maybe I can take you there in a future book of rambles.

Figure 8.10: '*Pahoehoe' or 'ropy' lava, quite different to the rubbly messy stuff on Raise. The lava surface I've sketched here is about the area of a large TV screen.*

From Raise, your views continue to be superb, especially of the great Blencathra ridge to the north (p. 234). **The next part of this route is the only part which does not follow a path. Head southeast, directly towards the Hole in the Wall path junction at the start of Striding Edge; you can see the horizontal path you followed towards Red Tarn quite clearly from here with St Sunday Crag behind. The moor underfoot is smooth short grasses and sedges and as the slope begins to increase, you see the main walking track from Whiteside Bank to Greenside directly in front. Join this and turn left onto it. It then begins to zigzag as it loses height to drop down towards Keppel Cove.** Catstye Cam and the great corrie of Brown Cove dominate the views as you descend (Fig. 8.11). Once you're on the zigzag, you can't miss the great Keppel Cove *terminal moraine* rampart (Fig. 8.12). And now other man-made features, which you'll have noticed earlier, stand out: a hideous concrete dam, altered water courses and *leats*.

Figure 8.11: *Catstye Cam and Brown Cove seen as you descend from Raise. It's not difficult to picture the glacier which once filled Brown Cove. The old leat seems to have tapped water impounded by the small Brown Cove dam.*

Figure 8.12: *Keppel Cove terminal moraine. The breach in the moraine dam is to the right of the sheepfolds and the later concrete dam is to the left centre.*

Man mucks about with Nature in Keppel Cove; a disaster: Locality 8

To best appreciate this locality, stop before you reach it and look at it from above. Find a place to sit if you can because there's quite a story to tell here. **If you prefer not to descend right down to the *moraine*, then simply continue on the main walking track. But if you're curious, you'll want to examine what has happened here closely.** But first, an historical account is overdue, don't you think? I've been keeping quiet about Keppel Cove (except for its *moraine*) though you've been able to see it since Catstye Cam. I wanted to keep you guessing a bit. What do you make of what you see below? The *moraine* is straightforward enough. But you can also see signs of the existence of a lake here once, both as a sort of 'tide mark' around its former edge and because there is a suspicious dark green marshy area where the lake bed must have been.

You'll also have spotted a deep rent in the *moraine* dam just beyond the sheepfolds. This cannot have been here whilst there was a lake for the Keppel Cove stream now runs at the bottom of it. And then there's all the evidence of Man's interference with water courses: you can see a rough stone channel which was built to capture the stream from Brown Cove, bringing its water into the Keppel Cove lake. And behind the *moraine*, there's the concrete dam and evidence of at least two *leats* which once conducted water (you can follow the main one on the OS Leisure Map) to Greenside Mine. So you'd conclude that a natural corrie lake formerly existed here, dammed by the *terminal moraine* of the Keppel Cove ice tongue 11,500 years ago.

What seems to have happened is that with the opening of Greenside Mine with its thirst for water to drive waterwheels and, later, turbines, men have tinkered with Nature's plumbing by raising the level of Keppel Cove lake (as they did at Red Tarn), presumably by building a small dam at the outlet stream and also by conducting additional water into the lake from Brown Cove. On the surface, this might have seemed like a clever way of avoiding spending much money to secure a year-round water flow.

But the increased hydraulic pressure exerted on the natural dam, made only of *moraine* – nothing more than a pile of wet boulders, gravels, sands, silts and muds – resulted in a fatal weakening of the dam. This finally must have failed catastrophically, for once the initial collapse had opened a breach, the dammed water had immense erosive power because of its hydrostatic 'head' – and would have ripped out the deep gully you see today. A surging wall of sediment-charged water must have then roared down the valley.

You only have to consult the written records (e.g. W.T. Shaw's book, 'Mining in the Lake Counties,' Dalesman Books 1972, page 81) to find that this dam burst happened on 29 October 1927. Heavy rains – the last straw – caused the dam to burst and the resulting flood swept down the valley to Ullswater, damaging both houses and shops in Glenridding. Remarkably no one seems to have died but the Greenside Mine company had to pay so much in compensation that the mine was nearly bankrupted. So that's the story of Keppel Cove.

Moraine dam bursts can be perfectly natural phenomena. In the Cordillera Blanca, central Andes of Perú, retreating glaciers left many huge dams which dwarf the Keppel Cove moraine. As with any dam and abundant meltwater, each collected a sizeable lake behind it. Peru has the misfortune to be prone to major earthquakes due to its location above a *subduction* zone. With each serious earthquake, some secondary disaster such as a moraine dam burst, may result, releasing a flood of boulders and debris known locally as 'aluviones'. This happens because the quakes cause enormous chunks of glacier to avalanche and collapse into the lakes. The huge waves set off by this, burst through the retaining dams and massive, fast-moving floods roar down from the high mountain valleys and lay waste to everything in their paths. Several of the small Andean towns such as the provincial capital, Huaraz, have been devastated in this way, with major loss of life. Peruvian government geologists take aluviones very seriously indeed, and have deliberately either opened the moraine dams to drain the lakes or built concrete spillways to prevent the rapid erosion and collapse of existing outlets. None of this has been easy to do since most of the moraine dams are at nearly the height of Mont Blanc. But at least it means that the people in the towns below have one less thing to worry about. Earthquakes are bad enough!

If you wish, leave the track and continue directly down to the *moraine* dam and examine the great gully cut by the surging mass of water from this former lake. Look back into Keppel Cove from this vantage point for here is a beautiful example of a fresh *alluvial fan*; an apron of debris brought down by the beck from the higher, *scree*-covered parts of the cove. As the sediment-laden stream entered the former lake, it lost all the energy with which it had moved its rocky load. So the fan built out into the lake just as at Elter Water (p. 155). But an interesting extra process has happened here since that fateful day in October 1927 when the dam burst: the stream has been given new life -geographers call it *rejuvenation* – by the sudden lowering of the level to which it can run without losing all its energy. As a result, it has cut down through its older fan (now covered in grass) and a new, post-1927 fan has built up, gradually encroaching on the old lake floor, now covered in soft rushes (Fig. 8.12). *Rejuvenation* plays an important role in the way landforms develop and is typically triggered by a fall in sealevel. So exactly what you see here happens on a large scale. When the sealevel falls, rivers which were previously mature with wide *flood plains* will suddenly start to flow faster and so cut down into their existing beds. If hard rock crops out in the old river bed, then rapids or a waterfall will form. Geographers can recognise whole series of *rejuvenations* by 'nick points' (usually a small waterfall or rapid) in present day streams or rivers. *Rejuvenation* also forms *river terraces* (p. 101).

Sealevels change almost continuously – and always have done so throughout time. We are getting panicky about the possibility of a few millimetres of rise in the next decade or so due to the supposed greenhouse warming of our climate, but during the last glaciations, sealevels fluctuated many times both above and below the present level. At times it was as much as 130 metres lower than at present; at others, up to 40 metres higher. Our embankments and barrages which we build to protect our fertile lowlands from the sea will amount to nothing if our present interglacial period warms up some more. On the other hand, if we plunge back into another glacial – and there's no reason we know of why this should not happen – then the amount of available dry land will enormously increase around the world as water becomes locked up in new ice sheets in northern Europe and North America. I'll leave you to consider the impact either scenario will have on the human race!

Figure 8.13: Dynamited dam below Keppel Cove.

As you head back towards Glenrdding along the farm track which starts by the sheepfold, you pass by the ugly concrete dam on your right. I haven't been able to find out anything about this, though I assume it was built after the 1927 disaster. But this flimsy, shoddily-made construction looks as if it was never used. There's no evidence of there ever having been a lake impounded behind it. Maybe the company changed its mind, for in 1928 they constructed a new water *leat* along to Mires Beck and built a powerhouse with a 300 HP turbine at Rattlebeck (where you crossed the bridge at the start of the walk). You'll notice that at some time, someone appears to have dynamited a gaping hole in the base of the dam (Fig. 8.13). This was presumably done to ensure that no further flood disasters would ever happen. I certainly wouldn't have put any faith in this dam, would you?

All that remains now is for you to walk back, via the old Greenside Mine buildings (which include a YHA and other outdoor pursuits centres, tastefully converted), to Glenridding. The track is broad and obvious all the way. I deliberately say nothing more about Greenside Mine since that is the topic of the next ramble.

ROCKY RAMBLE 9: GREENSIDE MINE AREA

How to get to the start of the ramble

As for the Catstye Cam and Helvellyn ramble, Glenridding (on the A592 at Ullswater) is the starting point. The village has large convenient carparks.

The ramble: needs, distances and times

The ramble is around 11.5 kilometres (just over 7 miles) depending upon how much wandering about you do looking for mineral specimens. It involves only around 570 metres of ascent (1,870 feet) if you follow my suggested route (no footpath for a while) via Stang and the great Chimney flue. If you choose not to do this and to return the way you came, back down Swart Beck, the climbing is only 450 metres (1,470 feet).

Be sure to take a hand lens with you to examine the various minerals that you'll certainly find on the mine dumps. On this occasion, a small hammer could be useful to help you break up the ore-bearing rock on the dumps and yield fresh, shiny *galena* and other minerals.

Whilst you can dash round this ramble in a half day, I'd recommend you allow yourself a full day if you're interested in poking around the old mine dumps and glory holes high up on Green Side. Beware of unstable rocks in some of these places though.

The OS Outdoor Leisure map is Sheet 5, North Eastern area.

Introduction: a brief history of Greenside Mine

Greenside Mine was once one of the largest lead producers in Britain, beginning production in the late 17th century. Working continued at the mine almost without ceasing until 1962 when it closed for good, the veins having been completely worked out. In 1890, it became the first mine in Britain to install electrical winding gear and was also the first to use an electric locomotive for underground haulage (Fig. 9.1). By the early years of this century, lead output from the mine reached 'highs' of 3000 tons per year. Between 1822 and 1962, it produced over 200,000 tons of lead concentrates (which totalled between 70 and 82 percent metallic lead), far in excess of all other Lakeland mines. It also produced around one and a half million ounces of silver. The rich Greenside Vein, averaging 7 percent lead, ranged from a few millimetres to 9 metres in

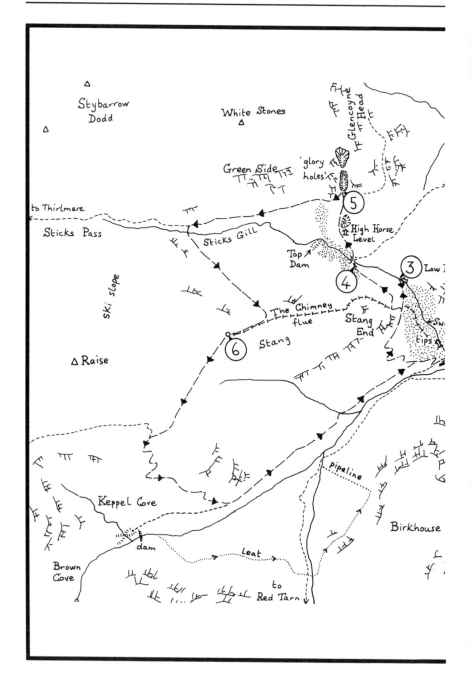

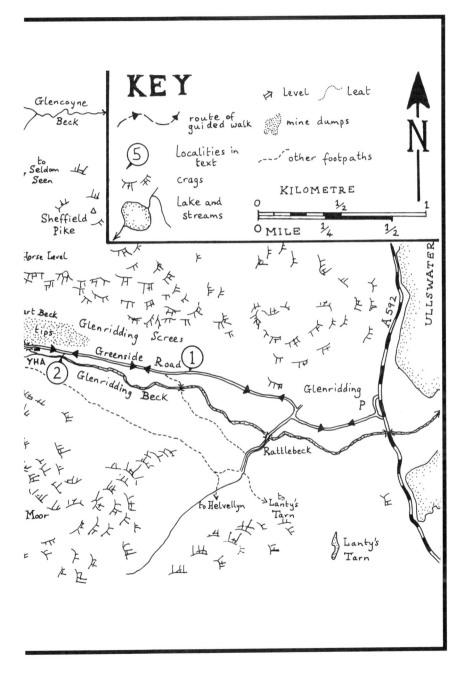

thickness, most of it being around 2 metres. It was first discovered at the surface, above Green Side at the head of Glencoyne, but was eventually worked to 790 metres (2,600 feet) depth. The deepest levels of the mine ran into the *Skiddaw Slates* which underlie the entire *BVG*. Though the veins continued in the slates, they were devoid of lead. The mine's history was not uneventful, involving a massive collapse of workings in the upper levels and two separate dam bursts.

Figure 9.1: *The first electric locomotive at Greenside Mine (drawn from an 1891 picture figured by W.T. Shaw in his book Mining in the Lake District, 1972, Dalesman Press.)*

This ramble is mainly concerned with the remains of the mine which you can still see. It is part geology and part industrial archaeology. In the upper reaches of the mine, you can find attractive mineral specimens in the old dumps, including the lead ore, *galena*, which the miners sought. I haven't attempted to desbribe the layout or detailed history of the mine, for this has been done by other writers such as W.T.Shaw in his book 'Mining in the Lake Counties' (Dalesman Press, 1972), the source of much of the information here.

Some mining lingo . . .

The idea of mining is to get at as much of the stuff you want (be it gold or lead) with the minimum of effort and expense. This gives you maximum profits. Before explosives, mining was carried out with little more than a pick, shovel, wedges and sledgehammers. Gunpowder changed all this; the miners could now simply bore shot holes with steel bars and heavy hammers. They then packed the hole with powder, stopped it up with 'stemming' (clay), lit the blue touch paper and retired. Bang! Later, trams began to be used with rails, and horses or people for haulage along 'levels' which are tunnels bored horizontally into the mountainside. Later still, electric locomotives carried out these tasks. 'Levels' gave easy access to all the workings and also acted as drainage channels for the inevitable water. Shafts were often sunk from the levels to get at deeper parts of the ore-bearing rock. At first, access was often by ladderways or some sort of windlass, though later, water- or electric-powered winding gear was used for hauling up both ore skips and, by means of a cage, the miners.

I once worked in a deep copper mine in western Canada. Access to the active workings was by a level 1$^1/_2$ miles long followed by a shaft nearly 2,500 feet deep. Travelling in the cage (which was double-decked) was at first a pretty scary experience when it stopped at the deeper levels. Because of the enormous length of steel cable suspending the cage in the deep shaft, the cage oscillated for half a minute like a heavy ball on an elastic band. You had to wait for the bouncing to stop before you could open the gate and step out into the '5850' (the deepest level below the surface workings and also below sealevel). The shaft did have an emergency ladderway but I never fancied 2,500 feet of climbing to get back up to the entrance level.

When deeper levels were only accessible by shafts, pumps (at first hand-powered but later powered by water or electricity) had to be installed to keep the workings below the access level from flooding. If water became a serious problem but the ore was good, a much longer drainage level might be driven from a lower altitude to intersect and drain the deeper workings. These were sometimes called 'soughs'. By the start of this century, compressed air was used for operating drills at the rock face. This enormously improved the speed and efficiency with which mining could be done as did the development of more powerful and safer explosives such as dynamite and gelignite.

The ore-bearing veins or 'shoots' at Greenside usually dipped fairly steeply and were worked by *stoping*. Where the level intersected the vein, the miners cut side levels along the vein and exploited the ore bodies by boring upwards (overhand *stoping*) into them, blasting and collecting the rock and ore which fell down to the level by gravity. If needed, pillars of rock would be left intact here and there to support the two walls of the vein (hanging wall and foot wall) and wooden props would be wedged in for the same purpose. This work, as you can imagine, was neither safe nor pleasant and needed both strength and great skill.

Once the ore was out of the mine, it was crushed, ground up and separated from the worthless or 'gangue' minerals (such as *quartz* and *calcite* which usually occur with it in the ore-bearing veins). This processing needed volumes of water, both for the washing and jigging separation process itself and for the waterwheels which drove the machinery. The sloppy waste 'fines' or 'tailings' were then disposed of in a tailings pond. Waste rock was simply dumped as close as convenient to the mouths of the levels from which it was hauled. Finally, the concentrates were roasted and smelted to yield the metal which was sought. This usually meant reducing metal sulphides to oxides and then to the pure metal and resulted in serious pollution (and you can still see the effect of this far above the mine at the last locality on this ramble).

Towards Greenside Mine

Initially, you follow exactly the same route as the Catstye Cam and Helvellyn ramble, up the road west from Glenridding but don't turn left to Rattlebeck Bridge as before; continue on (a right and then left turn, simply following the road) along Greenside Road past the Victorian miners' cottages, some of which have beautiful gardens. Above a footbridge about halfway between Glenridding and the Youth Hostel at Greenside is the first stop.

Common field and glacial features: Locality 1 [375 172]

Look across Glenridding Beck to the fields on the south side. Before the enclosures (p. 194), this was the site of a common field. You can still see the rectangular strips which formed these portions of fertile ground. The fields are located on the glacial *morainic* rubbish dumped by the melting *Devensian* ice around 15,000 years ago. This consists of a mix of clay (ground-up rock) and stones which is certainly an improvement on *scree* or bare rock, the only other alternatives in this valley. You'll notice piles of stones in the field above the footbridge reminding us of the backbreaking work people were once prepared to do to improve their land.

Below the footbridge, you can see that there are rock outcrops in the beck showing that there is very little glacial *moraine* in the valley bottom. The beck has cut down about 2 metres into its rock bed. This tells us something about the speed at which this downcutting occurs because we can assume that the valley floor was completely smooth whilst the ice was flowing down it, say 16,000 years ago. So this downcutting has all occurred within around 14 or 15,000 years.

Two metres in 15,000 years is 1.3 millimetres per decade! Not much, you might think, but remember that in geology, we're dealing with huge periods of time. If this stream continued downcutting at this rate for a million years, the chasm it would cut would be over 130 metres deep; 1,300 metres in 10 million years. As you know by now, geologists bandy about 'millions of years' as if they were mere flicks of the finger in overall geological time. It makes you think, doesn't it?

Above you on the north side of the valley are crags of *BVG,* part of Sheffield Pike, which have given rise to active *screes* higher up. The lower *scree* slopes are now stabilised, colonised by grass and bracken.

Continue along Greenside Road towards the mine. You can now see its unattractive dumps above the remaining mine buildings as you pass a plantation of spruces and larches on the opposite side of the beck. The beck is again cutting slowly into its rocky bed and the steep slopes between the track and the beck have been planted with ash and oak (Fig. 9.2). The trees in the intake above the track are mostly ashes though there are a few old hawthorns (Fig. 9.2) dotted about in the lower *screes.* Parsley fern grows in the wall beside the track.

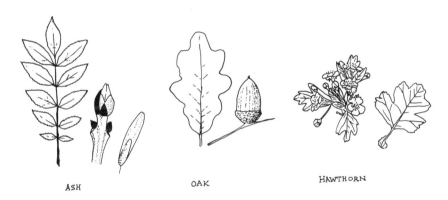

ASH   OAK   HAWTHORN

Figure 9.2: Ash (with leaf, black-tipped buds and seed), oak leaf and acorn, and hawthorn leaf and cluster of leaves and flowers (May blossom).

Shortly, you pass a stone building, roofed with concrete and partly built into the hillside on the right. It has a steel door and may have been a strongroom for the mine. Perhaps they stored silver here once? Or maybe it was a powder magazine. Every mine has one of these, usually located away from other buildings for obvious reasons. Greenside Mine used to have a brass-hubbed powder cart (brass does not emit sparks when accidentally knocked as steel can do) and gunpowder came from the Elterwater factory (p. 123) in 25 pound casks, made without nails. To ignite the gunpowder in the shot holes, the miners used fuses made out of straw filled with fine gunpowder and a twist of touchpaper at the end. Dynamite, both easier and safer to use, came at the end of the last century as did safety fuses for igniting it.

Some years ago when I was working in Fiji (South Pacific), I learnt to use explosives and even obtained a licence to do so. This allowed me to use them for geophysical surveys in which you fire off a charge buried in a hole. The resulting vibrations from the explosion are detected by a set of 'microphones' (called 'geophones') and recorded on special paper. Shock waves from the bang are reflected or refracted (as in optics) back to the geophones from rock layers below the ground. From the squiggles recorded on the paper, geophysicists can calculate the depths and likely composition of various rock layers. This is called 'seismic survey' and is used throughout the world with great success to find petroleum resources.

Water-polished jigsaw puzzles tell a steamy story: Locality 2 [3674 1737]

After the concrete-roofed house but before the YHA and group of houses ahead, there's an easy way down to the beck where you can examine clean and fresh *BVG* both in and by it, just below a fence. The rock is beautifully water-polished and if you wet additional parts that are dry, you see details of structures that you never normally see in the weathered outcrops on the fells (Fig. 9.3). Here you can see a complex and irregular network of pale grey veins which pervade a dark green rock, probably an *andesite*. At first, you might think that this was a *lava* which has been broken up by flow movement (like the 'aa' *lavas* you saw on the summit of Raise, p. 206). But when you look carefully, you see that this cannot be so because the fragments fit back together like a jigsaw puzzle. They have scarcely moved and many are 'frozen' in the process of beginning to break apart, not at all like the chaotic jumble of blocky 'aa' flows. Others are more rounded and knocked about – abraded – at their edges. But the message is clear: this rock has been broken up *after* it had solidified, probably by hydraulic fracturing due to the vigorous passage of hot fluids through it.

In fact this process – called 'hydrofracturing' – is well understood. It is deliberately used to break up rock at the bottom of boreholes which then releases entrapped oil or hot water (for geothermal generating stations). High-pressure pumps at the surface force superheated water down the borehole to create this sort of network of fissures and fractures.

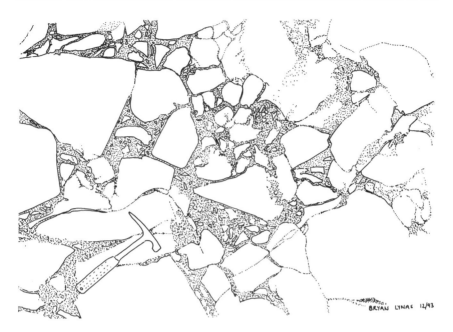

Figure 9.3: *Water-polished BVG breccias at Locality 2. My hammer gives the scale. Note how some pieces are just beginning to break up whilst others have become more broken and abraded.*

But where did the hot steamy fluids come from? We already know that much of the *BVG* was laid down under water. So if a molten rock such as this once was happened to be *intruded* into wet sediments, the water entrapped beneath it would become superheated and force its way upwards, fracturing the cooling and solidifying rock to create the jigsaw puzzle rock you see here. It could equally have been a *lava* which ran into a shallow lake. We can't see its relationship with the other *BVG* rocks here and without such evidence, whether it was *lava* or *intrusion* is just guesswork.

Return to the track and walk up through the old mine buildings (formerly stores and part of the old smelting mill), now appropriately converted to an outdoor pursuits centre, Striding Edge Hostel and Greenside Youth Hostel (which used to be the miners' hostel). Above you on your right are the vast tips of mine debris, much of which was crushed and ground up in order to separate the lead ore from the waste. Heroic attempts have been made to tidy up these dumps and plant grass and trees on them, both to cover them and to stabilise them for no one wants another Aberfan disaster.

The Aberfan tragedy happened on the morning of 21 October 1966 when a coal tip avalanched down onto a Welsh mining village, killing 144 people including 116 children in school.

As you can see, this has only been partly successful. **After the hostels, you come to a junction. Take the right-hand Sticks Pass track which climbs towards Stang End with the fenced-off dumps on your right.** The sheer size of these tips (and there's much more higher up which you can't yet see) tells you just how big this mine was. **Cross an old *leat*, once bringing water to drive waterwheels for the crushing plant, and zigzag up.** This track was for many years used to carry loads of lead ore from the oldest mine workings at Green Side down to Glenridding. From there, it was hauled to a smelter at Alston (20 miles northeast of Penrith) until in the 1830s, a smelter was built here, thus avoiding the tedious long journey to Alston. Below Stang End, there's a veritable forest of dwarf juniper trees on the steep stable *scree* slopes. The track passes through some of these gnarled, wind-blasted junipers. They are mostly not much higher than a tall man and many will have been here much longer than the mine. **After two zigzags through the juniper forest, the track emerges to follow the junction between crags on the left and *scree* on the right.** The crags host both juniper bushes and alpine lady's mantle (Fig. 2.11, p. 50) as well as ling and bell heathers. The rocks themselves are covered by a kaleidoscope of grey and vivid green lichens.

Lichens are not primitive plants as used to be thought. They are in fact the result of an association – symbiosis – between a fungus and an alga. The fungus provides a home and certain nutrients to the alga. The alga, in return, supplies the fungus with sugars from its own photosynthesis. Thus both survive where neither could otherwise. As you'd expect, there are many examples of this sort of relationship in the astonishing world of living organisms. Lichens are sensitive to air pollution so their abundance here tells us that Lakeland's air is still fairly pure.

The rock under the lichen is a red-weathering, dark-coloured *lava* or *intrusion*, probably similar to that at Locality 1 although here, you simply cannot tell whether it is fractured in the same way.

At the end of the longest zigzag, the track doubles back to the left again, but here you go straight ahead along a smaller track towards Swart Beck (also called Lucy Tongue Gill), above the tips. The path ends in an alcove just above the beck by a small larch tree.

Low Horse Level: Locality 3 [3622 1789]

From here, you can see clearly an actual vein like those which contained the lead minerals sought by the miners. **If you're reasonably agile – and careful – you can climb down to the stream here, cross it and actually examine the vein and level at first hand.**

The Low Horse Level was said to be '35 fathoms' below the High Horse Level (the remains of which you see shortly). The latter was at about 1,850 feet (= 560 metres). So the Low Horse must have been 210 feet lower – 1,640 feet (= 500 metres) which is precisely the height here. Another level, Lucy Tongue Level, was later driven to give access (and drainage) to the deeper levels of the mine. This level, started in 1845, took 18 years to drive, was $^3/_4$ mile long and was the main haulage and drainage level for the entire deeper mine. Its mouth was at about 1,100 feet (= 334 metres) above sealevel, further down Swart Beck. It is now inaccessible.

A constant chilling draught of cold air blows out of the Low Horse Level (Fig. 9.4) which as you can see is still open, telling us that there must be other open entrances to this mine. The entrance has partially collapsed and I emphatically recommend that you stay out of this.

BRYAN LYNAS 12/93

Figure 9.4: All that remains of Low Horse Level, whose entrance has mostly collapsed. You can see the barren vein (dotted and dipping steeply from left to right) clearly in the rocks above the entrance. The footwall is the dipping surface under the vein (labelled) and the hanging wall is the 'hanging' surface above.

The vein here *strikes* northwest, *dipping* at 78° to the east. It is barren, containing only brownish *calcite*, *quartz*, a little *hematite* and *barite* (or 'barytes'), a white or pink barium mineral which is notably heavy; hence its common name of 'heavyspar'. But in good mining tradition, the level was driven northwards along this vein, partly to explore its possibilities and partly to link into the higher workings of the productive part of the mine. It was successful in both these aims as the miners found a new ore shoot – the southern Greenside ore shoot which was covered by glacial *moraine* in the lower part of Sticks Gill valley.

Today, it's hard to believe that this was once the main haulage level for this mine. All that remains, apart from the partially-collapsed level entrance, is a rusted iron pipe draining water from the level. Yet had you been here over a century ago, you'd have seen men and ponies going in and out dragging iron 'cars' or 'skips' along the narrow rail track. Those coming out then sent their ore-filled skips down an inclined tramway to the dressing (processing) plant about 150 metres below, beside the beck.

Before retreating from this sombre gully, look at the rock which contains the veins. It is again a dark green-grey *massive lava* or *intrusive* of (from the colour) *andesite* to *basalt* type. It is not fragmental like so much of the *BVG* but it is slightly affected by *cleavage*. Other thin *quartz*, *calcite* and *barite* veins crop out in the gully occupied by the beck though they are never more than a couple of finger-breadths thick. The *barite* has a curious 'beef' appearance due to its occurrence as needle-like crystals tightly packed together.

Now, the local plant communities are recovering so you can find harebells, lady's mantles, foxgloves, heathers, cranesbills (Fig. 9.5) and ferns growing in and around the gully.

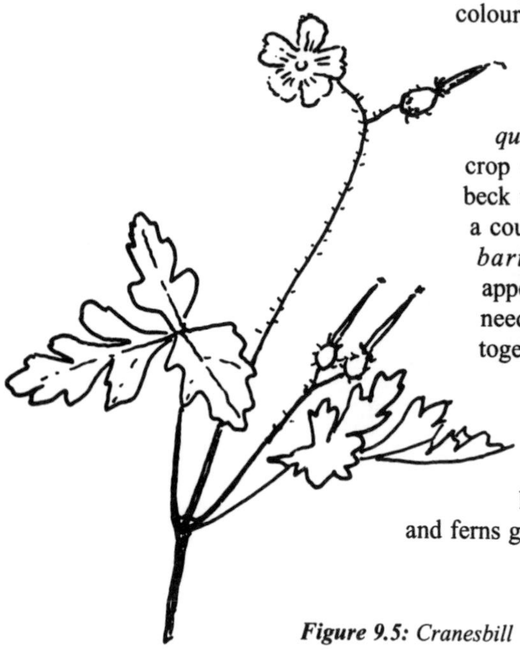

Figure 9.5: Cranesbill

Retrace your steps to the main zigzag track and continue on up. For the final 'zig', the track follows the line of the flue which ran from the smelter far below to run right, up Stang, to The Chimney (Locality 6). **Then the track flattens out as you arrive in the netherworld of Sticks Gill valley, the site of the original Greenside Mine workings.** The familiar view of Ullswater has disappeared and before you is the desolation wrought by mining: huge holes in the mountainside and vast areas of dumped waste rock. Yet all is not ruination: nature and time, great healers of wounds made by man, are gradually repairing the damage. Silence prevails once again, save for the croak of a raven, the trill of a meadow pipit and the soft tinkle of water in the beck. And plants are slowly colonising the dumps, starting with lichens and mosses.

In fact this rather surprising upper valley is a fine example of a 'hanging' valley (p. 11). The glacier which once filled it was small with a minimal snow catchment area; no match for the great ice streams coming down from Brown Cove, Helvellyn, Red Tarn valley and Keppel Cove. These powerful glaciers quickly cut down the bed of Glenridding valley leaving the Sticks Gill ice marooned high up on the north side, and chopping off the lower ridges – spurs – of the side valleys. Today, Swart Beck plunges down as rapids and small waterfalls, albeit partly choked by mine debris.

Geologists and geographers often refer to 'truncated spurs', 'hanging valleys'and "'U'-shaped valleys' as typifying the effects created by mountain glaciations. By now, you'll be aware that you can see these features everywhere in Lakeland and you might be surprised that it took geologists many years to even realise that mountains like these, and their Welsh and Scottish counterparts, had once been covered by ice. A delightful little book – which I have – by A.C.Ramsay, dated 1860 ('The Old Glaciers of Switzerland and North Wales') was the first to point this out in great and clear detail. The first geologists were no fools; they were merely encumbered by the religious dogmas of the time which insisted (as some people do to this day) that God created the Earth just 4,000 years ago.

Dressing areas and dumps: Locality 4 [3594 1795]

This locality is the area around the footbridge and was once the site of much hustle and bustle. On the north side of the bridge, the whole area is covered by fine grained sand and gravel. This was the site of the original ore dressing plant set up as long ago as 1690 by Dutch 'adventurers'. At that time, the 'adventurers' were *stoping* out their ore from the highest parts of the Greenside vein, well over 600 metres (around 2,000 feet) above sealevel. Conditions then must have been pretty rough. Winter freezes and snow would have brought the mine to a standstill for several months. The processed ore had to be carried out by packhorse over Sticks Pass to a smelter near Keswick. There were then no workings or dumps at all back down Swart Beck and Glenridding valley. These all date from a later period of development after the Low Horse and Lucy levels were driven.

The main ore-bearing veins were all to the north of here, the original one being found high up at the top of Glencoyne, *striking* almost north-south. The mineralising fluids (p. 180) had forced their way up along a *fault breccia* in which the minerals you'll see shortly were precipitated. The Greenside Vein ceases abruptly at its southern end when it meets an east-west *fault* known as the 'Clay Vein', Where you are now is probably about the position of this underground vein intersection. But the miners, eternal optimists, couldn't believe that the powerful Greenside Vein could simply disappear south of the Clay Vein and they made a major attempt to find it, assuming logically that it had been displaced sideways by the Clay Vein *fault* movement. This was one reason for the construction of the Chimney flue. (You passed this on the final zigzag after continuing on from Locality 3.) The idea was that by cutting a trench across the entire rock outcrop west from Lucy's Tongue (Swart Beck), they would be sure to cut across the southern extension of the Greenside Vein, if it existed. So they made their cut, found no veins, but at least had a flue for their smelter!

About a century after the 'adventurers', the Greenside Mining Syndicate formed. They probably built the former Top Dam which for a time impounded a tarn in the marshy bottom of Sticks Gill valley on the other side of the tips so you can't see it from here. This dam supplied water to the crushing and washing mill waterwheel which the Syndicate built here.

Much later, in the 1870s, heavy rain burst the Top Dam (sounds familiar? Keppel Cove again) and the resulting flood destroyed the silver refining house, sweeping off a 1000-ounce lump of silver as it poured down Swart Beck. Although men searched for it for weeks after, it was never found or so they claimed. Incidentally, the silver was extracted from the *galena* ore, for it often occurs in 'solid solution' within *galena* crystals.

During this period, the High Horse Level was driven to enable the miners to get at rich ore shoots at lower levels in the vein. Most of the tips here came from this important level and the ore was dressed right here before being carted down to Glenridding (using the specially-built zigzag track you've just ascended) and thence to the Alston smelter. It was also here that the miners lived because at that time, Glenridding scarcely existed. As you see, there's practically nothing left of all this former activity.

But it's here that you should take a little time to look for mineral samples if you're interested in doing so. They're easy to find along the edge of the tips. *Quartz* is obvious, being white and hard. *Calcite* is softer (you can scratch it with a knife, unlike *quartz*) and often quite brown (it is normally white or colourless) because it contains iron. You should easily find samples with thin veins of well crystallised *galena*, the lead ore which was the reason for this mine's existence. This mineral is an attractive shiny silver when fresh though weathering dulls it to a (surprise) lead colour. A brownish-black mineral -*sphalerite* or 'blackjack', the chief ore of zinc – is also common. Less common are traces of copper minerals such as *malachite*. You'll find this as thin green coatings on some surfaces. Figure 9.6 shows some of the crystal forms in which these minerals occur.

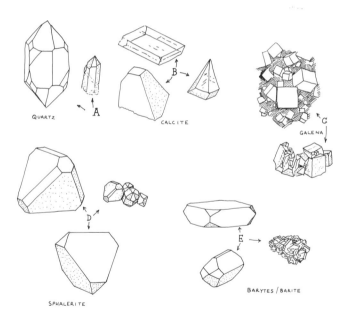

Figure 9.6: *A: Quartz (SiO$_2$), usually white or clear six-sided pyramids. B: Calcite (CaCO$_3$), also called 'dog-tooth' or 'Iceland' spar. This mineral has the curious property known as double-refraction. If you place a tabular crystal of calcite over a dot on a sheet of paper, you see two dots! C: Galena (PbS), which usually occurs as beautiful silver cubes (and often, as at this mine, contained extractable silver). D: Sphalerite (ZnS), variable in colour and not often forming large crystals . E: Barite (BaSO$_4$) cystals in their typical modes of occurrence. Barite is noticeably heavy.*

Times change and with them, our perception of 'waste'. *Sphalerite,* zinc ore, used to be regarded as waste because no industry used it. Yet now we use large quantities as rust-resistant coatings for steel; we mix it with copper to form the alloy we call brass and even use it in certain types of batteries. The Derbyshire mining area, once mined for lead, also yielded the 'worthless' *sphalerite* which was thrown out on the dumps. Yet in recent years, the dumps themselves have been 'mined' to extract this now-valuable source of zinc. *Quartz* too, in its purest form, is needed for glass-making and, when reduced to silicon, is the basis of the electronics industry. And *barite* is used today in rubber- and paper-making, by the drilling industry for drilling muds and in diagnostic medicine for contrast X-radiography (barium meals and enemas). I should add that lead, no longer as valuable as it once was, is still used in flashing or cladding for roofs and in lead-acid batteries for cars. It used to be used extensively as an additive (lead tetraethyl) in petrols but this is being phased out because of the inevitable health hazards associated with pumping thousands of tons of this poisonous heavy metal into urban atmospheres. Likewise its use in paints is much reduced. It has a lesser role as radiation shielding in the nuclear industry and in certain types of alloys.

Walk north towards the great 'glory holes' in the flank of Green Side. A path meanders up through mounds of *moraine*, past the wheel-less rusting hulk of an old rail car and past an obvious collapsed level, source of the rock waste dumps around here. This was almost certainly the High Horse Level, the deepest level of the mine until the Low Horse Level was driven (Locality 3). The High Horse was driven at the end of the 18th century and was the source of all the crushed and processed material you've just been looking at at Locality 4.

Continue on northwards to pass a curious funnel-shaped depression about 30 metres wide [3588 1820]. Underground workings have here broken through to the base of the soft, water-saturated *moraines* which are quite thick. As a result, the muddy and bouldery debris has slid down into the workings rather like sand in an egg timer, leaving this large hole at the surface. The process has now ceased and the egg-timer slopes are stabilising. **Now ascend to the lip of the lowest glory hole.**

'The Great Crush' of Gilgowars Level: Locality 5 [3588 1841]

Gilgowars Level was 35 fathoms (64 metres) above the High Horse. There's nothing left of it! This was the site of a monumental collapse of workings in 1862. Some 120,000 tons of rock, left virtually 'hanging' because of removal of an unsupported 'V' of *stoped* veins, collapsed, obliterating Gilgowars Level but fortunately not killing anyone because it was a Sunday and the mine was idle.

Since that time, the instability set up by *stoping* of the thick veins underground has continued to enlarge this and the higher glory holes you see up the mountainside (marked as disused quarries on the OS map). There were formerly two more levels (the original Adventurers' levels) above Gilgowars: the Middle (25 fathoms above Gilgowars) and Top Level (40 fathoms below the summit of the mountain). Again, these workings have all caved in because of the *stoping* right to the surface. As a result, much of this area is still unstable and best avoided. But the bottom of the lowest glory hole, just a few metres of easy downward scrambling, seems safe enough and is worth a visit.

About 20 metres from the lip of the hole is a huge boulder whose upper face is mostly formed of *galena*. This mineral is again easy to find in the numerous fallen blocks, occurring in veins together with *quartz*. At one outcrop on the west side of the hole, you can see a vein of solid *galena* almost the thickness of a brick.

I mentioned earlier how I once worked in a Canadian copper mine. Part of my job was to map in great detail the rocks exposed by mining underground. When the levels cut through an ore shoot, this was a sight to behold. At first, you saw nothing because the dust from blasting coated all the rocks with muck, so you always had to wash down the walls and roof with a hosepipe. (This annoyed the drillers who wanted to get on with their jobs for they were paid by productivity.) When you did this in the middle of an ore body, it was like the Midas Touch: one minute, you were looking at nondescript dirty rock; the next, glistening, lustrous, gold-coloured *chalcopyrite* made up the whole rock face and tunnel walls in front of you. It was like finding a treasure trove.

The host rock cut by these veins was *BVG*. Outcrops here show that it was an indeterminate greenish-grey *lava* or *intrusive*, filled with *feldspar* crystals and probably similar to that at Localities 2 and 3 – though here, it was highly altered by all the mineralising fluids which passed through it when the lead and other minerals were deposited, long after the *BVG*. Just how long is uncertain but *isotopic age* determinations suggest that the *galena* is around 325 million years old.

Return to the lip of the quarry to glance at the view. The lower part of the Sticks Gill valley below was very obviously a lake, now occupied like Keppel Cove, by marshy ground. This was the former Top Dam Tarn. In fact old OS maps – I have one engraved in 1868 – show both these former tarns quite clearly. Presumably, a smaller version of Top Dam Tarn existed here before the mine for the valley floor is also occupied by many *moraine* humps, partially buried by lake deposits lower down but clear along the valley sides. You can see the Chimney flue on Stang opposite, the upper end of which is the final locality. Notice how the 'birdsfoot' mine dumps fan out from the High Horse

Level, the idea being never to expend more energy in carting the waste out of the mine than necessary. So when one tip (which would have had a rail track along its top) became too distant, the miners would start another closer spur.

At this point, you have the option of retracing your steps or continuing on round to the Chimney (Locality 6, from which you have good views back to these enormous upper workings) and then down via Keppel Cove and so back to Greenside, passing the remains of the original mine hydroelectric generating plant on the way. Part of this route is devoid of paths though the walking is easy enough. So if the clouds are low and you don't like routefinding, you may prefer to potter about the lower workings here, searching for pretty mineral specimens and imagining what this large mine was like in its heyday. I do not recommend entering the higher parts of the glory holes as these are distinctly unstable and dangerous.

To continue, make your way west along a clear footpath on the north side of the valley which heads for Sticks Pass. At first, you can walk along an old grass-covered *leat* which soon merges with the main path. Follow the Sticks Pass track until the valley narrows to exclude the flat marshy bottom. The modern installations above you to the southwest (Raise) are for winter skiing. After the last *moraine* hump, branch left off the track and cross the beck. The old *leat*, almost totally overgrown by sphagnum mosses and sedges, joins the beck above a good crossing point. Now ascend the Chimney ridge – Stang – diagonally, keeping the disintegrating peat below you. Head (southeast) for a rocky outcrop at the lowest visible point on Stang. (These directions are necessarily a bit imprecise. The idea is simply to intersect the great flue on the ridge top, something you can't fail to spot when you get there.)

When you reach the ridge top, look back to Greenside Mine. Now you can see that the *moraines* in Sticks Gill valley form a distinct irregular crescent (Fig. 9.7), clearly the remains of a former *terminal moraine* from a small tongue of ice which may have existed here during the *Younger Dryas*. The mine dumps partially cover some of this *moraine* but certainly don't obscure it.

The Chimney, Stang: Locality 6 [3519 1755]

Join the flue along the ridge crest and walk up it to its west end and highest point where you'll find the ruins of the Chimney itself. The Chimney and its long flue (1 mile) were built in the 1830s at the same time as the new smelting plant. You might rightly ask why the flue should have been so long. Firstly, it was, as I mentioned at Locality 4, an exploration cross-cut, trenching through the bedrock to search for the supposed southern extension of the Greenside Vein. Secondly, it was to conduct the poisonous gases (mostly sulphur dioxide) away from the valley. But a third important reason for building this long flue was that it meant that any lead driven off by sublimation during the smelting process would condense on the inside of the flue and so could be collected every so often. They'd thought of everything, hadn't they?

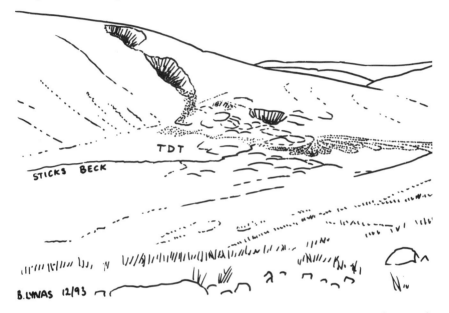

Figure 9.7: *Sticks Gill valley with crescent of moraines and mine dumps, rather mixed up together. 'TDT' is the site of Top Dam Tarn. The dumps just below Locality 5 probably came from the collapsed Gilgowars Level.*

This lead-condensing flue had the unintended benefit of minimising the lead poisoning of the landscape around the Chimney which nevertheless, as you can see, is still devoid of plant life near the flue or Chimney. The smelter closed at about the time of the First World War so we are looking at the effects of pollution from an operation which lasted for no more than about 80 years and which ceased about 80 years ago. Notice that the ground seems to have been more poisoned to the north side of the (presumably leaky) flue and Chimney, an effect almost certainly due to prevailing southwesterly winds.

After the closing of the smelter, the lead concentrates were hauled by a traction engine (the 'Helvellyn') to the nearest railhead (Troutbeck, on the now-defunct Keswick-Penrith railway) from where it travelled to Newcastle for smelting into lead. It proved more economic to take the ore to the source of coal – Newcastle is built on a formerly flourishing coalfield – than the other way around.

On the final sector of the ramble, you head for Keppel Cove to join the main walking track from Helvellyn and Whiteside and descend to Glenridding once again. You cannot see this track from here but it's easy to find: all you need to do is contour round the eastern flank of Raise, towards the southwest. Don't lose any height – just keep level – and you cannot miss the main track after about $^3/_4$ kilometre ($^1/_2$ mile) of easy walking. By then, you have splendid views into Keppel Cove, site of a former lake like Top Dam (p. 209). On meeting the track, turn left and drop down rapidly to Glenridding Beck and so back towards lower Greenside Mine.

As you walk down, you'll see quite clearly the *leat* which collected water, first from Keppel and Brown coves and then from Red Tarn Beck. I've marked this on the map. The *leat* contours its way around the fellsides until it reaches the top of what used to be a pipeline into which the water plunged. The pipe headed directly down the hill (labelled on the OS map 'not a path') to a powerhouse at the bottom [at 358 168] built in 1890 to supply electricity to the new winding gear and electric locomotive (Fig. 9.1). The powerhouse generated electricity at 600 volts yielding about 150 kilowatts (200 horsepower) of power. The electricity was carried by overhead cable to the Low Horse Level (Locality 3) and then down Willie Shaft to the Lucy Level. This was upgraded in 1912 when a 2,200 volt alternator was installed and the power taken direct to the Lucy Level where it was transformed down to 600 volts and rectified (from AC to DC) for the machinery. Looking about here today, there's almost nothing to be seen of the powerhouse and the pipeline has also been completely dismantled. All that remains are the ruined pier supports for the heavy steel pipe.

If you want to vary the final part of your return walk, take the footpath along the south side of lower Glenridding valley. It branches off just before the mine buildings and drops gently down towards Miresbeck and Rattlebeck. Above this path is another *leat*, built the year following the Keppel Cove dam burst in 1927. This fed water to a new powerhouse at Rattlebeck.

Some reflections . . .

Greenside Mine, on a small scale, encapsulates for me what we humans are doing to our planet. Certainly the mine brought prosperity of a kind to the area for a century or so. It provided work where there was none. But before the mine, there weren't any people save a few shepherds, so no work was needed. The wealth temporarily created is now vanished for ever and instead of a pristine valley, we have the unsightly scars and insidious pollution of the old mine. I mention pollution, even though the mine has been closed for 30 years, because the acid rainfall inevitably leaches out heavy metals such as lead from the dumps and flooded old workings. Before the mine, the lead minerals were safely sealed away underground. Lead is very poisonous as everyone knows and yet this metal inevitably will slightly contaminate any water that drains through the dumps for centuries to come. The waters flow into Glenrdding Beck and thence to Ullswater. Will the quantities involved injure people if they drink the water? Will they affect the ecosystem in beautiful Ullswater? Probably not, but no one knows.

The good news, perhaps suggesting a little hope for the future of our race on the planet, is that big efforts have been made to tidy up the mine remains, as you have seen. The lower dumps will soon be colonised by grasses and trees and little will remain to show that there was a mine there at all. The dumps from High Horse Level and the glory holes at Greenside will take Nature longer to reclaim. Meanwhile, they serve to remind us of how we desecrate our planet; they help reinforce the message that we have to tread carefully when exploiting natural resources.

ROCKY RAMBLE 10:
BLENCATHRA

How to get to the start of the ramble

This is easy since the fast new A66(T) runs right past Threlkeld village where you can park. There is a new carpark in the village itself, up a cul-de-sac to the hospital on the right, but for the purposes of this ramble, it is easiest to turn right immediately after turning off the main road (at the east end of the village) up a road to Gategill and the old mine. You can park in several places here [326 258], beside the old mine remains, labelled 'Wks' on the OS map.

The ramble: needs, distances and times

Blencathra is one of Lakeland's higher mountains (868 metres, 2,847 feet) so you need to take the usual clothing and boots suitable for cold, wet and steep slopes. Most of the ramble is on easy paths but part traverses Sharp Edge (though you can chicken out if you want and go an alternative easier way!) for which you must have good boots and not be too bothered by vertigo.

The distance is just over 11 kilometres (less than 7 miles) and the total climbing is around 750 metres (2,460 feet) though there are a number of alternative paths which you can either ascend or descend as you can see from the map. I'd recommend that you should allow a full day for this ramble, preferably one in which the weather is both fair and clear for the views are splendid. There is a wealth of fine places for picnicking, in particular beside Scales Tarn, but also near the various summit points of the long ridge.

The OS Outdoor Leisure map is Sheet 5, North Eastern area.

Introduction

'Blencathra' is a lovely name for a mountain; much more attractive than the functional 'Saddleback' which certainly describes its distinctive shape when seen from the east. Its name is Old British, though in part it comes from the Welsh 'blaen' meaning top. No one knows what 'cathra' may have meant. Perhaps the Old British just liked the romantic sound of the name. Wainwright verged on the baroque in his description of the dramatic southern front of the mountain: 'a tremendous convulsion . . . tore the heart out of the mountain and left the ruins . . . in a state of tottering collapse' (from 'Fellwalking with

Wainwright', Michael Joseph, 1985). By now, you will realise what this 'convulsion' was: glaciers.

This ramble takes you right round Blencathra including the Saddle itself (between Sharp Edge and the summit) and the entire ridge. From a geological viewpoint, there's not a great deal to see underfoot since the rock is entirely *Skiddaw Slates* (*Kirkstile Slates*) though you can see a good deal of distant rocks and landscape for the views are unsurpassed from this massive outpost of the Lakeland fells. And some of the effects of the glaciers are almost as fresh today as if the ice had melted only yesterday. In addition, there's a small mine to visit: the Threlkeld lead mine which closed in 1928.

'Threlkeld' is Old Norse meaning the 'thrall's spring'. What is a 'thrall'? you wonder, as I did. 'Thraell' is the Old Norse word for slave. 'Threlkeld' certainly sounds more attractive than 'Slavespring' but it does beg the question: who was the slave?

Figure 10.1: Gategill Farm and fell

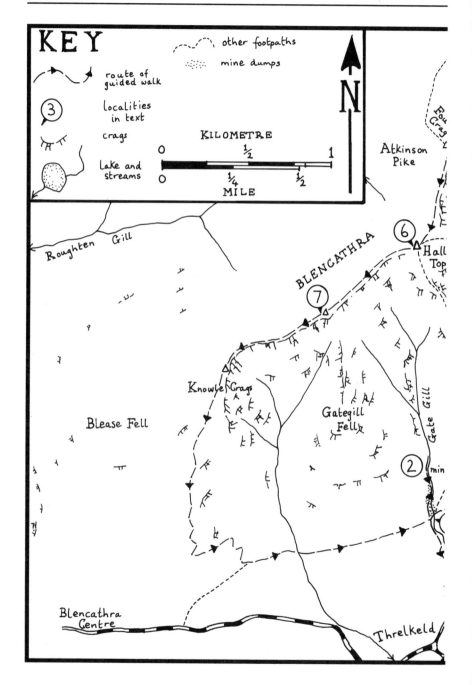

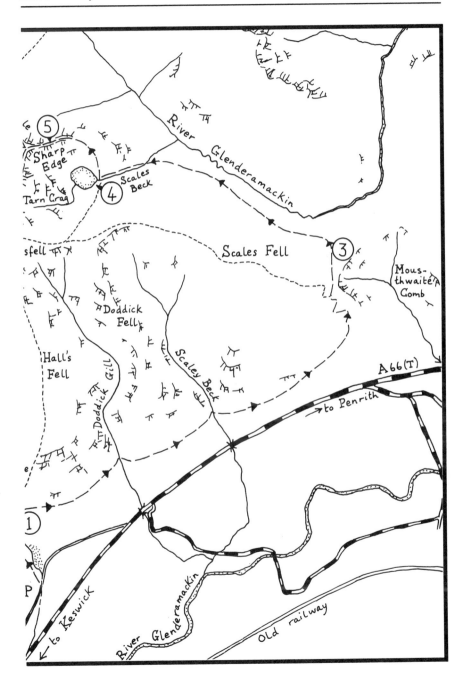

To Gategill and Threlkeld Mine

Walk straight up the public path towards Gategill Farm (Fig. 10.1), passing the old mine tips on your right. Follow the path through the farm buildings (it is signposted clearly) and through a gate to a track up the left side of Gate Gill. The gill has cut its way down into the *Skiddaw Slates* since the glacier retreat to form a little gorge, now shaded by a good stand of oak, birch, sycamore and ash trees.

Gate Gill and Skiddaw Slates: Locality 1

Just before the end of the wood, before you reach the top wall and gate, drop down to the beck. Here, just above a small waterfall, you can examine the Skiddaw sediments where they have been smoothed and polished by the water. Water-polishing often allows you to see details within the rock that you never see in the weathered and broken outcrops on the fellsides where only *cleavage* is visible. And this is the case here where you can also wet the rock to see the full detail. Notice that the rock is well *laminated* with some of the pale *sandstone laminae* reaching the thickness of your little finger. Most of the *laminae* are finer with five to ten packed into the same space as that occupied by the thickest ones. You saw very similar rocks (also *Kirkstile Slates*) to these on the Haystacks ramble and I mentioned then (p. 14) how the *laminations* may tell us something about the ancient climate: storms which caused distant rivers to disgorge suspended sediments into the ocean (which is where these rocks formed) or stirred up the muddy seafloor, creating small *turbidites*. The beds *dip* at about 30° to the west whilst the *cleavage* dips gently downstream (only visible in the walls of the little gully).

Return to the path and walk through the gate to join another well-used path which skirts the base of Blencathra, giving access to several different possible ascent routes. Here you have the option of walking up to the remains of the upper workings of Threlkeld Mine. If Greenside Mine was enough for you, skip the next locality. Otherwise, continue on up the left bank of Gate Gill. Where the paths cross, just after the gate, the beck has built up quite a delta of debris, washed out from the mine dumps which you can now see ahead of you. A little scrambling is needed here and there as you walk up through the dumps (Fig. 10.2) which, you'll notice, consist entirely of *slate* and chunks of *quartz* vein.

BRYAN LYNAS 12/93

Figure 10.2: *Remains of mining activities in Gate Gill. Blencathra summit (Hallsfell Top) forms the backdrop.*

Threlkeld Mine remains: Locality 2 [324 266]

Lead was the main mineral sought in this mine though there was some zinc production too. The main lead vein was found by the miners to be displaced (i.e. *faulted*) by a later vein rich in *sphalerite*. *Isotopic age* dating techniques tell us that the minerals apparently invaded the rocks around 320 million years ago. Several unusual minerals were found here. Cerussite, a white lead carbonate mineral, was actually mined along with the more usual *galena* and is formed from *galena* by exposure to atmospheric oxygen and circulating groundwaters. *Malachite*, also formed by oxidation of copper sulphide ores such as *chalcopyrite*, was found here too along with a rare zinc and arsenic mineral called adamite. Many other unusual or rare minerals occur in veins in the Caldbeck Fells north of here including tungsten, bismuth and molybdenum minerals at the once-important Carrock Mine. Underlying the whole Skiddaw area is a large *granite intrusion* (about which more later). Geologists usually expect to find a *granite* somewhere around when there are swarms of mineral veins as there are in the Caldbeck Fells (p. 180).

You would expect the *granite* to have roughly the same *isotopic age* as the minerals it is supposed to have produced. Unfortunately, the Skiddaw Granite seems to be considerably older (about 390 million years) than the mineral veins in the Skiddaw Slates which overlie it. Puzzles like this crop up with regularity in geology. Are the dates wrong? Did the minerals have nothing to do with the *granite* at all? Was there another later granite below the one we can see at the surface?

What we now lump together as 'Threlkeld Mine' was once two separate mines: Gategill and Woodend. Woodend Mine was close to where you started the ramble, the principal Horse or Woodend level being near the main road whilst what you see around here are the remains of Gategill Mine. This mine was producing lead well before the introduction of gunpowder. The miners used the laborious 'stope and feathers' system of wedges for prising rocks apart. In its last 40 years of life, the mine produced 14,000 tons of lead concentrates and 18,000 tons of zinc concentrates. As at Greenside Mine, silver was a by-product extracted from the lead. A fall in the price of lead had made the mine uneconomic by 1928 when all working ceased, though it was not abandoned until the second world war when the plant was dismantled and sold.

This locality includes the whole mined area which continues up Gate Gill for around 300 metres (the OS map marks 'levels, disused'). You pass two collapsed levels on the right (east) bank of the beck but the highest level is on the left bank (Fig. 10.3) where the lead-bearing veins (not now visible) were asscociated with small *dolerite dykes*. These *dolerites* are rather broken up by *fault* movements along these veins. Probably after the *faults* had first developed, they became conduits not only for the mineralising fluids but for the *dolerite magma*.

Figure 10.3: *Highest workings at Threlkeld (Gate Gill) Mine. My son is standing at the bottom of old stopes where the vein has been mined out to the surface. He is pointing to the contact between the Skiddaw Slates and a dolerite intrusion (see text).*

Most *faults*, once established, continue to be lines of weakness and so move from time to time as stresses in the rocks build up. It is because they are lines of weakness that veins often form along them. In some cases, you can see evidence for several pulses of movement and mineralisation: early minerals may be crushed or *brecciated* by movement and then recemented by later mineral fluids. Sometimes, figuring out the history of the various associations between mineralising 'pulses', different types of mineral 'assemblages', and fault movement can become quite complex. Geologists can usually work out the sequence of events (called 'paragenesis') by careful study of both the veins in the rock and of small, highly polished mineral samples under a special type of microscope.

There isn't much left to see of this mine. Here and there, segments of rail track emerge from collapsed levels to remind us that this steep gill was, probably for centuries, the site of much activity. Now, like Greenside Mine, there is silence save only the splashing of the beck and the bleating of sheep. If you're lucky, you might even see a dipper (Fig. 10.4).

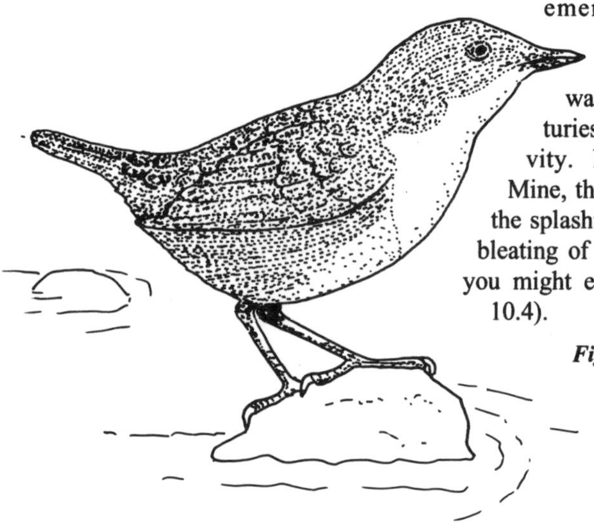

Figure 10.4: Dipper, a little bird with a white bib and quite astonishing ability to swim and walk underwater in search of its food.

Return to the main path above the first locality. From here, you can ascend directly to Hallsfell Top (Blencathra summit) via a relentlessly steep path (curiously not indicated on the OS Outdoor Leisure map) up Hall's Fell ridge. That is not my recommended route and this ramble continues northeast around the base of the Blencathra range on a pleasant and easy walking track crossing first Doddick Gill and then Scaley Beck before beginning to ascend towards Mousthwaite Comb, the next locality.

Mousthwaite Comb and the Glenderamackin: Locality 3 [343 277]

After passing Scales Farm (below on your right), the path starts to climb up the flank of Scales Fell. After a stiff climb over grass and bracken slopes, another path branches off to the left, heading directly up Scales Fell. Your route continues on round towards the Glenderamackin River valley, levelling out and turning to head northwest almost along the contours. Stop (for a breather if nothing else) at the point where you have a good view both into Mousthwaite Comb and into the Glenderamackin valley. This is the locality.

'Thwaite' is an Old Norse place name meaning 'clearing'. But what are we to make of 'mous'? The river name 'Glenderamackin' is equally odd.

Even odder than the name 'Glenderamackin' is the course of this river. If you glance at the map, you'll see that it rises on the north slopes of Blencathra and starts to flow southeast. Then it suddenly does a 120° turn to head first north and then northeast. Then (off the OS Leisure map), it turns again through almost 180° as it runs through Mungrisedale, to head due south. Finally, east of Mousthwaite Comb, it turns southwest and runs down to Keswick. Further to the north, the larger River Caldew does almost the opposite. It rises below Skiddaw, heads southeast and then turns abruptly to run north. The distance between the two rivers at Mungrisedale is about $1^3/_4$ kilometres (just over a mile) and there is no separating ridge. My guess is that the present river courses have something to do with modification of older courses by ice sheets. Maybe the Glenderamackin used to join the Caldew and run north. This curiosity means that little Comb Beck which rises at the head of Mousthwaite Comb and is only just over a kilometre long is at its start a mere 300 metres from the Glenderamackin (where the latter does its 120° kink). The little beck does then join that river – but not until the Glenderamackin has run almost 10 kilometres (just over 6 miles) further down its course. This is a very odd drainage pattern. If the Glenderamackin had cut away just a little further to the southeast, it would run out where Mousthwaite Comb now is. Alternatively, had the small corrie glacier which gouged out Mousthwaite Comb cut just a little further to the northwest, the same thing would apply. The obvious question to ask is why the Glenderamackin *didn't* in its younger days cut through directly across where Mousthwaite Comb now is?

And the obvious explanation is that the rocks forming the head of Mousthwaite are hard and it was simply easier for the river to cut down its bed towards the north. A stream will always take the easiest option.

Continue on the pleasant path along the side of the Glenderamackin valley to join Scales Beck which you cross, ascending its right side until you reach Scales Tarn (not labelled on my map because there was no space, but it's the only tarn so you can't mistake it). The path meanders its way beside the little beck with its small waterfalls formed by harder bands in the *Skiddaw Slates*. The beck's gradient is steep too because this is a rudimentary 'hanging valley', the main ice stream having been in the Glenderamackin valley below.

Scales Tarn: Locality 4

Take a seat in this natural amphitheatre, both to rest and relax and to admire the grandeur around you.

Scales Tarn is a perfect glacial corrie lake, partly dammed by a small *terminal moraine* which almost certainly dates back to the *Younger Dryas* cold event around 12,000 years ago. On these rambles, you've seen a good selection of such tarns: Stickle Tarn, Angle Tarn, Red Tarn, Goat's Water and Levers Water. But Scales Tarn is certainly one of the best, set in its deep northeast-facing corrie and overshadowed by that triumph of glacial sculpture, Sharp Edge.

The tarn is supposed, according to legend, to be bottomless. Tradition also has it that because of its position, the sun never reaches its surface (untrue!) and you can see stars reflected in it during the day. Sir Walter Scott, the famous Scottish novelist and poet (1771-1832) mentioned Blencathra and its tarn as part of his 'Bridal of Triermain':

King Arthur has ridden from merry Carlisle/When pentecost was o'er/He journ'd like errant-knight the while,/And sweetly the summer sun did smile/On mountain, moss and moor,/Above his solitary track/Rose huge Blencathra's ridgy back/ Amid whose yawning gulfs the sun/Cast umber'd radiance red and dun./Though never sunbeam could discern/The surface of that sable tarn,/In whose black mirror you may spy/The stars, while noontide sun lights the sky.

In the summer of the year 1800, Samuel Taylor Coleridge (English Romantic poet, 1772-1834, probably best known for his poem 'The Rime of the Ancient Mariner') spent a good deal of time exploring Blencathra and made notes of what he saw. He was, incidentally, probably one of the first people to walk for pleasure in the Lakeland fells. Of Scales Tarn, he had this to say:

A round bason of vast depth, the west arc an almost perpendic precipice of naked shelving crags (each crag a precipice with a small shelf) – no noise but that of the loose stones rolling away from the feet of the Sheep, that move slowly along these perilous ledges.

That seems a fair description to this day, a good deal more realistic than Daniel Defoe's overblown account of the 'barren and frightful . . . almost unpassable' mountains which he gave just over 70 years before (Daniel Defoe 'A Tour through the Whole Island of Great Britain').

You may think that your route up Sharp Edge will be 'barren and frightful', looking up at it from Scales Tarn. But fear not because, as always in the mostly unfrightul Lakeland fells, there is an alternative route (again oddly not marked on the OS Outdoor Leisure map) from the tarn more or less directly to Hallsfell Top, first running southwest and then west. This is clear; an easy and popular alternative for those who suffer vertigo and will mean that you simply skip the next locality. If you found Swirral Edge a doddle, then Sharp Edge is hardly worse, so begin your steep climb up the clear (but again unmarked) track beside the great *scree* slopes which fan out down to the lakeshore below Sharp Edge. At the ridge crest, you turn west onto the Edge itself. Unless you particularly like balancing and teetering along the very knife-edge of this ridge, you'll find a well-used track a little below the Edge on its north side.

Sharp Edge, classic glacial *arête*: Locality 5

You are perched on the *arête* which formed between two glacial corries (p. 198) (Fig. 10.5) . Underfoot are strongly *cleaved Skiddaw Slates*. The corrie to the north, its back wall formed by Foule Crag, is not anything like as impressive as that now occupied by Scales Tarn. Now you see the tarn from a very different perspective. It is, of course, slowly filling in and you can see this happening here where the *screes* from Sharp Edge have filled a little of its north side, and a tiny beck descending from Tarn Crags is busily building (in times of flood) a small *alluvial fan.*

When my son Richard and I were coming down Sharp Edge several years ago, we came across a couple who were stuck: petrified by vertigo. Richard (then aged 10) is as nimble as a mountain goat (from long experience of mountains with his family) and the unfortunate pair were so impressed by his virtuosity that they said to me, as we approached, 'Well if you can do it, so can we'. And they did.

Even so, do take care as you begin the very steep sector where the Edge joins the main bulk of the Saddleback ridge (Atkinson Pike). The chief concern here is others above you who may dislodge stones, for though part of the scramble is steep, there are plenty of handholds. I have deliberately included Sharp Edge in the ascent rather than descent because climbing *up* difficult bits is always easier.

Figure 10.5: *Sharp Edge.*

Soon you emerge onto the summit ridge, a nearly-flat grassy haven of safety after the trials of Sharp Edge. When you've recovered your breath and admired the view, walk along the broad track to Hallsfell Top, the highest part (868 metres, 2,847 feet) of Blencathra ridge. The climbing is over and from here on it is easy ridge walking and a long, grassy descent.

To the right of the path, between Atkinson Pike and Blencathra summit, you'll notice a large white cross made up entirely of quartz lumps set into the thin turf. This was made – over a period of years – by a Threlkeld man who started his self-imposed task in 1945. Why he did this I do not know.

Hallsfell Top, Blencathra summit: Locality 6

For once, here is a mountaintop not disfigured by a concrete trig point erected by the Ordnance Survey for their mapmaking work. All that marks the top is a small pile of *slate* lumps; not even a respectable cairn. This is because the *Skiddaw Slates,* of which (as you have seen) the mountain is entirely made, tend to break up into small jagged pieces due to the strong *cleavage* which affects them. There is no suitable rock anywhere nearby for cairn-building.

On a clear day, you can see most of the higher Lakeland fells, the Pennines and the hills and mountains of Galloway, across the Solway Firth. You can also see, closer at hand, various bits of scenery which are worth thinking about. The most obvious you'll have already noticed: the great contrast between the rounded forms of the uplands between here and Skiddaw and northwards to the Caldbeck Fells, when compared with the jagged, craggy scenery which is formed of *BVG* rocks to the south and southwest.

The Derwent Fells (Grassmoor, Causey Pike, Grisedale Pike, Robinson etc. away to the southwest) are also made of *Skiddaw Slates* but are quite respectably high. Why should this be, you might wonder, when the *Skiddaw Slates* are so soft compared to the *BVG*?

The answer is at least twofold: firstly the slates are by no means all soft. Parts of this enormously thick group of early *Ordovician* sedimentary rocks are composed of quite hard *sandstones.* Secondly, much of the slaty sediment has been altered and hardened by enormous *granite intrusions*, little of which we can actually see at the surface, but which we know must exist because of a large *thermal aureole.*

Whenever a hot liquid such as *granite* is forced into cold rocks, it heats them up and stews them in their own juices – plus a few others from the *granite;* hence many mineral veins. This slow cooking has the effect of causing new minerals to grow inside the original rock, transforming it in some cases into a very tough rock indeed.

Geologists know from careful gravity measurements that a very large body of *granite* must underlie the Lake District, and this is confirmed by several quite substantial areas of *granite* outcrops (Appendix: Geology Map). You saw some of this *granite* on the Haystacks ramble (p. 33) and you can see others from here (I'll tell you where to look in a moment). Also, geologists have found and mapped in detail the *thermal aureole* created in the *Skiddaw Slates* which tell their own story of being cooked up long after they were laid down. Just how long after is more complicated, for the *granites* and other similar rocks seem to have been forced up into both the *Skiddaw Slates* and the *BVG* at different times, mostly ranging from 400 to 330 million years ago.

The *thermal aureole* formed by the Skiddaw *granite* (dated at around 399 million years) is well known. If you were to walk northwest from here, you'd start to see the effect of it before you even reached Roughten Gill. Glendera-terra Beck (west end of Blease Fell) shows beautifully the evidence for the increasingly high temperatures to which the *Skiddaw Slates* have been subjected, as you walk north along it. The actual *granite* crops out in Sinen Gill, just north of Roughten Gill, though the outcrop is quite small for most of the *granite* has not yet been exposed by erosion.

If you look due south, you can't miss the large disused Threlkeld roadstone quarry on the opposite side of the Glenderamackin valley. Its stone used to be conveniently transported on the now-dismantled Penrith-Keswick railway spur, the same that was used for the lead concentrates from Greenside Mine and, presumably, from Threlkeld Mine too. The quarry exploited what geologists call 'the Threlkeld microgranite'.

'Micro' simply means, as you'd expect, that the crystals which make up the rock are smaller than in normal *granites*.

Its *isotopic age* is older than that of most of the other *granites*, at around 438 million years. It was *intruded* into the highest part of the *Skiddaw Slates*.

The fact that the *granite* – which, as you know, has been *isotopically dated* – was intruded into the *Skiddaw Slates* gives us a minimum age for these slates. If the slates didn't already exist, the *granite* couldn't have forced its way up into them. Therefore they must be older than 438 million years. An obvious point I know, but a vital part of the simple logical steps which geologists use to establish true ages of rock formations.

To the west of St. John's in the Vale – southwest from here – is Low Rigg. This is a second lump of the same *granite* mass and of about the same size. For some reason, this was hardly quarried at all. A third much smaller part of the *intrusion* is further south up St. John's in the Vale, south of Lowthwaite Farm. This was once quarried (Bramcrag Quarry).

Now head for the next high point – Gategill Fell top – along the great ridge. This is the next locality. As you walk along the wide and easy track, look down at what Wainwright described so graphically as the 'heart' of the mountain 'torn out' and left in 'tottering ruins' (which I quoted earlier): the precipitous and unstable slopes below you on your left, drained by Gate Gill. What do you think has happened here?

Gategill Fell top: Locality 7

Before looking again at the distant scenery and considering the rocky devastation that is Gate Gill far below, look first at the rocks which form this summit which crop out rather well just below it. Here you can see well *laminated* 'flags' (an old term meaning that they split well and would make good flagstones for paving) built up by alternations of *sandstone* and *siltstone*. The beds dip at about 30° to the northwest and, remarkably, show no sign of the usual *cleavage*. As you'll have noticed, normally the *cleavage* in the *Skiddaw Slates* is so strong that it obliterates everything else. Somehow, this bit of rock has escaped the intense stresses which have affected almost all the Lakeland rocks, including the much tougher *BVG* as you saw at the various quarries in the *Tilberthwaite Tuff* (e.g. p. 163).

Look to the south, across the valley to St. John's in the Vale. On the west side of the valley is a prominent north-south-trending ridge, called High Rigg on the OS map, with Thirlmere just visible behind. You can see there the remarkably clear *bedding* features in the *BVG* which forms most of the ridge. The actual contact (junction) between the *Skiddaw Slates* and the overlying *BVG* runs more or less east-west just beyond Low Rigg. Tewet Tarn nestles in the midst of the western part of the Threlkeld *granite intrusion.*

Did you have any ideas about what happened to the south face of Blencathra? There could scarcely be more contrast than that between the tumbled rocky wastes of Gate Gill below and the dreary gently sloping landscape to the north and west – Mungrisedale Common. Obviously glaciers are the culprit here. It was ice which 'tore out the heart' of the mountain. It also gave the mountain its unique appearance and character. But wait, ice as you have seen, typically forms 'U'-shaped valleys yet Blease Gill, Gate Gill, Doddick Gill and Scaley Beck all have a pronounced 'V'-shape.

What I think has happened is this: as the ice sheets waxed and waned over the 2 million years of glacial activity, the broad valley to the south, now occupied by the Glenderamackin River, must have been a major conduit for vast ice streams from the Helvellyn-Thirlmere area.

We know quite a lot about which ice moved where by studies of the boulders which it carried and then dropped. Some of these 'erratic' boulders were of rocks which are unique and immediately recognisable as having come from one particular source. The classic example is the granite from Shap (east Lakeland) whose distinctive boulders were widely scattered by the ice sheets and have been found as far away as York and the Midlands.

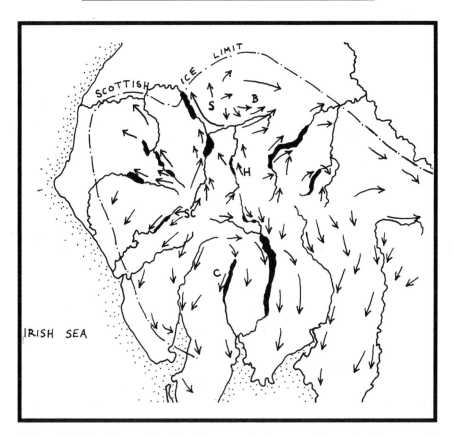

Figure 10.6: *Sketch map of ice flow directions which occurred during the glaciations of the Lake District, deduced mostly from studies of movement of distinctive rock types, glacial 'erratics'.*

Today, you can still find boulders of the Threlkeld *granite* (from the outcrops opposite Blencathra which I pointed out earlier from Locality 6) spread out both to the west (towards Bassenthwaite) and to the northeast (Matterdale and Troutbeck), ripped up by the ice sheets moving north from the Helvellyn area (Fig. 10.6). The glaciers didn't move far to the northeast because they met a much larger body of ice moving south from Scotland. What probably happened just east of here is that there was something of a tussle between the local Lake District ice and the Scottish ice. In this battle of behemoths, Blencathra suffered considerable damage, the remains of which you see below. Its southern and southeastern flanks were heavily cut into by the huge ice streams, and later small corrie glaciers continued the devastation as they began to carve out each of the deep gills which drain the southern rampart of the mountain. (The biggest of these was that which formed Scales Tarn and Sharp Edge.) After the ice melted finally, the small south-facing corries quickly fell apart as *screes* formed on a large scale, obliterating the usual glacial landforms and leaving what you see today: deep 'V'-shaped valleys with masses of loose *scree* and unstable outcrops of broken up *Skiddaw Slates*.

From your vantage point, you can see the much-photographed Castlerigg stone circle [291 236], about 4 kilometres southwest of here. This, the most famous of seventeen such circles in Lakeland, has 39 stones and dates back to the late Neolithic period around 4,000 years ago (Appendix: Timescale). Other circles may be older still.

Now begin the long and pleasant grassy descent via Knowle Crag and Blease Fell to rejoin the track which runs along the base of Blencathra above Threlkeld village, passing along below Gategill Fell. At Threlkeld Mine, turn right to retrace your steps through Gategill Farm to the starting point of the walk.

So ends the last of the ten rocky rambles which make up this book. I hope you have enjoyed them and got as much fun out of doing them as I have had in devising them. I hope, too, that you now have a real feeling for the geology beneath your feet in this lovely area we call Lakeland.

Glossary of
Geological Terms

accretionary lapilli	pea-sized blobs of volcanic ash which formed round nuclei such as raindrops during eruptions.
acritarch	microscopic plankton which floated around in the ancient seas and oceans of the world. Their skeletons were very tough so that they can often be found in old marine sedimentary rocks where no other larger fossils survived.
alluvial fan or *cone*	a mass of silts, sands and gravels deposited by a river at a point where its gradient decreases.
andesite	a fine grained volcanic rock, usually green-grey in colour, often forming large lava flows. Typically erupted by the volcanoes of the Andes mountains.
anticline	a fold in a rock sequence which is concave-downwards (q.v. syncline).
apparent dip	the inclination of rock beds which you see in a rock face not at right angles to the strike (q.v.). It is always less than the true dip (q.v.). The beds in Rossett Pike (p. 108) appear to be flat-lying because the outcrops you see there are almost parallel to the strike direction of the beds. In practice, most outcrops give you several sections at different orientations so that it is easy to calculate the true dip.
arête	sharply chiselled, knife-edge ridge formed by glaciers grinding away on both sides of the ridge e.g. Sharp Edge, Striding Edge.
ash	pulverised rock blasted out of a volcano, with a maximum particle size of less than 4 millimetres.
Ashgillian	the name given to the youngest epoch of Ordovician (q.v.) rocks. *See* Appendix.
barite, barytes	heavy white mineral which occurs in veins; sulphate of the metal barium.

basalt	a fine grained, dark, heavy lava low in silica (q.v.), consisting of feldspars (q.v.) and dark iron/magnesium silicate minerals such as olivine and pyroxene. Gabbro is the plutonic (q.v.) intrusive equivalent of basalt. Basalt eruptions are normally the least destructive of all, usually being non-explosive.
basaltic andesite	a hybrid igneous (q.v.) rock, halfway between basalt (q.v.) and andesite (q.v.).
bedding, beds, bedded	the layering or layers, sometimes called 'strata' and usually flat (planar), in which sedimentary (q.v.) rocks are laid down. q.v. laminated.
bedding plane	the dividing planes (flat surfaces) which separate beds or layers of strata. q.v. bedding.
bergschrund	deep crevasse which separates the head of a corrie glacier from the steep mountain wall against which it rests.
block	angular lump of volcanic rock larger than 32 millimetres. q.v. block tuff.
block tuff	tuff (q.v.) made up mostly of blocks (q.v.).
blockfield	area of shattered rocks characteristic of periglacial (q.v.) weathering in which rock outcrops are broken up into 'fields' of blocks.
bomb	lump of lava larger than 32 millimetres, blasted out of a volcano. q.v. pyroclastic, block, ash, lapilli.
Boreal Period	warm period after the ice age. *See* Appendix: Timescale.
Borrowdale Volcanic Group	*See* BVG and Appendix: Timescale.
brachiopod	sea-dwelling invertebrates (='no backbones'), commonly called lamp shells. They have two unequal-sized valves (a valve is one half of the shell) and are rather uncommon today. From 'brachio' = arm; 'pod' = foot.
Brathay Flags	sedimentary rocks of Silurian (q.v.) age. See Appendix: Timescale.
breccia	a rock made up of large, angular fragments of other rocks.
brecciated	*See* breccia; rock which was broken up to form breccia.
BVG	Borrowdale Volcanic Group of the Ordovician Period (q.v.); the name given to a group of volcanic lavas, pyroclastic (q.v.) rocks and interbedded sediments which forms much of the Lakeland fells. *See* Appendix: Timescale.
calcite	white or colourless crystalline mineral composed of calcium carbonate. It occurs in mineral veins and also forms limestones (q.v.).

caldera

a volcanic crater over 1 kilometre wide, usually resulting from the collapse of the upper part of a volcano into the underlying, partially evacuated magma chamber (q.v.).

Caledonian

usually refers to earth movements (folding, faulting and resultant cleavage) associated with the collision of the two great plates of America/Greenland and South Britain/Applachia. *See* p. 55 and Appendix: Timescale.

Caradocian

rocks of late Ordovician (q.v.) age. *See* Appendix: Timescale.

chalcopyrite

a lustrous yellow ore of copper (copper iron sulphide), usually found in mineral veins.

chlorite

a green secondary mineral similar to mica (q.v.) which grows in a rock as a result of the alteration of original, primary, minerals. This usually occurs during earth movements when the rocks are both heated and squeezed. It can also occur in igneous (q.v.) rocks as a result of slow cooling and hot watery fluids permeating the rocks.

clast

an individual particle of a rock, which may vary from hardly visible to the size of a boulder. q.v. volcaniclasts.

cleavage

a series of normally parallel, closely spaced planes within a rock, produced by the high temperatures and pressures of large earth movements. If the rock is strongly cleaved, it usually splits easily along these planes and is often quarried for roofing slates and other building materials (e.g Honister, Tilberthwaite, Loughrigg and Coniston).

cleaved

the state of a rock after it has been subjected to cleavage (q.v.) formation.

Coniston Grits

sedimentary rock of Silurian (q.v.) age. *See* Appendix: Timescale.

Coniston Limestone

complex formation of distinctive, fossil-rich limy rocks of Ashgillian (q.v.) age; now renamed 'Dent Sub-Group'. *See* Appendix: Timescale.

cross bedding

sedimentary (q.v.) rock unit in which individual beds are laid down at an angle to the original dip of the unit, such as at the front of an advancing delta or sand dune. Also called current bedding.

dacite

a fine grained volcanic rock composed mainly of plagioclase feldspar (q.v.) and quartz (q.v.).

debris flow

another rather more descriptive term for mass flow (q.v.). Also known as gravity flow since it is gravity which gives the flow its energy.

Devensian

the last major cold period of the ice age, lasting from between 114,000 to 11,500 years before the present. Also called Weichselian.

dewatering	removal of water from wet sediments, usually because of compaction from the weight of overlying material. This can result in characteristic structures such as the injection – upwards squirting – of water-saturated sludgy sediment. Usually, the water migrates slowly as diagenesis (q.v.) proceeds, causing no disruption.
diagenesis	process which occurs within sediments after their deposition in which they eventually become hardened into rocks. q.v. dewatering.
dip, dipping	*See* strike.
dip slope	land surface slope parallel to the true dip of the bedded rocks below. q.v. dip, strike.
dolerite	medium grained igneous rock, the intrusive (q.v.) equivalent of basalt (q.v.).
dyke	a thin sheet of igneous (q.v.) rock injected along a line of weakness such as a fault (q.v.) and usually steeply dipping or vertical, generally associated with volcanic activity. When a dyke reaches the surface, a fissure eruption occurs. q.v. intrusion.
englacial stream	meltwater stream contained within a glacier.
extrusion, extrusive	a body of igneous (q.v.) rock, once molten, which has flowed out at the Earth's surface and then solidified as it cooled.
eutaxitic foliation or *texture*	streaky texture characteristic of welded tuffs (q.v.) due largely to drawn out, extremely flattened pumice (q.v.) lumps.
fault	a fracture in the Earth's surface along which the rocks on one side have moved relative to those on the other. Faults may have horizontal (q.v. strike-slip), oblique or vertical displacements which range from millimetres to hundreds of kilometres.
feldspar	an important rock-forming mineral (silicate), often white or pink in colour. Two important types exist: orthoclase feldspar (potassium aluminium silicate) and plagioclase feldspar (of which there are six distinct mineral types), sodium – calcium aluminium silicate.
fiamme	from Italian for 'flame' used to describe flattened lumps of pumice (q.v.) looking like candle flames which are a characteristic of welded tuffs (q.v.). The flattening which compresses lumps to squeezed-out pancakes, is caused by the intense heat of the welded tuff flow and by the weight of the upper layers of the flow. q.v. ignimbrite.

flame structures   the result of squeezing of soft, wet sediment when a lower bed irregularly 'squirts' up into the overlying bed, giving structures which look like small flames. q.v. load casts, fluidisation.

flood plain   the flat area which mature rivers build up on one or both sides of their course due to repeated flooding, with consequent dumping of sediment. As the flood level drops, the waters return to the lower level river bed, excavated by the water in non-flood times. The Mississippi showed how large its flood plain is in the great floods of 1993 as did many British rivers in the wet 1993-94 winter.

flow banding   layering in a lava (q.v.) due to flow movement within the liquid rock before it solidified.

flow brecciation   the breaking up of a body of lava into angular fragments by the moving lava as it cools and solidifies.

flow folding   the folding which can develop in thick, sticky lava (q.v.) as it flows.

flow foliation   *See* flow banding

fluorite   a variably-coloured mineral, usually occurring as cubes, found in mineral veins. Calcium fluoride.

foliation, foliated   planar structures within a rock which may be due to a variety of causes such as cleavage (q.v.) and flow (in lavas, q.v. flow foliation).

fluidisation, fluidise a change of state of loosely consolidated, water-laden sediments which makes them behave like fluids rather than solids. This means that, once fluidised, they flow or squirt through other beds. Usually caused by earthquake shocks. Fluidisation also occurs in ignimbrite (q.v.) flows where violently expanding hot gases keep the solid volcaniclasts (q.v.) separated so that the entire mass behaves like an extremely mobile liquid. This may even occur in rare types of landslide.

formation   the name for a set of strata which is internally consistent and which forms an easily-recognised unit. The Tilberthwaite Tuffs (of the BVG, q.v.) are a distinctive example. In geology, 'beds' and 'members' make up a formation (they are really miniature formations) and several formations make a 'group', such as the Windermere Group (*See* Appendix, Timescale).

galena   the principal ore of lead, lead sulphide. It occurs as silvery cubic crystals associated with quartz (q.v.) and other sulphide minerals in veins. There are many good specimens to be had above Greenside mine (*See* that walk for details).

glacial striations	scratches and shallow grooves cut in the polished rock surfaces over which glaciers ground their downward course. The striations are made not by the ice, but by lumps of rock stuck in the base of the ice sheet, rather like sandpaper on a giant scale. They show us the direction of the former ice flow.
grading, graded beds	a graded bed shows sorting of its constituent particles, usually with the coarsest at the bottom and the finest at the top. This phenomenon gives the geologist a 'way-up criterion' (q.v.): it shows whether the beds are upside down (as sometimes happens in strongly folded rocks like the Alps and some of the sequences in the Scottish Highlands) or not. Grading is characteristic of turbidites (q.v.).
granite	a coarse grained, plutonic (q.v.) igneous (q.v.) rock made up chiefly of quartz (q.v.) and feldspar (q.v.). The intrusive equivalent of rhyolite (q.v.).
graptolites	an extinct group of small, free-floating planktonic animals which existed only as colonies. Some are used for dating the rocks in which they are found since they changed (evolved) rapidly over time and so are characteristic of particular time periods; graptolite zones.
gravimeter	sensitive instrument which detects minute variations in the Earth's gravitational field.
gravity flow	*See* mass flow and debris flow.
hematite	simple iron oxide, a high grade ore of iron, also spelt 'haematite'. *See* p. 181.
hyaloclastite	from 'hyalo' = glass, 'clast' (q.v.) = fragment and '-ite' = rock. Glassy lavas (such as obsidian) form when the molten lava is so quickly cooled that crystal structures have no time to form. Water-quenching of such lavas may cause them to disintegrate just as a hot glass bowl would if you poured cold water into it. This results in a highly distinctive rock.
ignimbrite	a hard rock formed from a hot, rapid, fluidised (q.v.) gassy flow of volcanic debris from a particularly violent form of *nuée ardente* (q.v.) eruption. In certain cases after the flow stopped (often tens of kilometres from the volcanic source), the internal heat was so great that the component particles welded together to give a very characteristic-looking rock: welded tuff. q.v. pyroclastic flow, welded tuff, fiamme, shard.
igneous rocks	those which have crystallised or solidified from a molten state such as lava. q.v. magma.

intrusion, intrusive	a mass of igneous rock which is injected into and cools within existing rocks. q.v. dyke.
isotopic age	the age of a rock (in years) determined from careful study of natural radioactive elements occurring within a (usually igneous) rock. *See* Appendix. Also known as radiometric age.
joints	fractures in a rock along which no movement has occurred. q.v. fault.
kettleholes	deep holes in moraines (q.v.) due to the melting away of large detached pieces of glacier ice, entombed beneath the moraine.
Kirkstile Slates	one of several sedimentary formations which form the Skiddaw Slates (q.v.) Group. *See* Appendix: Timescale.
lamina, laminae	very thin layers of sediment which collectively form beds.
laminated	very thinly layered sedimentary rocks.
lapilli	volcaniclasts (q.v.), from the Italian 'little stones', between 4 millimetres and 32 millimetres in size. q.v. ash, bombs, blocks, pyroclastic.
lateral moraine	moraine which develops at the edge of a glacier, found on the valley side after melting. These are uncommon save in areas which still have glaciers because they are quickly destroyed by later erosion or are buried by screes. q.v. terminal moraine, medial moraine.
lava	igneous (q.v.) rock in liquid state ejected from volcanoes or fissures in the Earth's surface. q.v. magma.
leat	small canal built to collect water from upstream of a mine or quarry, the water being used to power machinery. Leats typically almost follow contour lines (e.g. Dovedale and Greenside mine walks).
left-lateral	*See* strike-slip.
limestone	sedimentary rock made up mostly of calcite (q.v.) (calcium carbonate).
Llanvirnian	an epoch in the older part of the Ordovician Period (q.v.). *See* Appendix: Timescale.
load casts	when blobs or sections of denser sediment beds founder or sink into water-saturated underlying beds due to differential compaction, they form load casts. This is characteristic of water-lain sediments and you see examples on almost every walk. q.v. flame structures, fluidisation.
load casting	the process by which load casts (q.v.) are formed.
magma	molten rock within the Earth's crust. When this reaches the surface, volcanic eruptions occur. q.v. lava, magma chamber.

magma chamber the space underneath a volcano in which magma (q.v.) accumulates prior to eruption. q.v. caldera.

malachite green ore of copper (hydrous copper carbonate) which occurs in the oxidised part of a mineral vein.

mantle the thick, hot and almost solid interior of the planet above which the crust forms a thin skin. It is from the mantle that most magma (q.v.) originates, rising slowly into the crust either due to subduction (q.v.) processes or due to 'hot spots' in the mantle itself.

mass flow a jumbled mobile mass of sediment, rock and water or gas whose downslope motion is a response to gravity. q.v. pyroclastic flow, fluidisation, turbidite, gravity flow, debris flow.

massive without internal structures like bedding (q.v.) or flow foliation (q.v).

medial moraine moraine which develops in the middle of two merging glaciers due to the joining of their two lateral moraines (q.v.).

mica a platy silicate mineral, an important constituent of igneous and sedimentary rocks. Mica commonly grows in the rock during cleavage (q.v.) formation.

moraine debris produced by the erosive action of glaciers, often forming mounds. e.g. Mickleden moraines (p. 104). q.v. lateral, medial and terminal moraines.

nuée ardente 'glowing cloud'; violent type of volcanic eruption in which a heavy, ground-hugging cloud of incandescent gas and semi-molten rock is ejected at high speed from a volcano. q.v. ignimbrite, pyroclastic flow.

Ordovician Period the long period of time during which the Skiddaw Slates (q.v.), BVG (q.v.) and Coniston Limestone (q.v.) were formed in the Lake District. *See* Appendix: Timescale.

palaeontology, -ist geologist who specialises in the study of fossils

periglacial extremely cold conditions characteristic of the Arctic, usually associated with glaciers. Periglacial processes form blockfields (q.v.), tors and cause slow downslope movement of broken-up debris (q.v. mass flow), often called solifluction (q.v.).

phreatomagmatic type of violent eruption which occurs when groundwaters come in contact with molten magma in, for example, a shallow magma chamber (q.v.).

pillow lava the form taken by lava when erupted underwater, producing piles of concentric-banded 'pillows' which sag into earlier ones giving an easily identified rock.

plane, planar   flat surface, e.g. bedding plane (q.v.) or fault (q.v.) plane.
                           'Flat' does not imply 'horizontal' for a planar surface can
                           be tilted to any angle up to vertical.

planktonic   floating, usually referring to some organism in the sea
                           such as a graptolite (q.v.).

plate tectonics   study of the Earth's crustal structure in which the rigid
                           'plates' of the crust (lithosphere) slowly move about
                           relative to each other, floating on and driven by slow
                           convection currents in the hot plastic mantle below (q.v.).
                           This process has caused the drift of continents. When
                           plates (which can include entire continents like North
                           America) collide, mountain ranges (e.g. Himalayas) form,
                           or subduction (q.v.) zones and deep ocean trenches deve-
                           lop (as off the South American west coast) with associated
                           earthquakes and volcanoes. When they separate, new
                           ocean crust forms (e.g. Atlantic which is a 'young' ocean
                           formed when the Americas split away from Europe and
                           Africa). When plates meet with sideways motion, strike-
                           slip (q.v.) faults form (e.g. San Andreas) and earthquakes
                           are common.

plutonic   igneous (q.v.) rock intruded deep in the Earth's crust; e.g.
                           granite (q.v.).

porphyritic   igneous (q.v.) rock which contains large crystals set in a
                           much finer, microcrystalline groundmass of other
                           minerals, rather like currants in a cake.

protalus rampart   a ramp built of lumps of scree which have bounced down
                           a former snowpatch, now vanished, but leaving a rampart
                           at the base of the later scree slope.

pumice   very light volcanic rock which floats on water due to its
                           expanded polystyrene-like texture. The magma (q.v.) from
                           which it forms is typically highly charged with dissolved
                           gases. It is the sudden release of pressure in the violent
                           types of eruption such as nuées ardentes (q.v.) which
                           inflates the pumice, formed mostly of gas trapped by thin,
                           glassy bubbles. q.v. shards. The sharp, glassy bubble walls
                           give pumice its abrasive quality. Maybe you have a piece
                           in your bathroom.

pyrite   Fool's Gold, a common brassy yellow iron sulphide
                           mineral found especially in mineral veins.

pyroclastic   from 'pyro' meaning 'fire' plus clast (q.v.). Characteristic
                           of rocks formed by ejection of lumps by a volcanic
                           eruption.

pyroclastic flow	hot, ground-hugging, dense, gas-charged volcanic eruption which flows extrememly fast like a liquid (q.v. fluidisation) downwards into any convenient valley, being driven in part by gravity. It is made up of fragments of rock, usually almost entirely volcanic, of both primary (from the hot magma (q.v.) whose eruption causes the flow) and secondary (lumps ripped up into the turbulent flow) origin. q.v. ignimbrite, mass flow. Nasty and dangerous.
pyroxene	a major group of dark, heavy silicate minerals characteristic of igneous (q.v.) rocks which are less rich in silica (q.v.).
quartz	a glassy mineral (SiO_2), sometimes called 'rock crysta'', a very important constituent of most rocks.
radiocarbon	radioactive isotope of ordinary carbon (which has 12 protons and neutrons in its atomic nucleus). Radiocarbon has 14 (abbreviated to ^{14}C). Useful for isotopic age (q.v.) determinations of prehistoric remains and the later parts of the ice ages. *See* Appendix.
rejuvenation	literally, an old river system made young again due to a fall in sealevel or an uplift of the land. This increases the gradient and so the downcutting power of the river and its streams, leaving river terraces (q.v.).
rhyolite	a fine grained, quartz-rich volcanic rock; the extrusive equivalent of granite (q.v.).
right-lateral	*See* strike-slip.
river terraces	'perched' flood plains (q.v.) which formed at an earlier period in the river's development when its bed level was higher. As the river cuts its bed lower, it eventually reaches a point where it is no longer able to flood out over its old flood plain. Instead, it washes away much of it leaving only remanants in the form of a terrace (or several terrraces) and simultaneously begins to develop a new flood plain at a lower level. You can watch parts of this process happening, telescoped into minutes rather than centuries, when a stream crosses a sandy beach as the tide ebbs.
roches moutonées	from the French, literally 'sheep rock'; referring to the characteristic shape of rock outcrops in valley floors and sides, once moulded and ground by the passage of heavy glaciers q.v. glacial striations.
sandstone	a sedimentary rock composed of sand-sized grains.
scarp	abbreviation for 'escarpment'. Often used in geology to mean the cliff-like face which outcrops more or less parallel to the strike (q.v.) when the sedimentary (q.v.) beds have low dips. q.v. dip slope.

scree   a fan or cone of shattered rock fragments which have been prised off the crags above by frost action (q.v. periglacial). Water expands as it freezes, so any water that freezes in fractures in the rock gradually opens up the fracture. When the ice melts, the prised-apart piece falls away to the cone of rock debris below. All the screes you see today must have formed after the glaciers melted for earlier screes would have been removed by the flowing ice.

sedimentary   a rock deposited from either water, air, or ice. e.g. (q.v.) sandstone.

shards   fragments of glassy lava bubble walls blasted apart when the degassing during an eruption is extreme. The intermediate stage is pumice (q.v.). If expansion continues, the bubbles rupture leaving tiny fragments of glass. q.v. ignimbrite.

silica   silicon dioxide (SiO_2), a fundamental consituent of most rocks, commonly occurring as the mineral quartz (q.v.). q.v. silicification.

silicification   a form of diagnenesis (q.v.) in which a rock becomes enriched with silica (q.v.) due to circulating fluids. This effect hardens the rock and commonly obscures primary structures like bedding (q.v.) or glass shards (q.v.).

sill   intrusion (q.v.) of igneous (q.v.) rock which forces its way into a bedded sequence parallel to the beds. This occurs simply because the bed surfaces, like any fracture, represent a plane of weakness which is exploited by the molten magma (q.v.). q.v. dyke.

siltstone   sedimentary rock made up of silt.

Silurian Period   the period of time during which the sedimentary rocks which follow on from the Coniston Limestone were deposited: e.g. Skelgill Beds, Brathay Flags. *See* Appendix: Timescale.

Skelgill Beds   sedimentary formation of Silurian (q.v.) age, part of the Stockdale Shales. *See* Appendix: Timescale.

Skiddaw Slates   major group of sedimentary (q.v.) rocks, mostly in northern Lakeland and forming Skiddaw and Blencathra. *See* Appendix: Timescale.

Skiddaw granite   granite (q.v.) intrusion (q.v.) northwest of Blencathra (p. 248) underlying much of the Caldbeck Fells and Skiddaw Forest.

slate   a rock, usually sedimentary (q.v.) which has well developed planes of splitting usually due to cleavage (q.v.).

slump, slump fold

a fold which forms within a bed (q.v.) due to gravity-induced downslope movement (usually triggered by earth-quakes). Occurs only in soft and wet sediment before it becomes rock.

solifluction

slow downslope movement of debris or soil, partially due to freezing and thawing. q.v. periglacial, mass flow.

sphalerite

an ore of the metal zinc (ZnS), also called 'zincblende', 'blende' or 'blackjack'.

Stockdale Shales

sedimentary formation of Silurian (q.v.) age. *See* Appendix.

stope, stoping

technique used by miners for removing a steeply dipping, ore-bearing mineral vein involving as little waste rock material as possible.

striae

See glacial striations.

striations

see glacial striations

strike

the compass bearing, measured in degrees, of an imaginary horizontal line drawn on a bedding plane (q.v.). This, together with the dip (q.v.) of the plane (measured in degrees from the horizontal and perpendicular to the strike), uniquely defines that plane in space and allows the geologist to represent the three dimensional geometry of inclined or folded structures on a two dimensional map. The steeper the dip of a bedding plane, the easier it is to measure the strike. For vertical (upstanding) beds, the strike is easy to measure because the dip is vertical (90 degrees) but for flat-lying (horizontal) bedding, the planes have no strike. Are you confused? If so, try this experiment with this book: Hold it so that it is horizontal. Now you can see that if the book were a bed of strata, you couldn't measure any direction of dip – or strike. Now hold it so that it is vertical. The strike is the compass direction (bearing) of the book's spine and the dip is, obviously, vertical. Finally, hold it so that it is inclined about half way between horizontal and vertical (about 45 degrees). Move it (if necessary) so that its spine is horizontal. The spine now gives you the strike direction. The dip direction is always perpendicular to the strike (the book's spine), *measured in the plane of the book's cover*. So the actual angle of dip is the greatest angle you can measure between the tilted plane of the book's cover and the horizontal.

strike-slip	refers to horizontal movement along a fault (q.v.); e.g. Coniston Fault (p. 159). Strike-slip faults may be left-lateral (left-handed or 'sinistral') or right-lateral (right-handed or 'dextral') (q.v.). Strike-slip faults are also known as 'wrench' or 'tear' faults.
structure	describes the relationships of beds in terms of faults and folds.
subduct, subduction	process whereby two of the Earth's rigid crustal plates collide so that one is forced down as the other overrides it (p. 17 and 55). This produces a zone of subduction and is characterized by volcanoes and earthquake activity (e.g. Andes, Indonesia). q.v. mantle, plate tectonics.
subglacial stream	meltwater stream which runs beneath a glacier. q.v. englacial stream.
syncline	a fold in a rock sequence which is concave-upwards. q.v. anticline.
terraces	*See* river terraces.
terminal moraine	ridge of moraine debris dumped at the snout of a glacier and indicating its maximum advance. These may actually form a dam so that a lake forms after the ice has melted. e.g. Keppel Cove p. 207.
thermal aureole	belt of rocks altered by intense heat from a later intrusion (q.v.). Also called 'metamorphic aureole'. The Skiddaw Granite (see Appendix, Geological Map) has produced a large thermal aureole which affects most of the Skiddaw Slates (q.v.) north and northwest of Blencathra.
Tilberthwaite Tuff	cleaved BVG (q.v.) tuffs (q.v.) which have been much exploited by quarrying; *See* p. 85.
till	general term for the rubbish – ranging from boulders to clay – left by melted glaciers. q.v. moraine.
tor	bare, rocky outcrop surrounded by blockfield (q.v.) and the result of periglacial (q.v.) weathering. Characteristic of Dartmoor and other areas once subjected to intense cold but not covered by glaciers.
trilobite	extinct group of marine three-lobed arthropods, a little like modern woodlice. Trilobite fossils are quite common in parts of the Coniston Limestone (q.v.) (*See* p. 74).
tuff	volcanic ash (q.v.) hardened to form a rock.
turbidite	rock formed by turbidity current (q.v.).

turbidity current	turbid and dense current which forms, often triggered by earthquake shock, at the bottom of a water body (lake or sea). It flows into deeper water, carrying sand, silt and mud in suspension which, as the flow loses its energy, often fall out to form graded beds (q.v.); q.v. mass flow.
unconformity	a break in deposition during which erosion of rocks may occur. This can happen at any scale from small (p. 29) to very large, representing millions of years-worth of missing rocks as at the base and top of the BVG (q.v.).
Younger Dryas	a final cold period at the end of the Devensian (q.v.) ice age. Named ater the small Alpine flower *Dryas octopetala* (p. 84). *See* Appendix: Timescale.
vent agglomerate	a fragmental rock which chokes the vent of a volcano when an eruption ceases.
vesicle, vesicular	a lava (q.v.) with gas cavities. Sometimes called 'amygdules'. Commonly the cavities become filled with secondary minerals such as silica (q.v.), calcite (q.v.) or zeolites.
volcaniclasts	fragments of volcanic rock. q.v. pyroclastic, clast.
volcaniclastic breccia	impressive name for a rock composed of angular fragments of volcanic rock. q.v. volcaniclast, breccia.
way-up criteria	small structures, such as flame structures (q.v.) and load casts (q.v.) in sedimentary rocks, which always develop in such a way that they indicate whether the outcrop in which they occur is upside down (inverted) or right-way-up.
welded tuff	a tuff (q.v.) which has been hardened -welded — by its retained heat, individual fragments such ash, glass fragments — shards (q.v.) — and lumps of pumice (q.v.) being moulded and flattened together in a strikingly characteristic rock, common in parts of the BVG. q.v. ignimbrite, pyroclastic flow.

APPENDICES

1. Map Showing Simplified Lakeland Geology

The map shows only the older rocks of Lakeland. I have not shown the younger rocks (Devonian and later) because these aren't included in any of the rambles. The map also shows the approximate location of each numbered ramble. To keep the drawing simple, I have not shown any roads; merely the sea coast, a few rivers and, of course, the lakes. For more details of the ages and relationships of the simplified rock groupings, look at the Timescale. The 'cooked' *Skiddaw Slates* are those which have been affected by the heat from the nearby *granite intrusions* which have created a *thermal aureole*. Not all the *intrusions* labelled 'granite' on the Key are strictly *granite* though they are all *plutonic*. This is an inevitable consequence of keeping the map simple.

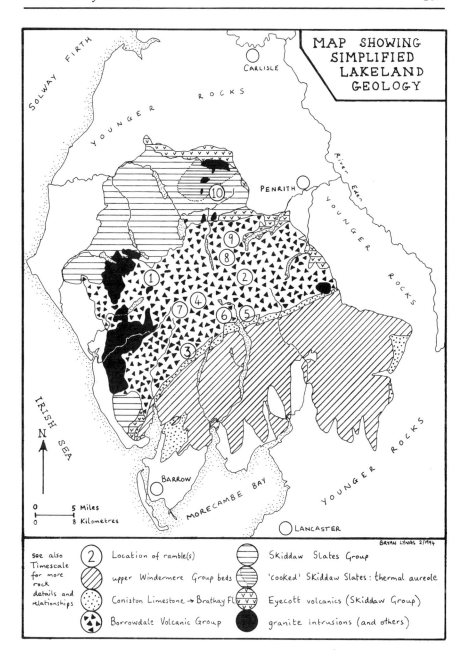

MAP SHOWING
SIMPLIFIED
LAKELAND
GEOLOGY

SOLWAY FIRTH

YOUNGER ROCKS

CARLISLE

PENRITH

River Eden

YOUNGER ROCKS

IRISH SEA

N

BARROW

MORECAMBE BAY

YOUNGER ROCKS

LANCASTER

BRYAN LYNAS 2/1994

0   5 Miles
0   8 Kilometres

see also
Timescale
for more
rock
details and
relationships

② Location of ramble(s)

upper Windermere Group beds

Coniston Limestone → Brathay Fl

Borrowdale Volcanic Group

Skiddaw Slates Group

'cooked' Skiddaw Slates: thermal aureole

Eyecott volcanics (Skiddaw Group)

granite intrusions (and others)

2. A ramble through Time.
The Timescale: what it is and how to use it

This is a seemingly complicated drawing which took me weeks to research and draft. But it summarises a vast amount of information in an accessible way – all in one go. My Timescale is really four timescales, labelled A, B, C and D, each showing much more detail than the previous one. The map of the geology only shows you where the rocks crop out underfoot but combined with this Timescale, you can form a clearer idea of how old they are relative to one another and of the enormous amount of time which has passed between their origin and the present day.

Column A

This is at the left side of the drawing and summarises the entire time history of the planet from its formation 4,600 million years ago to the present day. Geologists have divided up this unbelievably long period of time into a ranked family – a hierarchy – of ever smaller time chunks, each of which has some consistent feature which makes it different from the others. Top of the bill with the longest chunk of time is the Eon. As you see in Column A, the last 4,000 million years is broken up into three Eons: the Archean ('ancient,' the oldest), the Proterozoic ('earlier life') and the Phanerozoic ('abundant life'). All the rocks formed before the Phanerozoic are usually lumped as 'Precambrian' ('before the Cambrian'). The Phanerozoic Eon started about 550 million years ago with the 'Cambrian explosion' of new life forms. Suddenly, complex animals with shells appeared and quickly proliferated where before there had only been soft-bodied animals, simple plants like algae, and bacteria.

To learn more of this unique burst of life on Earth, get hold of 'The Book of Life' (see 5. Sources, No. 4, the last section of the Appendix). This excellent book dealing with life on Earth from the Archean to the present is superbly illustrated.

The Phanerozoic is itself split into three great Eras: the Palaeozoic ('old life'), the Mesozoic ('middle life') and the Cenozoic ('recent life'). But as you see from the actual scale of the column, these three eras together only amount to about $1/9$th of the time which has elapsed since the planet formed; almost 3,500 million years had already passed since the first life evolved at the start of the Archean.

These time scales are hard to appreciate, aren't they? To help put them even more into perspective, note that the first appearance of modern man (about 100,000 years ago) would be only $1/250$th of a millimetre (0.004mm) from the top of Column A. And the Roman conquest was only $1/12,000$th of a millimetre from the top! In relation to the age of the Earth and the first appearance of life at the beginning of the Archean, we humans have been around for a mere snap of the fingers. (And look what a mess we've made of our beautiful world already, one might add. Our industrial capability – which causes so much damage – only really started 200 years ago: $^{1}/_{125,000}$th of a millimetre from the top of Column A – that's only a few tens of atoms thickness!)

One way of looking at the various time divisions – the hierarchies – used by geologists is to think of them in terms of familiar units like months (= Eons), weeks (= Eras), days (= Periods), hours (= Epochs), minutes (= Stages) and seconds (= Zones). (The 'minutes' and 'seconds' don't concern us here, being rather specialised details.) But don't take this analogy too far because, of course, real clock time involves units which are always the same length. Also, there are always 60 minutes in a hour; 24 hours in a day and so on. Neither is the case in the Timescale where, for example, the 'hours' (= Epochs) can range between 10,000 and many millions of years. And there's no set number of Epoch 'hours' in a Period 'day.' You get the idea?

Column B

This column consists only of the Phanerozoic, now much expanded so that just over 550 million years occupies the same space as 4,600 million years in Column A. I've drawn tie-lines connecting the Palaeozoic, Mesozoic and Cenozoic Eras, to the Periods into which these Eras are split (from 'weeks' to 'days'). You may have come across some of the Period names – who hasn't heard of the Jurassic after the Stephen Spielberg film 'Jurassic Park'? You'll see that I've added small details about important new appearances (a tick) or extinctions (an X) of animals and plants during the Phanerozoic. 'E' denotes mass extinctions of many different life forms. These extinctions mostly coincide with Period boundaries. They are the main reason why geologists have divided the Phanerozoic into these 11 Periods for they represent important changes in the fossil record. The mass extinction everyone knows about is that at the end of the Cretaceous (65 million years ago) when the dinosaurs finally bit the dust, probably aided by an asteroid hitting the planet in what is now Yucatán in Mexico. But the granddaddy of all mass extinctions took place at the end of the Permian. This was far more important in terms of the number of species which died out, though in this case there does not seem to have been an asteroid impact.

Modern man at Column B scale appeared about $^{1}/_{30}$th of a millimetre from the top although there were many hominid species from which Man (ethnocentrically called *Homo sapiens*, 'wise man') evolved for several million years before this.

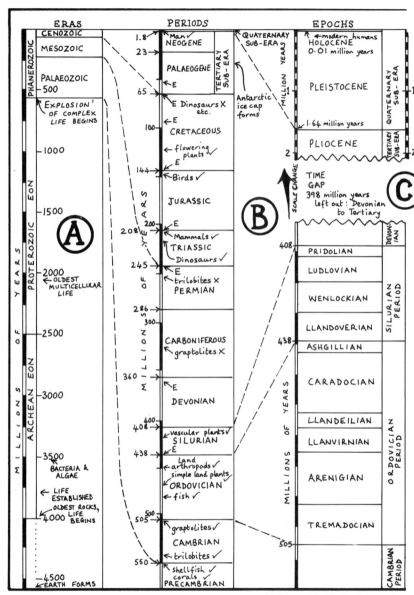

TIMESCALE

		TEMPERATURES	EVENTS	HUMAN CULTURES	CLIMATE	
COLD — WARM		-12 -10 -8 -6 -4 -2 +2 +4 °C				

WEICHSELIAN GL. — DEVENSIAN GL.
EEMIAN I — IPSWICHIAN I
SAALIAN GL — WOLSTONIAN GL
HOLSTEINIAN I — HOXNIAN I
ELSTERIAN GL — ANGLIAN GL

CROMERIAN — CROMERIAN
COMPLEX GL + I
GL + I

MENAPIAN GL
WAALIAN I

EBURONIAN G

TIGLIAN I — LUDHAMIAN I
↑ ↑
NW EUROPE   BRITAIN

GLACIALS & INTERGLACIALS
(GL)   (I)

CLIMAX OF
CALEDONIAN
MOUNTAIN–BUILDING
∿∿UNCONFORMITY∿∿
KENDAL SUB-GROUP
BANNISDALE SLATE
CONISTON GRIT
COLDWELL FORMATION
BRATHAY FLAGS
STOCKDALE SHALES
(BROWGILL & SKELGILL)
CONISTON LIMESTONE
∿∿UNCONFORMITY∿∿

} WINDERMERE GROUP

YEWDALE BRECCIA
TILBERTHWAITE TUFF
AIRY'S BRIDGE FORMATION
BIRKER FELL ANDESITES
HONISTER TUFFS
∿∿UNCONFORMITY∿∿

} BORROWDALE VOLCANIC GROUP (BVG)

LATTERBARROW SANDSTONE
TARN MOOR MUDSTONE
EYECOTT LAVAS
KIRKSTILE SLATES
LOWESWATER FLAGS
HOPE BECK SLATES

(OLDEST ROCKS
IN LAKELAND)
LAKELAND
ROCK
FORMATIONS

} SKIDDAW SLATES (SKIDDAW GROUP)

YEARS — THOUSANDS OF YEARS

'Little Ice Age'
'Little Climate Optimum'
← Viking raids

← Romans arrive in
Lakeland

* forest clearance, first
sheep, cereals cultivated
* stone circles
* Langdale axe exports
* elm decline + first
Langdale axes
* sealevel 6 metres higher
than today
*: first people enter
Lakeland
* complete forest cover
up to 600 metres
* Dover straits flooded

↑ rising sealevels

hazel woodlands

birch + pine forests
* final rapid ice melt

YOUNGER DRYAS STADIAL . cold!
Ice advances: corrie glaciers

ALLERØD   tundra, birch, juniper
              WINDERMERE
BØLLING   INTERSTADIAL
              mostly temperate
* ice sheets melt throughout
the world

Ⓓ

maximum glacier extension:
Lakeland submerged in
ice sheets;
ice reaches Cardiff – the Wash

coldest period: average
12 – 13°C colder than today

short warmer periods

BRYAN LYNAS 2/1994

IRON / BRONZE / NEOLITHIC — MESOLITHIC

SUB-ATLANTIC colder + wet

warm + dry
SUB-BOREAL

warm + wet
ATLANTIC

warm + dry
BOREAL

PRE-BOREAL warming

POST-GLACIAL — HOLOCENE EPOCH

LATE GLACIAL

GLACIATION

DEVENSIAN (WEICHSELIAN) GLACIATION

PLEISTOCENE EPOCH (top part only)

Column C

I've split this column into two parts, both now concerned with Lakeland rock units, events and timescales. The lower part is an enlargement of the Ordovician and Silurian Periods – between 505 and 408 million years ago. Here, the Periods ('days') are divided up into Epochs ('hours'). Some Epoch names crop up during the rambles though most don't, but I've included them all for the sake of completeness. So when I refer to a rock unit which was laid down sometime during the *Ashgillian Epoch*, you can see that this represents a time-slice of about 5 million years which ended 438 million years ago.

To the right of the time divisions, I've placed the simplified Lakeland rock unit names, some of which I have used in the book. The actual rocks are also divided up, just like the time divisions, into a hierarchy of units.

Rock units: Let's make a similar analogy to the time units (Periods = 'days' etc.) which I mentioned earlier. This analogy comes from the world of business: The biggest type of business is the Multinational, the equivalent of a rock 'Group' (not to be confused with a Rock Group like the geological-sounding 'Rolling Stones'). Multinationals are often made up of a number of Companies (= rock Formations) and Companies are made up of, say, Divisions (= rock Members, which don't concern us here) and so on down to the basic commodity, People (= Beds). Without people, companies are nothing. Without beds – the bricks and mortar – of rock (including volcanic rocks as well as sediments), none of the higher units can exist. Like the time clock divisions, this analogy has its limitations, but gives you the gist of the scheme for rock-naming.

So rock 'Groups' (= Multinationals) are made up of 'Formations' (= Companies) such as the *Tilberthwaite Tuff*. Ultimately, everything is built up of Beds (= People), though the Beds usually don't have formal names and are just spoken of anonymously as 'beds' (rather like the people in many companies, one suspects, so the analogy holds rather well here).

Unfortunately, there's a problem. Geologists are always refining their ways of referring to rock units (though the hierarchy of units is internationally agreed) and often 'promote' units by 'kicking them upstairs'. Sadly, this has happened to the Coniston Limestone (see p. 76) and many of the long-established Silurian formations. The poor old Coniston Limestone has not only been booted up into a Sub-Group, a sort of netherworld somewhere between Group and Formation (= a sub-multinational?), but has lost its name! The Stockdale Shales used to be a Formation but, like the Coniston Limestone, this unit has been pushed upstairs to form a Sub-Group. At least it kept its name. And the Browgill and Skelgill beds have now become 'formations'. It doesn't have to bother us here since I've stuck to the traditional names to try to keep things simple. Well, okay, reasonably simple. I just want you to be aware of these changes in case you wish to find out more about Lakeland rock names and wonder what's happened. (I'll probably be excommunicated by my geological colleagues for writing these heresies.)

The top part of Column C is quite different. This deals with the long period of cold we call the Ice Age. As you can see, I've left out 398 million years of time between this and the bottom part of the column, because nothing much happened in Lakeland over that long period. The rocks were deeply buried and that was about that. But by the late Tertiary Sub-Era, the old rocks were once again exposed to the forces of erosion -which now started to include ice sheets. The Quaternary Sub-Era (sub-era = 'a few days' in our time scheme) started – well, it's a bit embarrassing really – nobody quite agrees when. A date of 1.64 million years was fixed several years ago after much argument, but 1.8 million is also quoted. Again this doesn't have to bother us.

The timescale dates – all of them – are subject to constant revision as dating methods improve. (I explain how rocks are dated later in this Appendix.) They are probably all about right, but other timescales may give slightly different dates to mine which are the most recent I could find (1993).

What is important is that the world started to cool about 5 million years ago during the Pliocene Epoch. The first major ice sheets began to form in the northern hemisphere between 1.8 and 2 million years ago. But it was not all cold. The glacial freezes were punctuated by regular warmer spells ('interglacials' or 'interstadials') when the temperatures rose – sometimes remaining warm for tens of thousands of years, equalling or even exceeding those of today, and most of the ice sheets disappeared. I have crudely summarised what we know about temperature changes – glacials and interglacials – in a 'cold-warm' vertical graph to the right of the Epoch column. I've also given the names of some of these major climate change events in case you are interested. The last glacial is widely known as the Weichselian (in northwest Europe), but is usually called *'Devensian'* in Britain. Same thing; different name. Confusing but inevitable.

Some of the interglacials were sufficiently warm for macaque monkeys and hippos to flourish in southern England. Can you imagine?

What we like to call 'the end' of the glacial freezes occurred about 0.01 million years ago (we can be much more precise about this on Column D) with a change to warm conditions again. This is taken as the boundary between the Pleistocene and the Holocene (also known as 'Recent' or 'Flandrian') Epochs.

Actually, we are probably still in an interglacial and we have no means of knowing (yet) whether the world will plunge back into another glacial phase. Maybe our 'greenhouse effect' atmospheric tampering will prevent this happening, or maybe it will trigger something worse. No one knows.

Column D

This summarises the main events affecting Lakeland since the late Pleistocene. Note the tie-line running from '*Devensian*' on Column C to the base of Column D, emphasising my enormous scale expansion for this final 27,000 years of time. Here, I have (partly because of a wealth of new climate and dating information from the Greenland ice sheet drilling programmes) been able to plot temperature fluctuations over this timespan. As you see, they range from as much as 12-13 degrees Celsius colder than today to about 3 degrees warmer. The temperatures were never constant. Even in the depths of the *Devensian* ice age, they were shooting up and down, sometimes very rapidly. By about 22,000 years ago, the ice sheets reached their maximum extent for the Devensian/Weichselian glaciation in the northern hemisphere. In Britain, they reached as far south as Cardiff, though with a very irregular front.

Earlier glaciations were even more severe. The Wolstonian and Anglian glaciers (Column C, top) once reached further south than London. Only the southern strip of Britain – Cornwall to Kent – was never glaciated.

Around 14,500 years ago, there was a dramatic warming during which most of the continental ice sheets melted almost completely, liberating oceans of water and causing sealevels around the world to shoot up at least 100 metres (no, that's not an error: around 330 feet!). This mild spell (known as the Bølling and Allerød interstadial; the Windermere Interstadial in Lakeland) only lasted for about 1,800 years. Then the temperatures plummeted once more into the *Younger Dryas* cold event (also known in Britain as 'the Loch Lomond Stadial' or 'Loch Lomond Readvance') which lasted from 12,700 years BP (Before Present) to 11,550 years BP. It was this which caused the reappearance of glaciers in the higher Lake District valleys and corries such as Mickleden (p. 104) and Red Tarn (p. 196).

BP (Before Present, not the oil company) dates are almost always used by geologists. This is internationally taken to mean 'before 1950 AD' since we have to have a fixed time datum to measure back from. This is why most modern dates are given as Anno Domini, AD, rather than BP. Just to complicate the issue, always easy to do, many of the BP dates you see are '*radiocarbon dates*'. 'Radiocarbon years' are not exactly the same as calendar years so that 'radiocarbon years' have to be calibrated using a special curve to give the true number of years BP. Get it? If not, see page 280 for more details.

The *Younger Dryas* lasted about 1,200 years. Temperatures dropped right back to the way they had been during the Devensian/Weichselian glaciation. Lakeland became a freezing wilderness with sparse tundra vegetation and intense *periglacial* activity such as *scree* and *blockfield* formation. At about 11,550 years BP, the temperature shot up . . . within about 50 years. Suddenly, the frozen mountains were warm once again; the glaciers melted like snowballs in mild weather, dumping their *moraine* mounds and releasing floods of sediment-laden meltwaters.

Why did the temperatures climb so fast? Almost certainly due to major changes in deep 'conveyor belt' currents in the North Atlantic (p. 83) and a dramatic break-up of sea ice cover. The ultimate causes of these remarkable warmings and coolings remain elusive, though we now have some very good ideas. But we don't yet know how to predict another glacial deep freeze, the true test of how well we understand climate processes.

For the next 7,000 years, the climate stayed warm and mostly wet. The temperatures I have plotted on the Holocene sector of the curve are from a variety of sources including studies of pollen and beetles from the sediments laid down at these times. Knowing what types of insects and plants flourished – by linking the species you find with the same beetles and plants today, and their preferred climate zones – tells us a remarkable amount about what the temperatures were. The curve represents average July temperatures at latitude 55-60 degrees north (Lakeland is 54°N).

The early Holocene warming throughout the world meant that the sealevel continued to rise, reaching a maximum of nearly 6 metres (20 feet) higher than today around the Lake District coast.

How is it that sealevels have fallen again around Lakeland without a new ice age to lock up the water? In fact, they haven't; it's Lakeland which has risen. This is called 'isostatic readjustment'. If you lie on a mattress, your weight compresses it, but when you get up, the mattress springs back to its former higher level. The same happened in the Lake District (and Scotland and everywhere which was covered by glaciers): the enormous weight of the ice sheets pressed down the land surface to many metres below what it is today. As soon as the ice melted, the land surface started to rise, recovering its former level after a few thousand years. But because the ice melt was so rapid, sealevels rose much faster than the land rebound which is why by 6,500 years BP, the sealevel was higher than today around Lakeland. The sealevel rise was worldwide ('eustatic'), complicated in formerly glaciated areas by the slower isostatic recovery of the land. Parts of Scandinavia are still undergoing isostatic recovery though probably the process is complete in Britain. It is the interplay of eustatic sealevel rise and isostatic recovery which has formed the famed raised beaches you can see around many Scottish coasts.

The first humans probably appeared in the area around 6,500 years ago. Less than 1,000 years later, they had discovered the Langdale 'hornstone' *tuffs* and were making axes and other tools. Within a few centuries, these axes were so prized that they were exported throughout Britain and to the Isle of Man. Neolithic ('New Stone Age') people now started to use their stone tools for clearing the forest.

We are fairly certain that forests were being cleared – by both axe and fire – at around the time of the Langdale axe production because there is a sudden decline in the amount of elm pollen in sediments laid down at that time (for example in the Langdale Combe *kettlehole* ponds, p. 187). At the same time, there was a dramatic increase in grass pollen (and later, weed pollen) which tells us that Neolithic people were herding animals and creating pastures out of the formerly-total lowland forest cover.

By around 4,000 years BP, people were beginning to cultivate cereals.

Documented history begins with the arrival of the Roman legions sometime after AD71 (just under 2,000 years ago). By this time, the climate had cooled again, bringing the familiar rainy Lake District weather we all know and love. About 1,100 years ago, the Vikings (= Norse) began their raids and established small settlements (place names ending in *by* and *thorpe,* the latter nothing to do with the THORP reprocessing plant at Sellafield!). The Viking colonists were helped by a temporary climate improvement during which they reached Newfoundland (so much for Columbus 'discovering' America), Iceland and Greenland and established settlements in each place. Unfortunately for the settlers, the climate changed for the worse in these bleak outposts. Both the Newfoundland and Greenland settlers failed to adapt and their brief colonisations became extinguished by the colder 16th century. This latest cooling has been called 'the Little Ice Age' and during this time, the Thames would freeze over to such an extent that winter fairs were held upon it by Londoners. Since then, the climate has been warming slowly, possibly helped by industrialisation and fossil fuel burning and the rest, as they say, is history.

3. How old is a rock? Age determination.

Whole books have been written about this and it's a complex subject involving the union of several different approaches. The most important are *palaeontology* (the study of fossils and their relationship to the strata you find them in) and *isotopic age* determination.

The role of fossils

One approach to rock dating is to record fossil species which occur in *sedimentary* rocks. From extensive collecting for well over 150 years by *palaeontologists* all around the world (including Charles Darwin on his long 'Beagle' voyage), we know very well the relative ages of fossils in relation to one another. How should that be? Simply we know that if a rock contains a *trilobite*, then it must be Palaeozoic because these animals became extinct in the Permian (see Timescale). No *trilobites* have ever been found anywhere in rocks younger than the Permian Period or older than the Cambrian. We also know that certain types of *trilobite* existed only for brief periods during the Palaeozoic. Each new species evolved, flourished for a while and then became extinct. Let us assume a *trilobite* species – we'll call it Fred – is common in the *Coniston Limestone* but no one has ever found it in younger rocks that overlie it. If we find lots of Freds in some other rocks we are looking at in Wales, say, we can be sure that those rocks are the same age as the *Coniston Limestone.* Similarly, if you were to find a dinosaur tooth in a *sandstone,* you'd know that this rock would have to be older than Tertiary (see Timescale) in which rocks they are *never* found. And so on. This is the basis of what is called 'stratigraphic palaeontology'. It tells us accurately about *relative* ages: which rock is the same age, or older, or younger than another.

But how many years old is this rock? Absolute ages and atomic clocks.

I've worked on this explanation. Even so, I think I'd recommend that you read it over a pint of strong cider in a quiet pub somewhere.

How can you put actual dates in years on your Timescale? you ask. These figures are *not* guesswork; not a bit. They are the result of complex analyses and calculations based on certain well-known physical laws which govern the atomic disintegration of certain elements. Some elements (92 occur naturally) also exist as unstable forms called isotopes. Isotopes are chemically identical to their stable brothers, but have a different number of neutrons in their atomic nucleus which causes the instability. The isotopes break up – decay – to form lighter elements and in doing so, spit out tiny bursts of radioactivity. We know accurately how long it takes for most of these isotopes to decay. This is measured as 'half life.'

If you have a lump of uranium-235 (meaning that each atom of this isotope of uranium, the one we use in nuclear power stations, has 92 protons and 143 neutrons) weighing one gram, you'd have to wait 713 million years for it to lose half its mass by atomic disintegration: its half-life is 713 million years. So the uranium-235 acts as a very slow but absolutely constant ticking clock.

Ah ha! you say. But how can you apply this idea of 'half-life' to rocks because you can't tell how much isotope there was in the first place without going back to measure it, can you? Well yes, you can. The uranium that disintegrates doesn't vanish; it becomes something which wasn't there before: another (lighter) metal: lead-207. The 'daughter' lead-207 stays right there with its 'parent' uranium. So for every gram of 'parent' uranium that disintegrates, slightly less than a gram of 'daughter' lead-207 appears. The weight difference is because the atomic disintegrations emit radiation – radioactivity – such as an alpha particle. An alpha particle contains two neutrons and two protons – the nucleus of a helium atom. This accounts for the loss of mass. So if we can precisely measure (using a machine called a mass spectrometer) the amount of parent uranium remaining and the amount of daughter lead which has built up, we have a ratio which can tell us how much uranium was there in the first place. So from that, we can calculate the time interval which has passed because we can measure in a laboratory the rate at which uranium-235 disintegrates: its half-life. Thus our natural ticking clock is calibrated and it tells us the time very accurately.

Now for a practical example: Calculate the half-life of a pint of best bitter after a long day on the fells. You need several people to do this to obtain a statistically valid average!

I've simplified this example of what is called the uranium-lead series to illustrate the general principle. Fortunately, we have many isotopic clocks which run at very different speeds. Potassium-40 decays to argon-40 with a half-life of 11,850 million years. But carbon-14 has a half-life of only 5,730 years, decaying to nitrogen-14. Other clocks include uranium-238 to lead-206; rubidium-87 to strontium-87 and other elements most of us have never even heard of. As our analytical techniques become more sensitive, more isotopic clocks, requiring minute amounts of sample, become available to us.

Setting the clock

How is the radiometric (= time measurement using isotopes which naturally occur in rocks) clock set in the first place? Take the example of potassium/argon (abbreviated to K/Ar) dating, one of the most useful since potassium minerals are widespread in *igneous* rocks. The technique works only for rocks which start as liquids (like lavas) and which then solidify. It is the act of solidification that sets the radiometric clock ticking. Whilst the *lava* is liquid, any argon (a gas) liberated by the potassium isotope will bubble off and be lost. But from the moment the potassium is locked up inside a newly-formed *feldspar* crystal (for example), its 'daughter' product, argon gas, is trapped with it. And there it stays (we hope, because in some cases our radiometric clock can be reset by later geological events which may release some of the 'daughter' argon) until a geologist analyses it to measure the relative amounts of argon and potassium. She can then calculate the 'absolute' or 'isotopic' or 'radiometric' (same thing; different names) age of the *lava*.

You might wonder how we know that the age of the Earth is 4,600 million years given that the oldest rocks ever found on the planet's surface are less than 4,000 million. The answer lies in meteorites from space: these are assumed to have formed at around the same time as the proto-Earth (a globe of molten rock initially) and all of them give around 4,600 million as their *isotopic age*.

Fossils + isotopic ages = accurate dates

It follows from what I've said that if you *isotopically* date a *lava* within the *Borrowdale Volcanic Group* as 452 million years old, then the *Skiddaw Slates* (and their accompanying *trilobites* and other fossils) must be older than 452 million years. Obvious, I know, but this is the interlinking – the merging – between the two different approaches to rock dating. So if you find a *trilobite* called Jane in the *Skiddaw Slates,* you know that Jane lived over 452 million years ago. If a colleague finds a *trilobite* identical to Jane in rocks in the Antarctic, then you can be pretty certain that the rocks containing Jane are also older than 452 million years. But then assume that the Antarctic geologist later finds that the Jane-bearing rocks also include some *lava* flows. Samples from these flows give K/Ar dates of 473 million (±3 million, for example, which gives the expected limits of any error and which geologists always quote with their isotopic dates) which means that not only are the Janes in the *Skiddaw Slates* older than 452 million years, they are very likely to be about 473 million years old.

It is this constant fine-tuning by comparison of strata and their fossils –

stratigraphic correlation – with rocks which have yielded *isotopic ages* that enable geologists to build up an accurate overall timescale.

There – that was easy, wasn't it? And by the way, what *is* the half-life of a pint of beer? Is it different from cider? Or lager? Isn't science wonderful?

Radiocarbon and the end of the last ice ages.

I mentioned carbon-14 as being a useful isotope for measuring ages, but because its half-life is quite short (5,730 years), it is only useful for measurements over the last few tens of thousands of years. Because it occurs in almost all traces of plants and animal life – shellfish shells, bones, peat, wood and even lumps of charcoal from ancient campfires – it is enormously useful to us for dating many recent events (such as the time when men started to make the Langdale axes; p. 187). But nothing is ever simple. Radiocarbon ages are subject to variable amounts of error – sometimes considerable error – and they are continually being refined by checking with other dating methods. One such check is counting tree rings (dendrochronology) which obviously give calendar (real) years, linking *radiocarbon* dates of the same tree to the true dates. Another new technique is to count the years in ice cores from Greenland. This can be done in several ways, rather like tree-rings. From the same core, we can establish when warm and cold periods occurred, using a sophisticated technique involving isotopes of oxygen. (Tiny bubbles of this gas are trapped in the snow as it turns into ice due to the weight of later snowfalls on top of it.) So important climate 'events' like the *Younger Dryas* (Timescale, Column D), can be spotted in the ice core and dated accurately. The *Younger Dryas* is extremely well known throughout the northern hemisphere and has been repeatedly dated using *radiocarbon* methods. These methods give ages of around 10,000 years BP (before present) for the sudden warming which marked the end of the *Younger Dryas*. But the ice cores show that this warming took place around 11,550 years ago. This means that the *radiocarbon* ages are about 1,500 years too *young*: a 15% error!

But help is at hand, in the form of calibration curves. These are simply graphs on which an error curve is plotted. If you take a *radiocarbon* date of, say, 5,600 years, you simply look at the point of the curve representing that date and see instantly that you have to add 800 years to it to make it true, calendar years. So a *radiocarbon* (written ^{14}C) date of 5,600 years is actually 6,400 years BP. I've adjusted all the Timescale dates in this way though you may find many similar scales which are plotted in '*radiocarbon* years', a convention adopted by many scientists to 'avoid confusion'. Then, at least, you know you're dealing with incorrect dates which you can correct if you want.

How is *radiocarbon*, carbon-14 (^{14}C) formed? By cosmic ray bombardment from the Sun of the nitrogen gas which makes up most of our atmosphere. This changes the ordinary nitrogen into ^{14}C. But how does the *radiocarbon* get into shells and plants? The newly-formed carbon immediately combines with oxygen to form carbon dioxide (CO_2). And CO_2 is taken up by plants and shellfish (to make their shells) and some of the plants are eaten by animals. So the ticking isotope clock is set, waiting for someone to measure how much of the ^{14}C remains, centuries or millennia later.

4. Palaeomagic! How and why geologists study the ancient Earth's magnetic field.

Palaeomagnetism is the study of the orientation of the lines of force – like a bar magnet – of the Earth's magnetic field as it was in the ancient past.

The specialists who carry out these scrutinies are often known affectionately to other earth scientists as 'palaeomagicians'.

Fortunately for our understanding of the past, rocks such as *lavas* which erupt as liquids, contain magnetic minerals which, whilst the rock cools and solidifies, align themselves like tiny compass needles with the Earth's magnetic field, preserving this alignment effectively for ever – or at least until a palaeomagnet-ist takes a carefully oriented core sample and determines this alignment in the laboratory with a very sensitive device called a magnetometer. Because the inclination of the force lines depends on geographical position (latitude), the precise measurement of this inclination can tell us the ancient latitude at which the rock erupted and solidified. And because the minerals have a polarity – a positive and negative end like compass needles – we can tell whether the rock was north or south of the equator. When two independent lines of study tell the same story (i.e. fossils indicating tropical seas; palaeomagnetism indicating tropical latitude), we can be pretty sure that it's correct. .

This technique, then, dramatically illustrates just how far and how much continental plates move around on the Earth's surface – a process which continues today as the Americas and Europe/Africa drift apart several milli-metres per year.

5. Sources for Timescale dates and temperature curves

1. 'Global Palaeoclimate of the Late Cenozoic', by V.A.Zubakov and I.I.Borzenkova, Elsevier, 1990. Fig. S.2, p. 301; Table 9, p. 254-255. I've extrapolated radiocarbon dates and temperature estimates from this comprehensive work for the entire Holocene Epoch (with modification from #2 on this list). Most of the data for dates and temperatures of Pliocene-Pleistocene glaciations are extrapolated from Fig. 11.11, p. 381, modified at the top by GRIP data (#3).

2. New Scientist, 20 January 1990, p.52-55. 'Climate and history: the Westvikings saga' by John and Mary Gribbin.

3. Greenland Ice-core Project (GRIP) results: *Nature*, 15 June 1989, 532-533: 'The abrupt termination of the Younger Dryas climatic event'. *Nature*, 24 September 1992, 311-313: 'Irregular interstadials recorded in a new Greenland ice core'.

4. 'The Book of Life' edited by Stephen Jay Gould, 1993, Hutchinson.

5. *Radiocarbon*, 'Extended Sub1 Sub 4C database' by Stuiver and Reimer, 1993, 35 (1), 215-230. Calibration curve for correcting radiocarbon dates to calendar years.

6. 'The Pleistocene: Geology and Life in the Quaternary' by Tage Nilsson, D.Reidel Publishing, 1983.

The following are books directly relevant to Lakeland geology and history. I've used a few dates from some of these too for the Timescale (Column D):

7. 'Early Settlement in the Lake Counties' by Clare Fell, Dalesman Books, 1972.

8. 'The Lake District' by Roy Millward and Adrian Robinson, 1970, Eyre and Spottiswoode.

9. 'Geology of the Lake District' by Frank Moseley, the Geologists' Association, 1990. This is a useful series of geological excursions, but you need to know quite a bit about geology.

10. 'Lakeland Rocks and Landscape', a field guide edited by Mervyn Dodd, Cumberland Geological Society, Ellenbank Press, 1992. Another useful guide which requires less knowledge of geology than #9.

11. 'The Geology of the Lake District', edited by Frank Moseley, 1978, Yorkshire Geological Society. The definitive work, a little dated now but still useful to professional geologists.

12. 'Mining in the Lake Counties' by W.T.Shaw, Dalesman Books, 1972.

There are many other books and scientific papers about the geology and scenery, history and mining. The above is just a selection which I've found useful.

We have a wide selection of guides to individual towns, plus outdoor activities centred on walking and cycling in the great outdoors throughout England and Wales. This is a recent selection:

In and around the Lake District with Sigma!

CYCLING IN THE LAKE DISTRICT – John Wood *(£7.95)*

PUB WALKS IN THE LAKE DISTRICT – Neil Coates *(£6.95)*

A LOG BOOK OF WAINWRIGHT'S FELLS – Mark Woosey *(£7.95)*

WESTERN LAKELAND RAMBLES – Gordon Brown *(£5.95)*

LAKELAND WALKING, ON THE LEVEL – Norman Buckley *(£6.95)*

MOSTLY DOWNHILL:
LEISURELY WALKS IN THE LAKE DISTRICT – Alan Pears *(£6.95)*

THE THIRLMERE WAY – Tim Cappelli *(£6.95)*

THE FURNESS TRAIL – Tim Cappelli *(£6.95)*

CHALLENGING WALKS IN NORTH-WEST BRITAIN – Ron Astley *(£9.95)*

Cycling . . .

CYCLE UK! The essential guide to leisure cycling
– Les Lumsdon *(£9.95)*

OFF-BEAT CYCLING & MOUNTAIN BIKING IN THE PEAK DISTRICT
– Clive Smith *(£6.95)*

MORE OFF-BEAT CYCLING IN THE PEAK DISTRICT – Clive Smith *(£6.95)*

50 BEST CYCLE RIDES IN CHESHIRE – edited by Graham Beech *(£7.95)*

CYCLING IN THE COTSWOLDS – Stephen Hill *(£6.95)*

CYCLING IN THE CHILTERNS – Henry Tindell *(£7.95)*

CYCLING IN SOUTH WALES – Rosemary Evans *(£7.95)*

CYCLING IN LINCOLNSHIRE – Penny & Bill Howe *(£7.95)*

CYCLING IN NORTH STAFFORDSHIRE – Linda Wain *(£7.95)*

Country Walking ...